DATE DUE AT THE LIBRARY LAST NAMED BELOW

Application for renewal, quoting date due and all details in the panel
above, may be made in person, writing or by telephone

P. 12

CONCRETE

CONCRETE: Plain
Reinforced
Prestressed
Shell

R. H. EVANS
C.B.E., D.Sc., D. ès Sc., Ph.D., M.I.C.E.,
M.I.Mech.E., M.I.Struct.E. Professor of
Civil Engineering in the University of
Leeds.

C. B. WILBY
B.Sc., Ph.D., A.M.I.C.E., A.M.I.Struct.E.
Head of Department of Civil Engineering
Bradford Institute of Technology.
Formerly Development Engineer of Stuart's
Granolithic Co., Ltd.
Deputy Chief Engineer of Ferrocon
Engineering Co., Ltd.
Deputy Chief Engineer of Twisteel
Reinforcement Ltd. (Manchester)

LONDON : EDWARD ARNOLD (PUBLISHERS) LTD

624.0136/4
E VAN
H39459

Printed in Northern Ireland at The Universities Press, Belfast

PREFACE

This book, written for the use of students and practising structural engineers and architects, deals with the basic theory for the design of structural elements of reinforced and prestressed concrete. The structural analysis of building frames has been excluded as this would overlap with many specialist textbooks concerning the analyses of both steel and reinforced concrete framed buildings. Shells, however, as far as structural engineers are concerned, are structures ideally suited to reinforced concrete construction, and the analysis of such structures in a form suitable for design purposes has been presented without long expositions of basic theory, which are better treated in specialist textbooks on the subject. Approximate rules are given, based on practical experience, for the proportioning of shells for estimate and preliminary analysis; and it is hoped that the section on shells will give the practising engineer a clear method for the design of certain popular types of shells, and will provide the student and research worker with an introduction to the subject prior to further reading of basic mathematical analyses.

Prestressed concrete also is a subject which needs a textbook to itself for full treatment. The present work establishes the basic mathematical analyses free from *ad hoc* approximations. The analyses, and some of the approximations used in practice, are then used for the design of members commonly met with in practice.

Ultimate load designs are expounded for individual sections. Moment redistribution, however, is not considered as this has not yet been accepted by many authorities and Codes of Practice.

As no guidance on the resistance of members to torsion is given by the British and many other Codes of Practice, an attempt has been made to give recommendations to help designers. These recommendations have been based on a review of all the papers which could be found on this subject, and aim at reasonable conservatism and simplicity.

The American, as well as the British, Code of Practice is often quoted; this is not only useful for users of the American Code, but it illustrates the use of a foreign Code to the British reader and gives him useful experience, as British engineers design many schemes abroad using foreign Codes of Practice.

As an additional aid to the student, a number of miscellaneous examination questions have been included in the book.

The authors wish to thank C. P. Nazir, B.E., M.Eng. for his kindness in reading much of the manuscript and checking many of the examples.

R. H. E.
C. B. W.

CONTENTS

CHAPTER 1

PROPERTIES AND COMPOSITE ACTION OF STEEL AND CONCRETE

1.1 Cement

Cement is the most important ingredient of concrete and fortunately is the most reliable for consistency of quality. Portland Cement is produced by calcining in a furnace a mixture of clay and limestone with coal dust. The resulting 'clinker' is ground to a fine powder. The degree of fineness and the admixtures used in this grinding process can vary considerably the type of cement produced. High Alumina Cement (or 'Ciment Fondu') is manufactured in a different manner; chalk and bauxite are fused together at a very high temperature. The molten material is cast into *pigs*, broken up, and then ground into cement, without the addition of any other material whatsoever.

Lime was used for concreting purposes by the Romans, Saxons, Egyptians and Greeks. Limes obtained from certain localities were found to be stronger and more resistant to water; such limes we suspect were made from limestones with clay impurities, so that the lime contained cement as an 'impurity'. These 'limes' were called 'hydraulic limes'. An improvement upon these hydraulic limes was patented by James Arpdin in 1824 and he called his product 'Portland Cement' because it resembled Portland Stone.

High Alumina cement was first made by Bied for the French Lafarge Company in 1908, and named 'Ciment Fondu'. This discovery was made whilst searching for a cement which liberated no free lime upon setting. Portland cement liberates free lime upon hydration and this free lime in the resulting concrete is very vulnerable to attack from mineral sulphates, dilute acids, and other agents as described later.

The chemical reactions which occur during the setting and hardening of cement are not convincingly known, but it can be said very simply that lime and alumina are liberated on hydration. The lime combines with the alumina and in the case of Portland cement an excess of lime results; in the case of high alumina cement an excess of alumina results. Bearing this in mind, the properties of these two fundamentally different cements can often be predicted.

For example, when these cements are mixed together and hydrated, the excess of lime and alumina is liberated chemically, they react, and a

1

flash-set (almost instantaneous setting) can result. This can be useful for caulking small leakages in cofferdams, water retaining structures, and the like. The 'flash-set' phenomenon is however a reason for new Ciment Fondu concrete not being suitable for jointing to new Portland cement concrete, and *vice versa*. Time limits have to elapse so that there is no danger of unhydrated Portland cement coming into contact with unhydrated high alumina cement. The concrete which is to be extended should be 24 hours old if it is Ciment Fondu concrete, 2 days old if rapid-hardening Portland cement, and 7 days old if ordinary Portland cement.

When cement is hydrated we speak in terms of the *setting* and *hardening* of the cement or concrete. These terms are often used loosely, but in fact, are rigidly distinguished with reference to cement by the British Standards Institution. The word 'setting' is further refined into two expressions, *initial set* and *final set*. For full details of the tests imposed upon cement for initial and final sets, soundness, tensile and compressive strength, chemical composition, fineness of grinding, etc., reference should be made to the B. S. Specification 12 (1958). The definitions of 'initial set' and 'final set' suggest measurements which, unfortunately, bear no strict relationship to practice; such figures however enable the properties of different cements to be compared for their setting qualities. It can loosely be said that it is good practice not to disturb concrete after its initial set; this is normally not less than half an hour. The final set is not usually more than 10 hours. These figures are not directly related to practice however, since such operations as the trowelling of concrete floors and granolithic finishes, for example, usually need to be performed after the initial set, but before the final set has taken place.

There are now several varieties of cement available to the engineer. The most popular types are as follows:

(a) *Ordinary Portland Cement* (e.g. Earle's 'Pelican' cement). This is the most inexpensive cement and is consequently widely used for normal purposes.

(b) *Rapid-Hardening Portland Cement* (e.g. Earle's 'Ferrocrete' cement). As the name implies, concrete made with this cement hardens more rapidly than concrete made with ordinary Portland cement. Such a property enables early stripping of concrete formwork and this is especially advantageous for precast work where repeated uses are made of the same shutter. 'Extra rapid-hardening' cements can be obtained for special purposes.

(c) *High Alumina Cement* (e.g. 'Ciment Fondu' and Earle's 'Lightning' cement). This cement is not classed as a Portland cement. It hardens much more rapidly than any other commercial cement, and it has the further advantage of being sufficiently immune, for practical purposes, to attack from several important chemicals. Some examples are: many of the sulphates present in sub-soil waters and in sewage; sulphur compounds formed from the combustion of coal and oil; carbonic acid as experienced in sub-soil waters from moorland areas; many of the chemicals contained in sea-water; chemicals which attack Portland cement and which are present in important industries such as lactic acid (associated with milk), tar oil, cottonseed oil, beer, sugar juices, and so on. Ciment Fondu is the cement to use when high strength is required urgently, for example, on maritime structures when it is necessary to have a reasonably hard concrete before high tide; for the sealing of water leaks in emergencies when excavating in water bearing ground; for structural work which requires to be in use within say 24 hours; for structural work where formwork is required to be stripped early or where it is required to prop further shutters from the members as soon as possible; for prestressed concrete, especially pretensioned concrete, where economy requires release of the wires and removal of the members from the stressing beds as early as the strength of the concrete will permit.

The greatest disadvantage of high alumina cement is its cost, which makes it prohibitive for many purposes. Another disadvantage is the necessity for curing with water or dampness. Concrete using this cement has nevertheless been quoted as being more economical than steam cured Portland cement concrete for prestressed concrete work. Ciment Fondu costs about $3\frac{1}{2}$ times the price of ordinary Portland cement, and for a 1:2:4 mix (one part cement: two parts fine aggregate: four parts coarse aggregate) of concrete, Ciment Fondu gives a concrete slightly more than twice the price of a concrete made with ordinary Portland cement.

Ciment Fondu with a suitable aggregate can be used as a refractory concrete and is suitable for temperatures up to about 1,300°C. High climatic temperatures in combination with high humidities as experienced in the tropics reduce the strength of concrete made with Ciment Fondu rather alarmingly, and such concrete should not therefore be steam cured.

(d) *Cement for Use in Cold Weather* (e.g. Earle's 417 cement). Such cements are usually achieved by adding about 2% of calcium chloride to rapid-hardening Portland cement. The calcium chloride generates heat by reacting with the water used in mixing the concrete. This also enhances the rapid hardening qualities. These cements are reasonable in price and can very often be profitably used in cold weather to allow concreting operations to continue.

The high early strength properties are advantageous for prestressed concrete, more especially for pretensioned concrete. Unfortunately however there is recent evidence to indicate that the presence of calcium chloride can cause the wires to corrode, and that the steam curing of concrete made with these cements causes localized corrosion of the reinforcement.

(e) *Sulphate Resisting Cement.* This cement is made specifically to resist the attack of sulphates and it can be purchased for quite an attractive price. The strength of the concrete made with sulphate resisting cement at, say, an age of 28 days is fairly similar to that of the Portland cements. There is a cement known as 'super sulphated cement' which resists greater concentrations of sulphates than sulphate resisting cement.

(f) *Cements with a Low Coefficient of Shrinkage* can be specifically devised for highways, dams, water retaining structures, and similar purposes, to reduce the magnitude of cracks caused by shrinkage. Such a cement was devised and used for the mass concreting to the Boulder Dam, U.S.A. A cement which expands upon setting is claimed to be obtainable in France. This can be used as a means of prestressing, although limitations to this are probable, as an expanding cement is hardly likely to adhere very successfully to the reinforcement (see discussion later on *bond*, §1.14).

(g) *'Low-Heat' Portland Cements* generate less heat upon reacting with water than normally experienced with other cements and are thus suitable for mass concrete work. The heat generated with Portland cement in mass concrete work can literally boil off the water required for the necessary chemical reaction, the steam causing flash-setting of some of the cement and also voids in the resulting concrete. The special cement mentioned in (f) as having been used for the Boulder Dam had also 'low-heat' properties.

(h) *Coloured Cements.* These cements are used for reconstructed stones, renderings, and the like. Because of the high cost of these cements, coloured artificial stones usually have a facing about $1\frac{1}{2}$ in. thick made with the coloured cement, and a backing made with ordinary Portland cement. Coloured cements can be obtained by adding the following pigments to Portland cement: yellow ochre (yellow), brown oxide of iron (brown), green oxide of chromium (green), red oxide of iron (red), manganese black (black). The weight of the pigment should not exceed 10% of the weight of the cement otherwise the strength will be impaired. White cements are very popular and require to be specially manufactured.

(i) *Portland Blast Furnace Cement* is obtained by grinding granulated blast-furnace slag with the clinker which is normally ground down to make ordinary Portland cement. For further details refer to B. S. Specification 146 (1958).

(j) *Water Repellant Cements* are most effective in sealing leakages in water retaining structures.

1.2 Aggregates

Aggregates are classed as *fine aggregates* and *coarse aggregates*. Various sands are most popularly used as the fine aggregates. For good quality concrete the coarse aggregates are either water worn gravels or crushed rocks. The aggregates chosen are usually the most inexpensive to give the requisite quality of the concrete. The engineer must however be satisfied that the source selected will consistently supply the same quality of aggregate which he has approved. Sometimes the engineer requires stockpiles at the suppliers' works to meet with his approval. These are then drawn upon exclusively for the concreting operations.

Aggregates for normal concreting work are a fairly inexpensive commodity; consequently transport charges substantially influence their over-all cost. Local aggregates are therefore generally employed, but an expensive type of aggregate may warrant greater transport costs if the necessary stone does not occur locally. Examples of more expensive stones are: granites for granolithic finishes; various types of coloured aggregates for artificial (or reconstructed) stones (usually used for the surface layers of the stone only); and vermiculite for lightweight finishes (imported to this country from South Africa).

Reference should be made to the B. S. Specifications 882, 1198, 1199, 1200, 1201, which recommend various gradings of the particle sizes for both fine and coarse aggregates. These are a guide to good concrete practice; it is disputable however whether these are ideal gradings for concrete. The British Standard Specifications quoted specify tests of other relevant qualities of the aggregates, namely specific gravity, water absorption, bulk density, organic impurities, and crushing strength.

Figure 1 shows four desirable gradings for $\frac{3}{4}$ in. aggregates and one average grading curve for $\frac{3}{8}$ in. aggregate. The grading of a $\frac{3}{4}$ in. aggregate should lie within the curves 1 and 4, and preferably within the curves 2 and 3.

Coarse aggregates can be classified according to shape as follows:

(a) *Rounded aggregates*, for example beach and other well-worn gravels.

(b) *Irregular aggregates*, for example water-worn river gravels.

(c) *Angular aggregates*, for example crushed rock or manufactured materials. These are commonly granites, limestones, basalts, quartzites, flints, pumice, broken bricks, foamed slag, blast furnace slag, sometimes a strong sandstone, vermiculite and duromit, etc.

The grading, shape, porosity, and surface texture of the aggregates can affect the workability and consequently the strength of concrete. This will be discussed later in §1.3.

When a concrete is required to be 'lightweight', to have a good resistance to heat transmission and impermeability to water, and a high strength is not required, special lightweight aggregates are often used such as vermiculite, foamed slag, clinker, breeze, pumice, wood-wool, etc.

If water is added to 1 cu. ft of sand, the gross volume of this sand increases until it occupies about $1\frac{1}{4}$ cu. ft. After this volume is attained

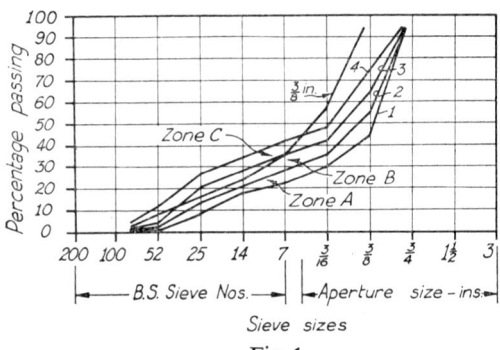

Fig. 1.

the addition of further water decreases the gross or bulk volume until when the sand is finally saturated the volume has returned to 1 cu. ft. When concrete is 'batched' by volume (i.e. the ingredients measured by volume) the water content of the sand greatly influences the quality of the resulting concrete. Consider a 1 (cement) : 2 (sand) : 4 (gravel) mix, the ratios referring to dry volumes of the respective materials (in accordance with standard practice). If we were using a sand experiencing its maximum amount of 'bulking' of say 25%, then the mix actually produced in terms of dry volumes would be

$$1:\tfrac{2}{1\frac{1}{4}}:4, \quad \text{or} \quad 1:1\cdot6:4.$$

If water is added to 1 ton of sand, the gross weight is increased by the weight of the water added to about 1·1 ton upon saturation. Hence, if the batching of concrete were by weight, the water content of the sand would still be troublesome but not to as great an extent as by volume. Consider again a 1:2:4 mix and let the sand be increased in weight by its maximum amount of say 10% due to its water content. Then the mix actually produced in terms of dry volumes would be $1:\tfrac{2}{1\cdot1}:4$ or 1:1·818:4.

In approximate figures, therefore, a proposed 1:2:4 mix (i.e. 1 cement:6 aggregate) can be as inaccurate as 1:1·6:4 (i.e. 1 cement:5·6 aggregate) if batched by volume, or as inaccurate as $1:1\cdot82:4$ (i.e. 1 cement:$5\cdot82$ aggregate) if batched by weight. This reasoning ignores the fact that the same phenomenon also affects coarse aggregates, but to a far less extent. Several devices can be purchased for measuring the water content of the aggregates, so that the mix can be adjusted accordingly. The water content often varies from place to place in a stockpile. When a large concreting programme is being conducted the stockpiles will sometimes be insufficient (especially on congested sites) and sand which arrives during the course of the concreting operations will have a different water content to the sand in stock. Aggregates are commonly exposed to the weather so that the water content will vary with the rainfall.

It is therefore difficult to allow accurately for the errors in batching caused by the water content of the aggregates. From what has been said above however it will be realized that batching by weight, in preference to volume, saves cement and gives a more consistent mix.

1.3 Concrete

Coarse aggregates, fine aggregates, cement and water are mixed together in suitable proportions; the mixture, placed and compacted wherever required, solidifies after a lapse of time into what is known as 'concrete'.

The mixes of concrete recommended for structural use by the British Standard Code of Practice 114 (1957) are 1 part (by dry volume) of cement; 2 parts (by dry volume) of fine aggregate; 4 parts (by dry volume) of coarse aggregate, and similarly, $1:1\frac{1}{2}:3$, and $1:1:2$.

Concrete, for structural purposes, is required to be of a certain strength. The proportions of aggregates to cement are by no means entirely relevant, however, and indeed the ratio of water to cement (measured by weight) is far more influential upon the strength of the concrete. Several engineers have regretted that prior to 1957 the British Code of Practice (which is essentially the same as the by-laws of most local authorities in this country) gave no incentive to the contractor to exercise keen control of the concrete, so that the proportion of cement in a mix could be lower than that required by the Code (and the concrete less expensive) yet the same strength as specified for the mix could still be achieved by carefully planned control of the water to cement ratio, grading of the aggregates, uses of admixtures, special cements, special compacting techniques, curing and so forth.

It is felt by many engineers that a concrete should be specified by its strength in compression. This has been standard practice in the U.S.A. for many years, and the 1957 British Code of Practice[3] now allows concrete mixes to be designed upon such a basis. The contractor is at liberty to design a suitable economical mix, so that there is an incentive to invest in the modern plant required to achieve a more scientific concrete practice. The concrete then becomes far more consistent in quality than a concrete batched in a primitive manner.

Many investigators have proved that most of the qualities desired of concrete are intimately related to its compressive crushing strength, for example, the strength in tension, shear, the resistance to weathering, abrasion and wear, and the impermeability. Exceptions to this rule are lightness (in density), thermal insulation and shrinkage. If a lightweight or thermally insular concrete is required then a lightweight aggregate is often used.

For most structural purposes then, engineers desire a concrete with a high compressive strength (refer also to §1.2). Compressive crushing strength is measured by compressing 6 in. cubes (4 in. cubes can be used for aggregates having particles not greater than $\frac{3}{4}$ in.). These are made and cured in a special manner as described by B.S. C.P. 114 (1957). Concrete cylinders (6 in. diameter × 12 in. long) are used in lieu of cubes in the U.S.A. It has been found that the strength of such a concrete cylinder is approximately equal to 0·85 of the strength of a 6 in. cube of the same concrete.

In passing, mention should be made of the only other test of strength described by B.S. C.P. 114 (1957), which is a bending test of a specified member over a specified span. The member fails in flexural tension, and a specified calculation derives the purported maximum tensile stress in the extreme fibres at failure, and this stress is known as the *modulus of rupture* of the concrete.

The factors which have the greatest effect upon the strength of concrete are the compaction of the mix, the water to cement ratio, and the method of curing.

It is easy to imagine that the strength of concrete depends upon the absence of voids, or in other words, upon the final density after setting and maturing. For example, 5% of air voids can give a loss in strength of 30%, 10% of voids can give a loss in strength of 60% and 25% of voids can give a loss in strength of 90%. Compaction of the concrete is therefore extremely important, and this is dependent upon the 'workability' of the concrete.

Workability is the ease with which concrete can be placed in moulds, compacted around reinforcement and screeded to a level. Scientists have devised several tests for measuring this property. All of these schemes however have been subjected to much adverse criticism. The test which has possibly been condemned the most, namely the 'Slump Test', is the most commonly used in practice in this country and the U.S.A., and was suggested and described by the B.S. C.P. 114 (1948), but only for 'ensuring uniformity in the consistency of the concrete' during the progress of the work. In this capacity it is a reasonably useful test providing the materials are of constant quality. The nature and the grading of the aggregates considerably affect the slump. It is therefore incorrect to say that specifying the slump (irrespective of an intimate knowledge of the particular concreting materials to be used) can control the strength of the concrete. The specification of the slump of a concrete by itself leaves no incentive for the contractor to employ methods giving greater workability and economy, without any reduction in strength, and hence a better finish to the concrete. Such methods would include, for example, attention to grading and type of the aggregates, and the addition of various proprietary chemical agents, as described later.

The Road Research Laboratory of the Department of Scientific and Industrial Research in Great Britain defines workability as the 'amount of useful internal work required to compact concrete' and on this principle suggests the following tests for measuring this factor:

(a) *The Heap Test.* A given quantity of concrete falls from a specified height on to a flat plate and the shape of the resulting 'heap' is taken as a measurement of the workability.

(b) *The Slab Test.* This concerns the surface texture of the concrete when deposited in a mould of a thin section.

Table 1 recommends suitable workabilities of concrete for various uses; the 'compacting factor' figures refer to the compacting factor test for workability described in the D.S.I.R. *Road Research Technical Paper* No. 5(a). The slumps specified in the Table are only an approximate guide, because, as explained previously, the slump test is unreliable when varying aggregates are encountered.

Good compaction of the concrete, and hence a high strength concrete with a good finish, can be obtained by manipulation of the grading and type of the aggregates, the use of proprietary additives, employment of vibration, and use of a high water content. This latter idea must be avoided as much as possible as it also decreases the strength of the concrete as explained later; it can however be used with advantage when combined with a 'vacuum' process (see §1.4). As mentioned previously a high strength concrete requires to be as free from voids as possible. If water in excess of the amount required for the chemical reaction with the cement is present in the mix, this water remains in a free state and the concrete sets around the drops of water. Such particles of water eventually evaporate into the atmosphere leaving pores and voids in the concrete resulting in weakness and permeability.

The effect of the water to cement ratio on the strength of the concrete was first realized by Duff Abrams of Lewis Institute, Chicago, in 1918, who stated that the strength of any 'workable' concrete was dependent upon the water to cement ratio alone. In other words this theory of Abrams means that for equal water to cement ratios the strength of a concrete of say a 1:2:4 mix is the same as that of a concrete of a 1:1:2 or of a 1:1½:3 mix; assuming the same cement and degree of compaction

TABLE 1

Degree of workability	Slump in inches	Compacting factor		Use for which concrete is suitable
		Small apparatus	Large apparatus	
'Very low'	0 to 1	0·78	0·80	Vibrated concrete in roads or other large sections
'Low'	1 to 2	0·85	0·87	Mass concrete foundations without vibration. Simple reinforced sections with vibration
'Medium'	2 to 4	0·92	0·935	For normal reinforced work without vibration and heavily reinforced sections with vibration
'High'	4 to 7	0·95	0·96	For sections with congested reinforcement. Not normally suitable for vibration.

are used and the conditions of curing and the age at comparison of strengths are equal for all of the mixes. The types of aggregates used can be varied providing the concrete does not fail by the fracture of such aggregates. The workability of the above mixes would be considerably different; it would be necessary for example, with certain low water to cement ratios, to vibrate the 1:2:4 mix to achieve the same compaction as could be obtained without vibration in the case of the comparable 1:1:2 mix. The D.S.I.R. (*Road Research Technical Paper* No. 5. H.M. Stationery Office, 1947) extended this proposition to 'unworkable' mixes providing such mixes were fully compacted. The strength of concrete increases as the water to cement ratio is decreased, providing the water present is sufficient to allow the full chemical reaction to occur with the cement. If the water is less than this amount, then a decrease in strength is experienced, as would be expected, and in the limit, it is obvious that if no water were present at all, then no chemical reaction could occur and the concrete would have no strength whatsoever. Figure 2 shows the relationship between the crushing strength and the water to cement ratio for 4-in. cubes of fully compacted concrete for mixes of various proportions.

Only the compressive crushing strength of concrete has been mentioned so far; it is generally accepted that this is a fairly reliable guide to the tensile and shear strengths, the modulus of rupture, the resistance to abrasion, wear, durability to the weather, density, porosity and watertightness.

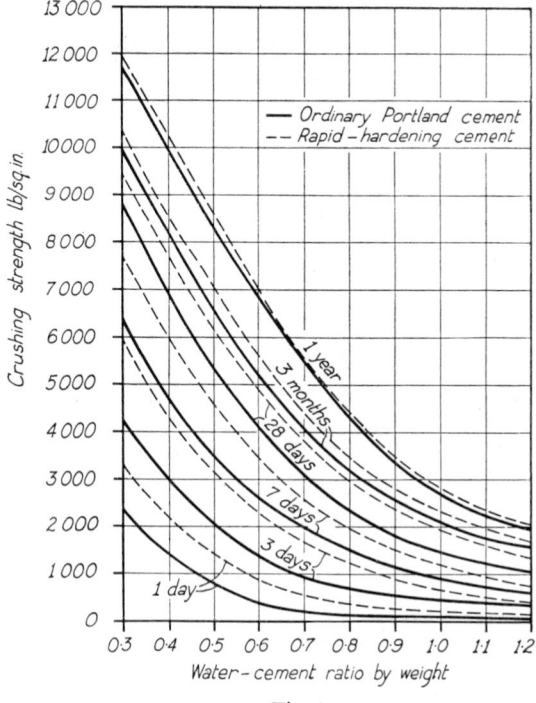

Fig. 2.

B.S. C.P. 114 (1957) specifies a standard compressive test as mentioned above, and also a standard test for the modulus of rupture. This latter test gives greater values than those obtained from tension tests made on say *standard briquettes*, which are described in B.S.S. 12 (1958). The cross-section of the briquette which is tested in tension is one inch square, the specimen being primarily designed for testing cements by determining the strengths of their sand and cement mortar mixtures. Larger specimens should be used for tension tests when the maximum size of the aggregate is greater than ⅜ in.

Shear in concrete beams is thought of in terms of *diagonal tension* and consequently the tensile strength of concrete is more relevant than the pure shearing strength. The pure shearing strength can be obtained from torsion tests of cylinders of concrete. The distribution of shear stress in such tests however is not the same as experienced in, say, a punching shear test.

1.4 Vacuum concrete

The concrete is made sufficiently wet to be placed and compacted easily and then the vacuum process removes water from the concrete, so that it finally has a low water to cement ratio. The water is extracted through mats placed in contact with the concrete. These mats are such that only water, and no cement, nor fines out of the aggregates can be sucked from the concrete by the vacuum pump. Side shutters can usually be removed immediately afterwards if desired as the concrete has almost zero slump.

1.5 Vibrated concrete

Concretes with low water to cement ratios can be placed and compacted by internal or external vibrators. External vibrators usually consist of motors with heavy cams on their shafts so that the shafts are out of balance. The vibrators are fastened to the mould. Internal vibrators are of a 'poker' type and can be held in the hand and immersed in the concrete where required. They are the more efficient for compaction and do not require the strong moulds, which are often necessary for the external vibrators. If sufficiently dry mixes are used the sides of the moulds can be removed immediately after vibration; there are in fact beam-making machines where the concrete is compacted by vibration, then the sides removed immediately, and the beam dragged away along skids on its pallet.

Most block-making machines employ pressure as well as vibration. Here again solid and hollow blocks can be removed immediately from the block-making machine on their pallets.

Workmen, when not strictly supervised, tend to make concrete extremely wet. Vibration does not increase the workability of such concrete and might easily be detrimental by causing segregation of the constitutents of the concrete, the gravel tending to sink to the bottom, and the sand and cement to float to the top of the concrete. Such segregation can even occur with very dry mixes if the vibration is sustained for a long enough period. The vibration employed with an apparently dry mix should be just sufficient to make the concrete flow into the sharp arises of the mould and around the reinforcement. Such concrete can have no slump so that the sides of the mould can often be removed in a few hours and a really excellent strength of concrete results.

1.6 Gap graded concrete

The principle of this method is to omit certain 'undesirable' sizes of aggregates from the gradings specified by the relevant British Standards (see Fig. 1). Such undesirable sizes are those which prevent the efficient packing of the other sizes. This does not apply to what is known as 'no fines concrete', in which coarse aggregate is mixed with cement, and sand is omitted. If desired the smaller sizes of the coarse aggregate can also be omitted, or one size only of aggregate can be used with cement. 'No fines' concrete is required to contain a multitude of voids to give good thermal insulation and these voids need to be large enough to prevent the movement of water through the concrete by capillary attraction. *In-situ* 'no fines' concrete walls have been used in Britain for housing, the idea being that good thermal insulation is achieved and that rain beating on a wall only penetrates a short horizontal distance into the wall before having dropped to the bottom of the wall, there being no capillary paths to conduct the water completely through the wall.

This section will now exclude 'no-fines' concrete and discuss the more common aim of *gap grading* which is to achieve strength from the efficient packing of the aggregate. By careful packing, a strong wall can be built without using any cement. If a cement paste were to fill all the minor voids in such a wall, then a very strong construction would result, and this would be the ideal aimed at by the advocates of the gap grading of concrete.

A multitude of spheres of diameter D have a rhombohedral form of packing. These can be termed 'major spheres', and spheres of diameter $0\cdot414D$, known as 'major occupational spheres', can fit into the voids between the major spheres. The latter spheres would, mathematically, constitute our coarse aggregate. The fine aggregate would consist mathematically of 'minor occupational spheres' of diameter $0\cdot225D$, which would fit into the remaining voids. The voids now remaining can be fitted by 'admittance spheres' of diameter $0\cdot155D$. Cement would then occupy the remaining voids and a mathematically-perfect compact mix would result. Such a mix however could not normally be cast in this ideal fashion and consequently some authorities[9] consider that only the 'major' and 'admittance' spheres are of practical value in designing a mix.

Mixes therefore are often designed with one size of coarse aggregate (for example $\frac{3}{4}$ in.) and a sand, all the particles of which can pass through the voids in the compacted coarse aggregate. The sand is designed to fill the voids in the coarse aggregate and the cement is designed to fill all the remaining voids. The particles of sand must not be smaller than necessary, as this will increase the total surface area to be wetted with water and cement, and consequently a wetter mix (giving a weaker concrete) would be required for any requisite workability. Irrespective of the calculation as suggested above, the sand should be sufficient to distribute itself uniformly throughout the mix under practical conditions. When the sand is less than 18% of the mix it is difficult to obtain uniformity even under laboratory conditions. Mixes are often designed and then modified to suit the particular site conditions of mixing and compacting.

To increase workability it is advantageous to reduce the surface area of all the aggregates in a unit volume; this can be done by using larger particles. The largest aggregate possible should therefore be used, consistent with the minimum clearances allowed; such as in the sections of beams.

Gap grading enables leaner and dryer mixes to be used, the absence of many intermediate sizes of aggregates having reduced the specific surface area of the aggregates and therefore having increased workability. The lean mixes usually utilized, however, make vibration almost essential. Such concrete, being made of leaner and dryer mixes than a conventional concrete of equivalent strength, will therefore experience less shrinkage and hence possess better weathering qualities than the conventional concrete.

Compressive forces on the gap graded concrete described are transmitted from particle to particle of the coarse aggregate and not through any cement and sand particles. Consequently the creep associated with such concrete is low. By using the coarse aggregate to the best advantage higher strengths should be obtainable than with conventional concrete. Owing to the efficient packing and good workability, a gap graded concrete will contain less cement (and therefore cost less) than a conventional mix of equal strength.

A coarse aggregate as used in a conventional mix, that is having a grading similar to those illustrated in Fig. 1, will experience a fair amount of segregation during transportation, and pouring into and out of the lorries. The rain also helps segregation of the stockpile. Gap grading avoids these disadvantages by requiring only single sizes of coarse aggregate.

Some authorities advocate two different single sizes of coarse aggregates to be used with sand and cement in a mix. Gap graded concretes as lean as 1 (cement):2·45 (sand):6·59 (gravel), with a water:cement ratio of 0·51, increase in strength with age in a similar fashion to conventional concretes.[9] Because of the packing of the aggregate of a gap graded concrete, vertical shutters can often be removed immediately after casting. Walls and columns can then be trowelled if desired or sprayed with a light water jet to expose the aggregate.

One disadvantage of gap grading is that if the single-size aggregates supplied contain over $2\frac{1}{2}\%$ by weight of undesirable particles, this upsets the grading which is very sensitive to such intrusions. If however such irregularities are to be expected in the supply then the mix can be calculated accordingly from the resultant bulk density of the aggregate.

1.7 Curing of concrete

After setting or solidifying, concrete increases in strength with age, for example see Fig. 3. The strength at a particular age can be further increased by suitable curing of the concrete whilst it is maturing. Such curing comprises the application of heat and the preservation of moisture within the concrete. The application of heat speeds up the chemical reaction and consequently the rate of hardening of the concrete.

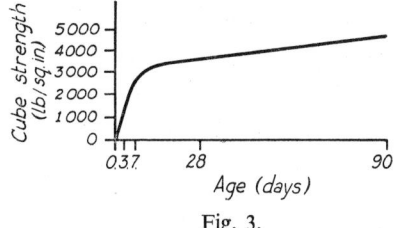

Fig. 3.

It can be imagined that preventing the escape of moisture from the concrete enables previously unwetted minute particles of cement to participate in the cementing action. If heat is applied to accelerate the hardening of the concrete it is therefore important not to expel the water held within the concrete.

In other words, if heat is applied a high humidity is also desirable; steam is therefore a most suitable medium for this purpose. Steam curing can be done at atmospheric pressure or under pressure. The latter method is more effective but far more expensive as pressure chambers have to be constructed for say the treatment of precast members. For example, the $\frac{1}{2}$-hour strength of concrete steam cured under pressure could attain the 28-day strength of an identical concrete maturing in air without any special treatment. Steam curing and indeed heat in any form must not be applied to high-alumina cement concretes. This is a further example of some of the widely differing properties of concrete made with high alumina cement and concrete made with Portland cements. Possibly because of the relatively great heat evolved during the hydration of high alumina cement, steam curing has a detrimental effect upon such concretes. At any age, the strength of high-alumina cement concrete is seriously reduced by the application of heat in conjunction with a high humidity (as in certain tropical climates).

Increasing the strength of concrete by preventing the water used in mixing from escaping is usually done in one of the following ways:

(a) Flooding or submerging the concrete in water. The floors of basements and reservoirs can fairly easily be flooded with water. Precast concrete units can be immersed in water in special tanks.

(b) Treating the surface of the concrete so that it cannot dry out. Proprietary products exist for painting the surface of the concrete or alternatively for applying coverings which adhere to the concrete. These latter coverings are often used for maturing concrete roads.

(c) Concrete is often covered with damp sand or hessian fabrics, which are always kept damp by watering periodically.

1.8   Design of concrete mixes

Most commonly a concrete mix is designed to give the specified strength at the minimum cost. The cost depends upon the value of the materials, upon the labour required for batching, mixing, transporting, placing and trowelling, and upon the method of curing adopted.

Codes of practice specify the minimum crushing strength required for a concrete at a particular age (often 28 days and 7 days). To comply with the minimum specification of strength, the concrete must be designed to have an average crushing strength in excess of this value. The magnitude of this necessary excess of average strength over minimum strength will obviously depend upon how consistent the quality of the concrete can be maintained during manufacture. Table 2 gives a relationship suggested by the D.S.I.R. between the minimum and average crushing strengths of works cubes for different works conditions.

TABLE 2

Conditions	Minimum strength as percentage of average strength
Very good control with weight batching, moisture determinations on aggregates, etc.; constant supervision ..	75
Fair control with weight batching ..	60
Poor control; volume batching of aggregates	40

After deciding upon the average strength of concrete required to give the specified minimum strength, the necessary water to cement ratio can be obtained from Fig. 2 (incidentally these graphs assume that the concrete is cured in air). The desirable workability can be ascertained using Table 1 as a guide, and then the most suitable aggregate to cement ratio can be obtained from Table 3. This table gives such ratios for different gradings (as specified in Fig. 1), workabilities, water to cement ratios, and types of aggregates.

TABLE 3

(1) ¾-in. Rounded Aggregate.

Degrees of workability	Very low				Low				Medium				High			
Grading of aggregate (Curve No. on Fig. 1)	1	2	3	4	1	2	3	4	1	2	3	4	1	2	3	4
Water cement ratio by weight 0.35	4·5	4·5	3·5	3·2	3·8	3·6	3·2	3·1	3·1	3·0	2·8	2·7	2·8	2·8	2·6	2·5
0.40	6·6	6·3	5·3	4·5	5·3	5·1	4·5	4·1	4·2	4·2	3·9	3·7	3·6	3·7	3·5	3·3
0.45	8·0	7·7	6·7	5·8	6·9	6·6	5·9	5·1	5·3	5·3	5·0	4·5	4·6	4·8	4·5	4·1
0.50	—	—	8·0	7·0	8·2	8·0	7·0	6·0	6·3	6·3	5·9	5·4	5·5	5·7	5·3	4·8
0.55	—	—	—	8·1	—	—	8·2	6·9	7·3	7·3	7·4	6·4	6·3	6·5	6·1	5·5
0.60	—	—	—	—	—	—	—	7·7	—	—	8·0	7·2	×	7·2	6·8	6·1
0.65	—	—	—	—	—	—	—	8·5	—	—	—	7·8	×	7·7	7·4	6·6
0.70	—	—	—	—	—	—	—	—	—	—	—	—	×	—	7·9	7·2

(2) ¾-in. Irregular Gravel Aggregate.

Degrees of workability	Very low				Low				Medium				High			
Grading of aggregate (Curve No. on Fig. 1)	1	2	3	4	1	2	3	4	1	2	3	4	1	2	3	4
Water cement ratio by weight 0.35	3·7	3·7	3·5	3·0	3·0	3·0	3·0	2·7	2·6	2·6	2·7	2·4	2·4	2·5	2·5	2·2
0.40	4·8	4·7	4·7	4·0	3·9	3·9	3·8	3·5	3·3	3·4	3·5	3·2	3·1	3·2	3·2	2·9
0.45	6·0	5·8	5·8	5·0	4·8	4·8	4·6	4·3	4·0	4·1	4·2	3·9	×	3·9	3·9	3·5
0.50	7·2	6·8	6·5	5·9	5·5	5·5	5·4	5·0	4·6	4·8	4·8	4·5	×	4·4	4·4	4·1
0.55	8·3	7·8	7·3	6·7	6·2	6·2	6·0	5·7	×	5·4	5·4	5·1	×	4·8	4·9	4·7
0.60	9·4	8·6	8·0	7·4	6·8	6·9	6·7	6·2	×	6·0	6·0	5·6	×	×	5·4	5·2
0.65	—	—	—	8·0	7·4	7·5	7·3	6·8	×	×	6·4	6·1	×	×	5·8	5·6
0.70	—	—	—	—	8·0	8·0	7·7	7·4	×	×	6·8	6·6	×	×	6·2	6·1

(3) ¾-in. Crushed Rock Aggregate.

Degrees of workability	Very low				Low				Medium				High			
Grading of aggregate (Curve No. on Fig. 1)	1	2	3	4	1	2	3	4	1	2	3	4	1	2	3	4
Water-cement ratio by weight 0.35	3·2	3·0	2·9	2·7	2·7	2·7	2·5	2·4	2·4	2·4	2·3	2·2	2·2	2·3	2·1	2·1
0.40	4·5	4·2	3·7	3·5	3·5	3·5	3·2	3·0	3·1	3·1	2·9	2·7	2·9	2·9	2·8	2·6
0.45	5·5	5·0	4·6	4·3	4·3	4·2	3·9	3·7	3·7	3·7	3·4	3·3	3·5	3·5	3·2	3·1
0.50	6·5	5·8	5·4	5·0	5·0	4·9	4·5	4·3	4·2	4·2	3·9	3·8	×	3·9	3·8	3·5
0.55	7·2	6·6	6·0	5·6	5·7	5·4	5·0	4·8	4·7	4·7	4·5	4·3	×	×	4·3	4·0
0.60	7·8	7·2	6·6	6·3	6·3	6·0	5·6	5·3	×	5·2	4·9	4·8	×	×	4·7	4·4
0.65	8·3	7·8	7·2	6·9	6·9	6·5	6·1	5·8	×	5·7	5·4	5·2	×	×	5·1	4·9
0.70	8·7	8·3	7·7	7·5	7·4	7·0	6·5	6·3	×	6·2	5·8	5·7	×	×	5·5	5·3

— Indicates that the mix was outside the range tested.

× Indicates that the mix would segregate.

EXAMPLE 1.8.1

To design a concrete mix for a pretensioned prestressed beam to have a minimum crushing strength of 5,100 lb/sq. in. at an age of 7 days.

The coarse aggregate to be used is a ¾ in. and down rounded aggregate with a grading curve approximating to curve 2 on Fig. 1. Vibration is to be employed and the prestressing wires cause little obstruction to the placing of the concrete. We shall assume however in this example that the beam is of I-section with narrow flanges and web. Hence it is decided that a 'medium' workability is desirable (see Table 1).

The concreting is constantly supervised, and weigh-batching is employed, frequent moisture tests being made on the aggregates.

Referring to Table 2, the minimum strength will be 75% of the average strength. The average crushing strength to be obtained is therefore $\dfrac{5 \cdot 100}{0 \cdot 75} = 6{,}800 \text{ lb/sq. in.}$

Using rapid-hardening Portland cement and consulting Fig. 2, the necessary water to cement ratio is 0·35.

From Table 3, the aggregate:cement ratio is therefore 3.

1.9 Shrinkage

When cement, sand, gravel, and water are mixed together the gross volume decreases as the finer particles arrange themselves in the interstices of the larger particles. This shrinkage continues as the concrete is being worked into place. Evaporation of water in the mix also decreases the volume of such concrete. It is possible to fill a mould, for example a 6 in. cube box, and observe the concrete retract into the mould. Shrinkage, when the concrete is in a fluid state, does not matter structurally because no internal stresses can be instigated.

There is an inaccurately known point at which the concrete changes from a fluid to a solid and fragile material; fragile because at this stage it is most immature. The exact time when this occurs depends upon the proportions of the mix, the type of the cement, and the humidity and temperature of the atmosphere.

After this point, further shrinkage of the concrete will cause internal stresses and even cracks to occur in the concrete. As mentioned above, the time when the transition occurs from liquid to solid is not precisely determinable, and therefore it is difficult to know exactly when to commence measuring the shrinkage of the concrete in its solid state.

Measurements of the coefficient of shrinkage are possibly commenced too late to be of real mathematical value, because such readings are commenced at no agreed age but just when the specimen is hard enough to strip and handle for the purposes of the test. On such a basis the shrinkage coefficient can be of the order of 0·0005 at an age of 12 months and a typical relationship between shrinkage and age is illustrated in Fig. 4. Initially the rate of shrinkage is high so that the error in not knowing the precise time to start measurements is quite appreciable.

With the above coefficient, and supposing, for simplicity, the modulus of elasticity (see §1.9) of concrete to be 4×10^6 lb/sq. in., then if the concrete were restricted from shrinking the tensile stress induced in the concrete would be $0 \cdot 0005 \times 4 \times 10^6 = 2{,}000$ lb/sq. in. The concrete would certainly crack as its ultimate tensile strength would only be about 400 lb/sq. in. The coefficient of shrinkage is less for a lean mix than for a rich mix (i.e., rich in cement content), it is less for a low water to cement ratio than a high one, is very sensitive to the method of curing, and is influenced by all the other possible variables to a less influential extent.

As implied above, shrinkage continues after the concrete has solidified as and when further water evaporates. The chemical reaction of cement with water is still subject to very divergent views. This reaction does however appear to continue in the concrete indefinitely and we do know

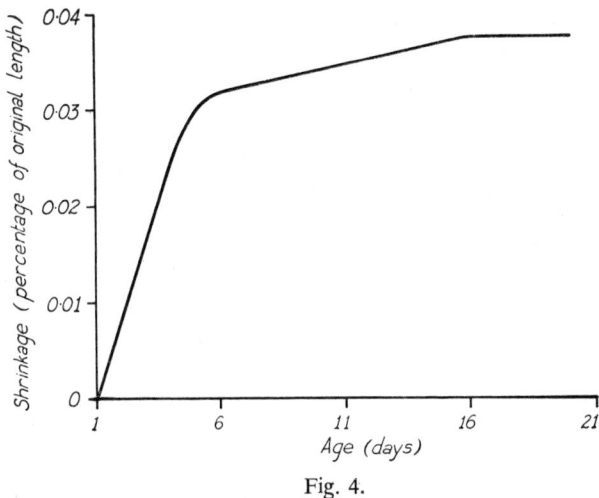

Fig. 4.

that a gel is formed which contracts upon desiccation and becomes very hard. If concrete is submerged in water this cement gel expands with considerable force, so that the whole mass of concrete expands. Such an expansion however can never equal the shrinkage which has already taken place. On drying this concrete in air shrinkage again occurs. Therefore, when concrete is subjected to continual wetting and drying, as for example due to tidal action, it experiences corresponding expansions and contractions. If concrete is cast beneath water then it does not shrink at all but expands, owing to the cement gel absorbing water.

If a mass of concrete shrinks (or expands) uniformly and its movement is not restricted by any external forces, then it is easy to imagine that no internal stresses can be induced in the concrete. This particular case seldom happens in practice; usually any movement of the concrete is restricted internally by reinforcement embedded in the concrete, and often externally by its surroundings. Also, the surface of concrete will often dry out (and therefore shrink) faster than the internal particles of concrete.

When the concrete of a beam containing reinforcement changes from the fluid state to the solid state, the concrete continues to shrink but also will commence to bond to the reinforcement (see §1.13). The resistance of the reinforcement to contraction opposes the shrinkage of the concrete. Consequently the concrete near to the reinforcement is in tension, a bond stress is developed between the concrete and the reinforcement, and therefore the reinforcement is in compression. For a minutely short length of the reinforcement bar the resistance to tension of the concrete will be greater than the resistance to bond, hence plastic yield will occur of this bond stress. For a long length of the bar the resistance to bond will be greater than the resistance of the concrete to tension. Consequently the concrete will crack. The spacing of the cracks will therefore be such that the bond resistance between adjacent cracks is sufficient to overcome the tensile strength of the concrete.

It seems almost certain that shrinkage cracks very often exist in reinforced concrete beams at intervals along the length of the reinforcement. Such cracks are usually too small to be observed with the instruments normally available for research in laboratories. When a reinforced concrete beam is tested, however, cracks can usually be observed at a lighter loading than predicted from the modulus of rupture of the concrete. This either indicates that such cracks are already present in the concrete due to shrinkage, or that the internal tensile stresses in the concrete due to shrinkage aid the externally applied moment in overcoming the modulus of rupture of the concrete. In other words shrinkage causes the concrete to be 'prestressed' before the member is subjected to the external loading. This prestress generally induces tensile stresses at unfavourable locations and causes cracks to appear sooner than if this shrinkage effect were not present. To reverse this process would give a concrete beam, for example, an increased resistance to cracking and would therefore be highly desirable. The science of 'Prestressed Concrete' (see later) concerns methods of performing this function.

The phenomenon of shrinkage is one factor limiting the permissible tensile stress in the reinforcement, specified by several authorities, when no attempt is made to ascertain the stresses due to shrinkage. Such a reduction in the allowable tensile stress in the reinforcement reduces the size of the cracks in the concrete in the immediate proximity of the reinforcement, and hence compensates for the detrimental effects of the shrinkage.

Designs concerning conventional reinforced concrete work do not usually attempt to estimate the quantitative effect of shrinkage, chiefly because such calculations cannot be made with any degree of confidence and the basic assumptions required to build up any mathematical analysis can be adversely criticised. Prestressed concrete designers only treat shrinkage in a very elementary fashion, namely as a 'loss' which will reduce the precompressing force. This is only substantially true in the case of post-tensioned concrete members containing no longitudinal reinforcement bonded to the concrete.

Even though shrinkage stresses can cause early formation of cracks, and prestressing the concrete with compressive stresses can retard the formation of cracks, the ultimate strength of a beam is not altered by either of these two effects, because when cracks do occur such initial internal stress systems are then released. The prime concern in design is the ultimate strength. The next important factor is the size of the cracks at working loads. Shrinkage only affects the latter consideration, and, as mentioned before, in practical design the permissible working stress in the tensile reinforcement is limited to compensate for this effect.

The particles at the surface of a member usually experience different conditions of curing to the internal particles of the member. The rates of shrinkage therefore differ in such zones and this 'differential shrinkage' can cause troublesome stresses, cracks, and movements. Such an effect is possibly a cause of the surface crazing which can occur on artificial stones for example. It can also cause ground floor and road slabs to warp. This effect can obviously be reduced by endeavouring to cure the surfaces in a similar fashion to the curing experienced by the internal fibres of a concrete member. These latter are fairly well sealed from the atmosphere so that to reduce differential shrinkage it is therefore desirable to seal the surfaces from the atmosphere. The most effective way of achieving this would be to immerse the concrete member in water for as long a period as possible. It is often more economical in practice to approach the ideal by either covering with damp hessian sacks, sand, or with proprietary waterproof sheets; or just spraying periodically with water. A granolithic topping on a floor is very vulnerable to the detrimental effects of differential shrinkage and is usually kept damp for as long a period as is practicable and this should be at least 7 days.

Shrinkage must always be borne in mind in the design and construction of structures. Whenever possible, (without undue expenditure), concreting programmes aim at minimizing the detrimental effects of shrinkage. For example, ground floor 'slabs on solid', that is floor slabs laid upon *blindings* which are placed over either suitable sub-soil or suitably consolidated hardcore, in other words, floor slabs which are not suspended are often concreted in numerous independent portions each of about 15 ft square. Such portions are able to shrink to some extent before being joined together. Plain concrete roads are also constructed in a piecemeal fashion. This is not considered necessary when reinforcement is present; possibly numerous minute cracks are formed, but as such reinforcement resists shrinkage the overall contraction is negligible.

Many engineers will attribute almost any serious crack in a structure to shrinkage. This is usually a fallacy because the reinforcement of most structures has a considerable resistance to the forces exerted by the shrinkage of the concrete, such that shrinkage cracks in a long structure will take the form of very small cracks fairly regularly spaced throughout the length of the structure. Certain individual large cracks are often caused by thermal expansion and contraction and settlement.

1.10 Relationship between stress and strain

If a graph is plotted relating stress and strain, the shape of the curve obtained is very much influenced by the rate or rates at which the stress is applied. Furthermore it is also dependent upon the strength of the

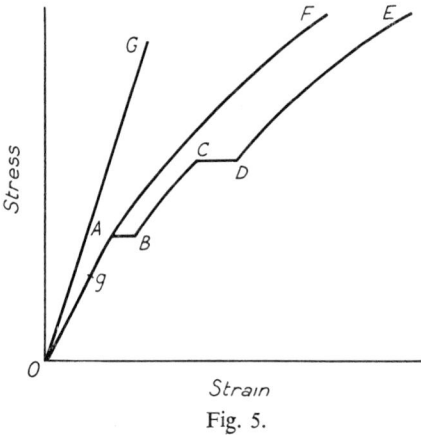

Fig. 5.

concrete under question and indeed to some degree upon all the other possible variables of the specimen.

Fig. 5 shows a graph OAF which is typical of a concrete specimen loaded at a uniform rate. If the process of loading had been halted at the point *A* the concrete would have continued to strain under this particular constant stress. After a certain lapse of time, when the strain had reached the point *B*, the loading is recommenced at a similar rate as previously. The relationship now traces out the curve *BC*, and supposing the loading is stopped at *C*, the same phenomenon of 'creep' occurs as on the stretch *A* to *B*, that is the specimen strains or 'creeps' under constant stress until the loading is recommenced at the point *D* and the relationship then takes the form represented by *DE* on the graph.

This phenomenon of *creep* (known in the U.S.A. as *plastic strain* or *time-flow*) has been the subject of many investigations. Fig. 6 shows a curve *CD* which relates the creep (or increase in strain) to time when the specimen is subjected to a particular constant stress. In this instance it took 5 seconds to apply the stress, so that the readings commenced from this time. It was originally imagined that if this loading had been instantaneous and the observations of creep had been commenced immediately then this curve would take the form *BCD* in Fig. 6. This is not so; a correction to the relationship is represented by *ACD* as explained later.

One of the authors[1] constructed an apparatus which could load a specimen and record the strains at an extremely high speed. This enabled him to obtain readings of creep after an instantaneous loading to the

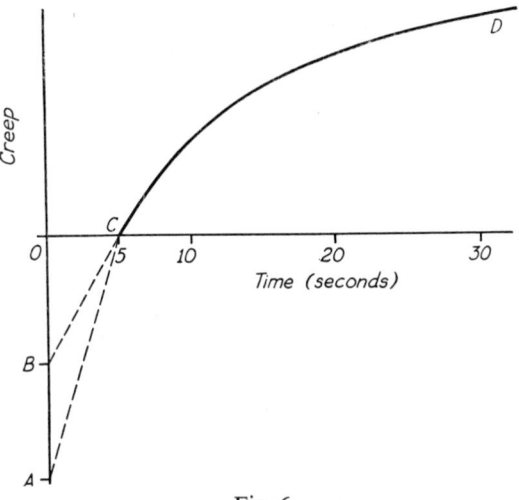

Fig. 6.

stress in question, and hence he plotted the curve *AC* in Fig. 6 mentioned above.

This same apparatus enabled an interesting relationship to be discovered between stress and strain. At any particular stress an instantaneous increase in stress always gave a directly proportional increase in strain. For example, supposing the stress was instantaneously increased from 400 to 410 lb/sq. in. then the increase in strain was found to be the same as would have been obtained if the stress had been increased from say 800 to 810 lb/sq. in. On such a basis the linear relationship *OG* shown in Fig. 5 was obtained.

Numerous investigators have endeavoured to relate creep to the other possible variables of concrete, and several different formulae have been proposed. The majority of these agree that the creep is directly proportional to the constant stress under which the creep occurs and also proportional to a function of the time the specimen has been subjected to the stress concerned. Furthermore all seem to consider that stress and time are the principal factors involved. The D.S.I.R. states that the creep is equal to

$$Kp(1 - e^{b-ct^n})$$

where K, b and c are constants, p is the stress, t is the time in which the stress has been applied and n is a constant equal to 0·4. To quote another example, Lorman states that creep is equal to

$$\left(\frac{mt}{C + t}\right) \cdot p$$

where C and m are empirical constants. If $t \to \infty$, this formula gives the creep as equal to mp, so that m is the ultimate creep for unit stress.

From the above, it is distinctly noticeable that with regard to the relationship between stress and strain, concrete is comparable in behaviour to natural stones and timber, but certainly not to steel, because there is no period of proportionality, no marked elastic limit and no yield point.

Apologies must therefore be made for mentioning the term *modulus of elasticity* in connection with concrete. It will no doubt alarm the scientifically minded student to read that prior to B.S. C.P. 114 (1957) most Codes of Practice required concrete to be designed principally as an elastic material.

The reason for this illogical state of affairs is that practice led design and design led scientific knowledge in the concrete industry, and the pioneers of design endeavoured to treat the subject in a similar fashion to the design of steel structures by the elastic methods with which they were well acquainted. Why do not all authorities in the light of modern knowledge try to design concrete in accordance with the way in which it behaves? Perhaps the answer to this question is because firstly, experience of multitudes of structures over many years gives engineers confidence in perpetuating the original elastic ideas; secondly, such methods are not highly erroneous for estimating stresses at working loads; thirdly, many engineers are reluctant to change design techniques which they have mastered. Codes of Practice, however, often illogically increase allowable stresses in the concrete in the light of plastic behaviour even though the elastic design methods are still employed.

For conventional design therefore some value or values must be attributed to a rather mythical modulus of elasticity. Fig. 7 illustrates a typical stress: strain diagram for a concrete specimen and shows various ideas which have been propounded for the modulus of elasticity. OT_0 is tangential to the function at the origin and represents what is known as the *initial tangent modulus*. TPT' is a tangent at the point P and is known as the *tangent modulus* at this point. Similarly T_1QT_1' is the tangent modulus at point Q. The straight line PQ is called the *chord modulus* for the range P to Q. OP is the *secant modulus* for point P, and similarly OQ is the secant modulus for point Q. In Fig. 5 the slope of the curve OG is Evans' 'short range' or *instantaneous modulus* of elasticity. This latter modulus is suitable for use in predicting the stresses caused in concrete structures due to shocks from earthquakes or blasts from bombing.

The maximum permissible compressive stress in bending at working loads is often specified to be about one third of the crushing strength. Up to such working stresses the relationship between stress and strain approximates with reasonable accuracy to a straight line, and most engineers utilize a secant modulus of elasticity corresponding to the

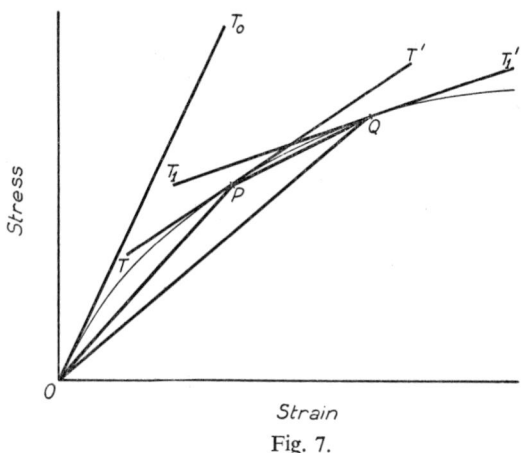

Fig. 7.

maximum allowable working stress. This is the modulus of elasticity which the authors will imply when subsequently referring to the modulus of elasticity of concrete, unless specifically mentioned otherwise.

Referring to Fig. 5 if, say, points A and B were at the allowable working stress of the concrete under investigation, then the moduli of elasticity at points A and B respectively are obviously different. The modulus of elasticity is therefore greatly affected by creep. It ought to be mentioned immediately that designers commonly make no separate calculation for creep (i.e. with the methods described above) but desire the value of the modulus of elasticity to take creep into account. Notice how this idea of an elastic modulus becomes more and more illogical, but in this instance it should be realized that it is not easy to separate elasticity from creep.

Concrete at the age of one year can have a modulus of elasticity of about one third of its value at the age of one month. This phenomenon is due to the effect of creep. The value obtained from a test at the age of one month might be say 4×10^6 lb/sq. in., the loading being applied over a period of say one hour. If the specimen is left to creep for a further 11 months under its working stress then the strain would have increased such that the modulus of elasticity could be say 1.33×10^6 lb/sq. in. When such tests are made, specimens are cast out of the same mix for the purpose of measuring the shrinkage which occurs, in the above case for example, between the age of one month and one year. This shortening due to shrinkage can then be deducted from the extensometer reading to give the true creep or plastic strain over this period independently of the effect of shrinkage.

It is generally acknowledged that the modulus of elasticity depends chiefly upon the speed of loading, the time the load is sustained (the creep which occurs), and the compressive strength of the concrete. From certain tests made in the U.S.A. it would appear that the type of aggregate should be added to this list. These tests conclude that concrete made with Waylite aggregate (which is similar to British foamed slag) has a modulus of elasticity of only two thirds of the value of a conventional type of concrete of the same ultimate compressive strength. The modulus is of course dependent to a lesser extent upon all the other possible variables associated with concrete.

The American Concrete Institute Code of 1956 gives the modulus of elasticity of concrete as

30,000/(the crushing strength of the standard concrete cylinder).

The British Code of Practice previously varied the modulus according to the concrete mix (i.e. strength) but now adopts a constant value of 2×10^6 lb/sq. in. The only merit of this idea is that of standardization, the value taken being an average value of different concretes of varying ages.

The ratio of the moduli of elasticity of steel and concrete respectively is known as the *modular ratio*. For example the modular ratio adopted for all concrete mixes by the current British Code of Practice is 30×10^6 divided by 2×10^6 which equals 15.

The fact that the modulus of elasticity decreases with the lapse of time causes effects which characterize reinforced concrete construction. In general, there is a tendency for the concrete to deform continually under the sustained load.† In beams this causes the deflection to increase with the age of the concrete, and a redistribution of the relative stresses sustained by the concrete and steel respectively. The concrete might be said to relax, consequently decreasing the maximum stress to which it is

---

† The remainder of this paragraph will be understood better when later sections of this book have been read.

subjected and increasing the stresses in the compression and tensile reinforcements. Columns behave similarly in that the stresses in the concrete are decreased at the expense of the stresses in the reinforcement.
If a column is subjected to an eccentric loading, then creep allows the
lateral flexure to increase and consequently the eccentricity of the loading is increased. In a similar fashion the lateral instability of columns is
slightly increased.

It is interesting to notice here an illogicality of ideas in the British
Code of Practice prior to 1957. The stress allowed in the compression
reinforcement of beams was required to be computed from an elastic
analysis, whereas the stress allowed in the compression reinforcement of
columns could be computed such that the concrete was acknowledged to
have 'crept' and the design in this instance could be described as 'plastic'
as opposed to 'elastic'.

When concrete is prestressed, the phenomenon of creep is associated
with a relaxation of the stresses in the concrete, and this constitutes an
undesirable loss of prestress. This will be more fully discussed later.

1.11 Types of reinforcement

The majority of reinforced concrete construction employs 'black' mild
steel bars of circular cross-section complying with B.S. 785 (in Britain).
On the Continent poorer quality steels are also used for reinforced concrete work. In the past, engineers have often been worried that such
bars might not grip or 'bond' to the concrete. Consequently numerous
bars have been devised to create mechanical bonds between the steel and
the concrete. As concrete practice and scientific knowledge advanced,
it became accepted that a mild steel bar of circular cross-section could
grip adequately to the concrete to develop its full tensile strength. Lugs
and other devices on such bars are therefore superfluous from a commercial point of view.

The British Code of Practice, for example, now allows high tensile
steel to be used in conventional reinforced concrete providing the bar
mechanically bonds with the concrete. If a mild steel bar of square cross-
section is twisted, this 'cold working' converts it into high tensile steel (e.g.
'Square Grip' or 'Twisteel'). The bar has then such a shape that it can
mechanically grip to the concrete. Another popular bar in this country
and on the Continent is of Danish origin; a mild steel bar is
rolled with a slight patterning on its surface; this is then subjected to
'cold working' which consists of a tensioning and twisting action;
a high tensile bar with a mechanical bond results (known as 'Tentor').

Other types of high tensile bars recently produced in Britain for
use in conventional reinforced concrete are Unisteel 60 and GK 60.
These are both hot rolled high-tensile bars with deformed surfaces.

An advantage of using such bars is that the weight of steel required in a structure is reduced, so that although the cost of high tensile reinforcement is more than that of mild steel per ton, less is used, and the manufacturers of these proprietary bars often claim that the total cost of the reinforcement can be reduced. Less reinforcement requires to be bent and fixed so that this can usually be considered to be a saving, although sometimes higher rates have to be paid for bending and fixing certain bars with surface irregularities.

A disadvantage of high tensile bars is the phenomenon of 'overstrain' which occurs at bends of small curvature. For example it is often specified that a high tensile deformed bar should be capable of being bent around a pin six times its diameter without fracture, whereas a mild steel plain bar would be bent around a pin of twice its diameter for the 'cold bend test'. On this basis, stirrups should not therefore be made with high tensile deformed bars. * It has been recommended[2] that high tensile deformed bars should not be bent around a bend with an internal radius of less than eight times the diameter of the bar because of the danger of locally overstressing the concrete. Such a regulation makes difficult the detailing of the reinforcement transmitting bending moment from a beam into an external column. Haunches simplify this particular problem but such a solution is expensive in Britain. A disadvantage of high tensile bars, which is ignored by Codes of Practice, is that the percentage of longitudinal tensile reinforcement is reduced, and it has been proved by several investigators that this reduces the strength of beams in shear.

High tensile wires are used to make fabrics for reinforcing slabs (refer for example to B.S. 1221). Cross wires are welded to the main wires and enable the main high tensile wires to be mechanically bonded to the concrete. The chief advantage of such fabric reinforcements is the ease and consequently low cost of fixing. A disadvantage is the high cost of fabrics. Also fabrics do not commonly allow comparable economies to those effected by bending up or curtailing alternate bars in slabs. The steel over the supports of continuous slabs is far more rigid for concreting purposes when bars are used as opposed to fabrics. The main steel in a slab is sometimes inadequately anchored into the supporting beams when fabrics are used. The cross wires of B.S. fabrics do not satisfy the recommendation in B.S. 114 (1957) to the effect that the reinforcement in any direction should be not less than 0·15% of the gross cross-sectional area. Sometimes additional bars are laid on the fabric to supplement the area of the cross wires to comply with this

* Further information on this subject is given in 'Overstrain in high-tensile reinforcing bars at bends and in stirrups' by C. B. Wilby, *Indian Concrete Journal*, Jan. 1962. This shows that the problem is not always so difficult as it might appear.

regulation, but quite often the recommendation is ignored. It must not however be ignored when substantial temperature stresses are liable to occur or when the slab is of a substantial length (or width) in the direction of the cross wires.

For design purposes the British Code of Practice[3] allows round mild steel bars to have a tensile working stress of 20,000 lb/sq. in., and mechanically bonded high tensile bars to have a tensile working stress of 30,000 lb/sq. in.

The Code of Practice quoted in reference[4] for water retaining structures limits the stress in both mild steel and high tensile steel to 12,000 lb/sq. in. for reinforcement in liquid-retaining face. The idea is that if the steel stress is kept low then the adjacent cracks in the concrete are similarly small. This is not the full story however as mechanically bonded bars distribute such cracks far more uniformly, and at a given stress in the reinforcement the cracks will be more numerous and smaller for a mechanically bonded bar than for a plain bar[2]. Consequently the above mentioned regulation is inadequate for a high tensile bar which has a periphery which can develop a mechanical bond with the concrete.

Recommendations by the Ministry of Works for the design of structures with resistance to air raids and atom bombing do not allow high tensile steels to be stressed to anything like as great an amount as the stress allowable for mild steel reinforcements. The logic behind this idea is roughly that high tensile steel is more brittle than mild steel, so that its strength would be impaired by sudden shocks from the blasts of bombs.

For prestressed concrete, the wires commonly used at present in Britain are 0·08 in. (2 mm), 0·2 in. and 0·276 in. (7 mm) diameter and can be obtained with an ultimate strength of 130/140, 100/110, and 95/105 tons/sq. in. respectively. Such wires are also sold with indented surfaces and some types of wires are crimped. These endeavour to create a mechanical bond with the concrete, which, of course, is a desirable feature. Another method of attempting to obtain such a bond is by twisting together numbers of plain wires (usually two and three respectively). High tensile Lee-McCall bars are a proprietary system of bars used for prestressing purposes. Similar systems are in use on the Continent.

1.12 Advantages of conventional and prestressed reinforced concrete

Reinforced concrete has greater durability than competitive forms of construction, such as structural steelwork and timber. Prestressed concrete generally utilizes high grade concrete, has no cracks at working loads, and the wires can often be given a thicker covering of concrete; so that it can be claimed to be yet more durable than conventional reinforced concrete construction.

Reinforced concrete has greater resistance to fire than structural steel-work, aluminium, and timber, and indeed most multi-storey structural steelwork buildings are required to be completely clad with reinforced concrete, apart from the top storey, by many local by-laws in this country. The fire resistance of prestressed concrete in particular has been adversely criticised. Much of this criticism has been unfair; prestressed concrete can fail by sufficient exposure to fire, but when it does fail many forget to mention that conventional reinforced concrete would often also have failed. Not enough is possibly known about this subject and one must be very careful not to generalize because the particular design adopted has its own bearing upon the subject. A dense concrete as is more often associated with prestressed concrete has greater thermal conductivity but, of course, greater strength. Greater cover can often be used in prestressed concrete design, and in general the more the concrete cover to the steel, the better the fire resistance.

Costs are constantly fluctuating but it has been stated that a reinforced concrete structure is often less expensive than the equivalent structural steelwork structure clad with concrete[5] and the speed of construction is approximately the same. One of the authors has known of two identical buildings which were constructed, and in this particular instance the one of reinforced concrete construction was cheaper and erected quicker than the similar building in structural steelwork.

Reinforced concrete is usually acknowledged as being the cheapest method of resisting compressive forces. It has also been suggested in reference[5] that it is in the national interest to use reinforced concrete in lieu of structural steelwork as concrete materials are plentiful in this country, and the great saving in steel could be diverted to valuable exports.

In France and Germany reinforced concrete construction has made structural steelwork almost obsolete. In the U.S.A. the balance might be slightly in favour of structural steelwork. Very long span bridges and skyscrapers however are often far better designed in structural steelwork or aluminium.

Reinforced concrete lends itself to the advantages of monolithic construction, whereas steelwork has to be welded to achieve such an effect. This tends to give a structure with a wealth of latent strength. Concrete increases in strength with age so that the factor of safety of a reinforced concrete structure is forever increasing. It is also of course forever 'creeping' and 'shrinking' but experienced designers can master these troubles.

Reinforced concrete structures are more expensive to design commercially than conventional structural steelwork, and indeed many builders and architects use steel girders in buildings because their requirements are so easily obtained from simple tables, without having to employ an experienced designer.

The self weight of a concrete structure is greater than a steel framework (not clad with concrete). This has advantages where vibrations and light secondary loadings are experienced. The concrete structural element is often too massive for its natural frequency to be interfered with by many light vibrations which would affect lighter constructions such as structural steelwork or aluminium. The self weight of concrete members is a nuisance with structures carrying very light loads but this is largely offset by the cheapness of the material. Reinforced concrete purlins for example can even be less expensive than the equivalent angle irons in steel.

Prestressed concrete construction has no cracks at working loads, and usually employs a high grade of concrete so that it is a most durable construction. It is therefore ideal for exposed structures such as bridges, maritime structures, and water retaining structures. Prestressed concrete enables smaller quantities of concrete and reinforcement to be used but the materials are more expensive than those used in non-prestressed reinforced concrete work. Prestressed concrete involves additional labour in the tensioning of the reinforcement and better concrete control has to be exercised than with normal reinforced concrete construction. Generalizing must be avoided and each particular job must be judged upon its relative economies in different types of construction. It can however be said that the proportion of structures utilizing prestressed concrete is smaller in Britain and the U.S.A. than in France, Belgium, and Germany. This is due to several factors:

(a) The cost of labour relative to the cost of the materials is higher in Britain and the U.S.A.;

(b) The industry is organized differently in Britain from the Continent. Sometimes an architect will prohibit the use of prestressed concrete because he feels that the method is too young for its long term properties to have been fully encountered, and possibly because he is afraid that the designer might not have had sufficient experience of such structures. There are of course some architects who do not even trust conventional reinforced concrete and always specify structural steelwork;

(c) There is also the fact that the pioneers of this form of construction were Continentals, the most notable being Eugene Freyssinet;

(d) In Britain, prestressed design tends to utilize one or other of several patented systems. The prices of many of these systems including royalties and components seem high and often make prestressed construction uneconomical. A reduction in such prices would stimulate the industry considerably.

Deflection is important in most structures and indeed many clients desire large spans uninterrupted by columns but are most alarmed at the idea of any noticeable deflection occurring. The greater the deflection which can be allowed, the greater will be the economy of the construction in many instances. A reinforced concrete beam might weigh about one third of the load which it is required to carry, whereas the weight of the equivalent rolled steel joist might be negligible compared with this amount. The concrete is (after many years of creep have taken place) very approximately 15 times more elastic than the rolled steel joist. These factors tend to be unfavourable towards concrete, but some compensation is gained by the concrete beam being more massive than the rolled steel joist, thereby giving an increased moment of inertia to the cross-section.

Prestressed concrete is more rigid than conventional reinforced concrete, if the members are of the same size, but generalization is misleading because prestressed concrete can be designed to make great savings in the quantities of steel and concrete, full advantage being taken of high qualities of these materials. In such instances a prestressed design can be a very flexible construction.

Reinforced concrete members being more massive than the equivalent steelwork members are less vulnerable to vibrating machinery, earthquakes and atomic blasts. For lightness of construction prestressed concrete is generally somewhere between structural steelwork and conventional reinforced concrete.

From a design point of view concrete is very much stronger in compression than it is in tension; it can be as much as about 30 times, and is commonly about 13 times stronger in compression than in tension. If a beam were designed in plain concrete the tensile zone would therefore need to be very large for economy of the concrete in compression. With any such calculations the concrete beam is found to be phenomenal in size and its own weight is a very large proportion of the total load it can carry. Steel is very strong and efficient in tension, but often in compression its full strength cannot be utilized because of its lack of girth; in other words it is limited by lateral instability. Consequently a reinforced concrete beam represents an ideal structural companionship; the concrete in the compression zone is more massive than its equivalent steel member so that its strength is not limited as greatly by lateral instability, whilst the steel provides great strength in tension. The concrete is then required to transmit horizontal shear stresses from the compression zone to the tensile steel and to bond successfully to this steel, otherwise the beam would act like a carriage spring, the two independent members having very little strength.

Codes of Practice endeavour to limit the size of cracks in reinforced concrete by limiting the concrete and steel strengths which may be used. If the reinforcement is not mechanically bonded, for example, its safe working stress is limited to 20,000 lb/sq. in. by the British Code of Practice and the poorest of black steel rods made in Britain are adequate. (Certain Continental steels used for reinforcement however do not meet with the British requirements). Consequently, advantage cannot be taken of very high strength concretes and steels with conventional reinforced concrete design.

Prestressed concrete employs high tensile wires or bars which impose a compression before loading upon the zones where the subsequently superimposed loads would normally cause tensile stresses. This will be discussed in greater detail in Chapter 6. The overall effect is that the gross section of the concrete is utilized (in conventional reinforced concrete design the tensile strength in bending of the concrete is ignored) and also high strength concretes and steels can be used. For example it is common at working loads, for the concrete to be stressed to about 2,000 lb/sq. in. and the wires to 65 tons/sq in.

Prestressed concrete therefore has the advantage of eliminating tensile cracks due to strain, shrinkage, and creep at working loads. Other advantages (which will be discussed later) are: the greater bond strength obtained when pretensioning is employed, and the increased strength of the beam in shear at working loads.

1.13 Assumptions made in the elastic design of reinforced concrete

Firstly it is assumed that *plane sections subjected to bending remain plane after bending*, this proposition being well known from Bernoulli's Theorem. It is found to be reasonably true by experiment and means that the distribution of strain is linear.

It is also assumed that *stress is proportional to strain for both the steel and the concrete*. This is accurately true for the steel up to the limit of proportionality; but only approximately true for the concrete as far as the allowable working stress, and most inaccurate above this stress towards failure. The elastic method of design endeavours to compute the stresses at working loads, and limits these stresses to amounts dependent upon the yield stress and or ultimate strength of the steel and the crushing stress of the concrete. The respective factors of safety are obtained from the experience of engineers and scientists in the industry. It can therefore be appreciated that beams designed in such a fashion are safe but have varying load factors on their ultimate strengths. Many engineers and scientists prefer to specify a load factor on the ultimate strength of a beam, and hence try to base designs upon a prediction of the ultimate strength, such designs being described later, as 'plastic' design methods. The advocates of elastic design ideas feel that stresses and therefore the size of cracks at working loads are controlled, and this method of design has been used without cause for alarm since the early years of the industry. With regard to prestressed concrete the basic idea is to eliminate cracks at working loads, and provided this consideration is achieved, one is prepared to accept varying load factors on the ultimate strength for this type of construction.

Perfect bond is assumed between the steel and the concrete. The concrete shrinks upon setting and therefore exerts a pressure upon the steel; this creates a friction between the two materials. This pressure is reduced to some extent when the steel and surrounding concrete are stressed in tension because Poisson's Ratio is greater for steel (approx. 0·29) than for concrete (approx. between 0·20 and 0·14); the converse applies when the steel and surrounding concrete are stressed in compression. Irregularities on the surface of the reinforcement lock the steel mechanically to the concrete; several proprietary high tensile bars and prestressing wires are purposely manufactured to create such an effect. The French claim to have concrete which expands upon setting; such concrete will exert no pressure whatsoever upon the steel, so that the steel would need to be made with special surface irregularities if any adhesion were required between the steel and the concrete.

The *depth of the steel reinforcement is considered to be negligible compared with the depth of the beam.* This is usually an accurate assumption.

Normally, temperature and shrinkage stresses are ignored in the design of sections to withstand bending moments, shear forces, and axial forces. It can be mentioned here that fortunately the thermal coefficients of expansion of concrete and steel are sensibly the same. For the design of the structure as a whole temperature and shrinkage effects must definitely be considered. Temperature stresses are particularly important, for example in the design of chimneys, and in such instances these stresses must be studied. Losses in prestress due to shrinkage are important and are described in Chapter 6.

For conventional reinforced concrete *the concrete is assumed to be cracked in tension* when bending stresses are considered. This is because the tensile strength of concrete is only about one tenth (and can be as little as one thirtieth for high strength concretes) of its compressive strength. *The same concrete is, however, expected to resist diagonal tensile stresses* (to a safe working value not exceeding approximately 156 lb/sq. in.).[3] If the beam were prestressed it would be permissible for certain small tensile stresses to occur under bending; some engineers would allow as much as 250 lb/sq. in. both upon stressing and at working loads. The Code[4] for the design of water retaining structures assumes that the concrete will withstand tensile stresses so that no cracks occur, but nevertheless does not trust the concrete in tension structurally. In fact concrete has a most unreliable resistance to tension. The ultimate strength of numerous direct tension specimens made from the same batch of concrete in exactly similar fashions can vary enormously. The maximum strength can often be as much as 100% more than the minimum strength. The ultimate tensile stress in bending, judged on the extreme fibre stress, using the assumptions of the elastic analysis, (and known as the *modulus of rupture*) is higher and more reliable than the direct tensile strength. In tension the ultimate strength can be affected greatly by the number of pebbles of the coarse aggregate which happen to occur across the critical cross-section. Much therefore can be attributed to chance during the placing and compacting of the concrete.

Concerning the design of prestressed concrete beams in bending the modulus of elasticity for concrete in tension is assumed to be the same as the value of this modulus for concrete in compression.

1.14 Bond between concrete and steel

This is a most necessary requirement of reinforced concrete construction. If, for example, no bond existed between the tension reinforcement of a beam and the surrounding concrete, then the system would behave in the same way as a carriage spring having two leaves of different inertias and strengths, namely a relatively large concrete leaf (possibly with a modulus of rupture of only say 500 lb/sq. in.) and a comparably small steel leaf (relatively strong with a maximum ultimate fibre stress in bending of say 33 tons/sq. in.). Under these conditions the stiffer concrete member would resist most of the superimposed bending moment and its ultimate strength would very soon be realized; at such a load that the assistance of the reinforcement in resisting bending moment could be described as negligible. It is therefore essential that bond should exist between the tension reinforcement and its surrounding concrete. In other words, for the steel to be satisfactorily utilized it has to bond to the concrete so that a reinforced concrete beam, for example, would bend as though it were a homogeneous member (the strain in the reinforcement being the same as the strain in the surrounding fibres).

It is obvious that pretensioned wires (or bars) must bond to the concrete which is cast around them. Otherwise when the wires are released after the concrete has adequately matured, no precompression would be induced in the concrete, the wires just sliding relatively to the concrete (see Chapter 6).

Bond comprises two different actions. Firstly, there is the ability of the concrete to stick to the steel. This is usually referred to as *adhesion*. Secondly, there is the frictional resistance between the steel and the concrete. This is often called *grip*.

When a bar is tending to pull out of its surrounding concrete the relative movement of the bar to such concrete is known as *slip*. A bond stress cannot exist without its coexistent strain, that is without slip. Adhesion is an initial resistance to bond and occurs when the slip is minute. With a smooth cylindrical bar, for example, adhesion is often attributed to micro-mechanical locking (minute irregularities on the bar mechanically locking to the concrete). As soon as a small amount of slip occurs the adhesion is ruptured and takes no further part in the bond resistance. For such slips a bond resistance is developed by the 'friction' between the bar and the surrounding concrete. This is aided by the shrinkage of the concrete upon setting, as this causes the concrete to exert a radial pressure on the reinforcing bar, thus increasing the frictional resistance between the two materials.

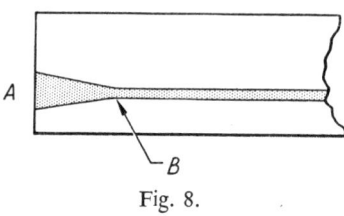

Fig. 8.

The frictional resistance can be assessed by multiplying such a pressure due to shrinkage by some suitable coefficient. Certain coefficients suggested by Armstrong[7] illustrate the sensitivity of the frictional resistance to the grease and rust on the surface of a bar. *Dilatancy* is a resistance to slip resulting from the wedging action of the small particles of concrete after an initial slip has occurred. This effect constitutes a part of the general frictional resistance mentioned above. The frictional resistance is enhanced at the locality of a crack where a *tangential friction* occurs because of the slight change in direction of the reinforcement bar.

Another contribution to the frictional resistance can be called *wedge action*. When the longitudinal stress in a bar changes due to its bond to the surrounding concrete, the effect of Poisson's Ratio will cause a corresponding change in the cross-sectional area. Thus such a reinforcement bar becomes slightly tapered and hence the name 'wedge action'. With conventional reinforced concrete this effect is extremely small and indeed reduces the frictional resistance. However in the case of prestressed concrete, where steel stresses are much greater the wedge action is a definite asset. To illustrate this point, Fig. 8 exaggerates the effect; the pretensioned wire is unstressed after release at *A* and has therefore a larger diameter here than at *B* where the wire is in its fully stressed condition; the 'bond length' in this instance being the distance *AB*.

Both the adhesion and the frictional resistance are increased by *mechanical locking*, that is by using reinforcement bars with surface deformations which mechanically lock to the concrete.[2]

Bond therefore consists of firstly an *adhesive resistance* and then a *frictional resistance*. As a simple illustration, Fig. 9 refers to a 'pull out test' of a steel rod from a concrete block. When the pull in the rod is P the portion of the graph AB represents the way in which the force in the rod is gradually transmitted to the concrete by frictional resistance. At the point B, the force still in the bar is insufficient to overcome the adhesive resistance of the remainder of the bar, and therefore BC represents the way in which the force in the rod is gradually transmitted to the

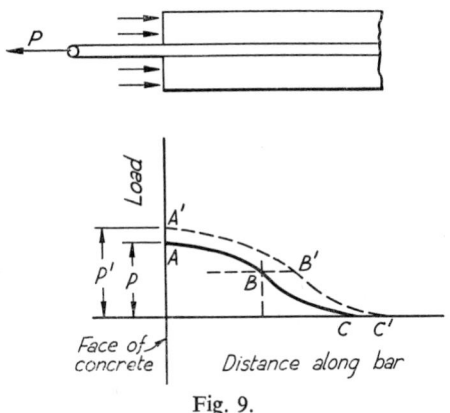

Fig. 9.

concrete by adhesion. When the load in the bar is increased to P', the slips increase and the curve becomes $A'B'C'$, $A'B'$ being the frictional stage and $B'C$ the adhesive stage.

When a reinforced concrete beam is subjected to bending, the tension reinforcement which is bonded to the concrete is such that both the steel and the concrete are in tension. This is a criticism of the above mentioned pull out test, in which the steel is in tension and its surrounding concrete is in compression. Tests of bond stress are therefore made by measuring the strain in the steel, and the strain in the concrete touching such steel, along the length of the bars provided as tension reinforcement in beams subjected to bending. The authors feel that the best method so far devised for obtaining these measurements of bond stress is that described in reference.[8]

The length (i.e. *bond length*) which a bar has to be embedded in concrete to develop its full tensile stress can be computed as follows:

EXAMPLE 1.14.1

Fig. 10 shows a bar anchored into a block of concrete. The necessary bond length l inches is to be computed so that the bar can develop its full tensile working stress t lb/sq. in. at section B.

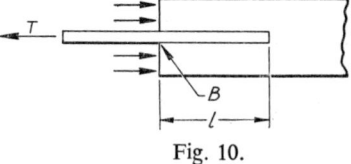

Fig. 10.

If the bar has a cross-sectional area A and a perimeter o, then the force in the bar T is given by

$$T = At$$

If c_b is the average bond stress between the steel and the concrete, this exists over an area of contact equal to ol.

$$\therefore \quad T = c_b(ol)$$
$$\therefore \quad At = c_b ol$$
$$\therefore \quad l = \frac{At}{c_b o} \cdot \qquad \qquad \dots(1,1)$$

For example, if the allowable working bond stress were 120 lb/sq. in. for a 1:2:4 mix of concrete according to reference (3) and the maximum permissible steel stress at working loads were 20,000 lb/sq. in. then

$$l = \frac{A(20,000)}{120o} = 166 \cdot 7 \cdot \frac{A}{o}$$

and therefore, for a circular bar of diameter d inches,

$$l = 166 \cdot 7 \frac{\pi}{4} d^2 / \pi d = \frac{166 \cdot 7}{4} d = \underline{41 \cdot 7d} \qquad \dots(1,2)$$

or for a square bar of side D inches,

$$l = 166 \cdot 7 \frac{D^2}{4D} = 41 \cdot 7D \qquad \qquad \dots(1,3)$$

If this latter bar is twisted (to create a mechanical bond), then the permissible bond stress at working loads is allowed to be increased by 25% of the above value by reference (3). The twisting of such bars gives the high tensile properties associated with the cold working involved, and reference (3) allows the maximum permissible working stress of these bars to be 30,000 lb/sq. in. Thus for such square twisted bars we have

$$t = 30,000 \text{ lb/sq. in.}$$
$$c_b = 120 + \tfrac{25}{100} \times 120 = 150 \text{ lb/sq. in.}$$

$\therefore$ from equation (1,1),

$$l = \frac{D^2 \times 30,000}{150 \times (4 \times D)} = 50D \qquad \qquad \dots(1,4)$$

1.15 Monolithic construction

In riveted structural steelwork construction, the factory produced rolled steel joists are often connected together by cleats to form a building skeleton of beams and columns. These connections are not tight or rigid enough for the beams to be designed as continuous, or for the bending moments in the beams to be transmitted to the columns.

With *in-situ* reinforced concrete construction the structural members are cast in the situation required and to whatever shape desired. Advantage is therefore generally taken of making the beams continuous and also of allowing the columns to contribute to the bending resistance of the continuous beams. This makes a more economical structure than one consisting of a multitude of simply supported beams with columns taking direct load only, and the structure exercises a better control over the distribution and maximum size of cracks in the frames, floors and finishes. Such a structure also has a superior resistance to lateral loads due to wind, earthquakes, and explosions.

Many *in-situ* reinforced concrete buildings have continuous slabs which are designed as independent structural members to the beams and columns; but in construction everything is cast to make all these structural members a monolithic mass. This gives such a construction a wealth of latent stiffness and strength. Precast concrete construction cannot be as strong in this respect, unless all the elements are post-tensioned together.

1.16   Assumptions of the plastic design methods

Plastic design concerns two ideas. Firstly, with regard to the assessment of the bending moments in a redundant frame, plasticity is the ability of highly stressed sections to what might be termed yield, and allow a redistribution of the bending moments (as obtained from an elastic analysis) towards failure. Secondly, plastic design can be employed in the design of individual sections of structural members. In this latter instance the assumptions outlined below are employed.

It is assumed that plane sections subjected to bending remain plane after bending (Bernoulli's Theorem). This means that the distribution of strain is linear.

Some relationship is then assumed between this strain, and stress. This is where plastic design methods differ.

As in the case of the elastic design of reinforced concrete (refer to §1.13), the concrete is assumed to have no resistance in flexural tension, perfect bond is assumed between the steel and the concrete, the depth of the steel reinforcement is assumed to be small compared with its effective depth, and normally temperature and shrinkage stresses are ignored in the stress analysis of sections.

CHAPTER 2

THE ELASTIC ANALYSIS OF REINFORCED CONCRETE MEMBERS IN BENDING

2.1 Elastic analysis

Elastic analysis deals with that conventional method of design which excludes the resistance of the concrete to tensile stresses, the concrete being cracked in the tension zone. It is probably safe to say that authorities throughout the world* permit this method of design, and indeed most reinforced concrete structures in existence illustrate the safety (and conservativeness) of such designs. The assumptions of the method are as described and discussed in §1.12.

2.2 To evaluate the concrete and reinforcement stresses for a fully defined rectangular section subjected to a given bending moment

Fig. 11(i) shows the breadth b and *effective depth* d of the steel reinforcement. The *effective depth* is measured to the centroid of the total cross-sectional area A_s of the tensile reinforcement.

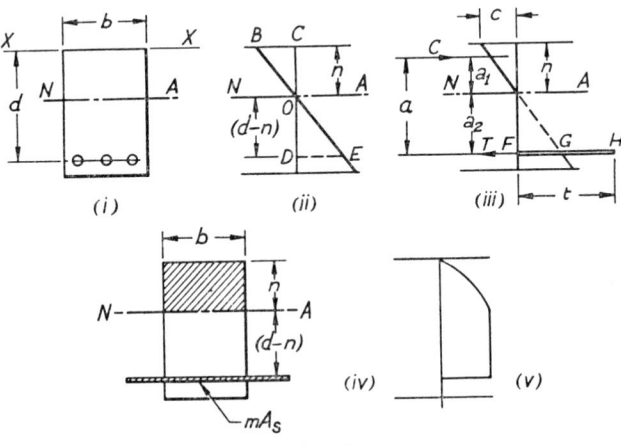

Fig. 11.

Fig. 11(ii) shows the distribution of strain when the section is subjected to bending; this is linear in accordance with the assumption that plane sections remain plane. Therefore triangles OCB and ODE are similar,

$$\therefore \quad \frac{BC}{CO} = \frac{DE}{DO} \qquad \qquad \ldots\ldots(2,1)$$

* The U.S.S.R., since 1938, has been one exception to this rule.

40

Fig. 11(iii) shows the corresponding distribution of stress. Assuming that, for concrete, stress is proportional to strain, then this diagram is also linear, but it is also assumed that the concrete cannot withstand tensile stresses. The part of the linear relationship shown dotted in Fig. 11(iii) does not therefore exist, and EH represents the stress t in the tensile reinforcement. The maximum extreme fibre stress in the concrete is denoted by c.

Applying Hooke's Law,

$$\text{the strain } BC = \frac{c}{E_c}, \qquad \text{and}$$

$$\text{the strain } DE = \frac{t}{E_s},$$

where E_c = Young's Modulus for concrete (see §1.10) and E_s = Young's Modulus for the steel reinforcement. Substituting these values in equation (2,1)

$$\frac{c/E_c}{n} = \frac{t/E_s}{(d-n)}$$

where n = the depth of the neutral axis NA

$$\therefore \quad \frac{t}{c} = \frac{E_s}{E_c} \cdot \left(\frac{d-n}{n}\right) = m\left(\frac{1-n_1}{n_1}\right) \qquad \ldots\ldots(2,2)$$

where m = the *modular ratio* (i.e. E_s/E_c), and $n_1 = n/d$.

The longitudinal compression C must equal the longitudinal tension T, as there is no external thrust in this direction; i.e. $C = T$,

$$\therefore \quad \frac{c}{2} \cdot nb = A_s t$$

$$\therefore \quad \frac{t}{c} = \frac{nb}{2A_s} = \frac{nb}{2A_s} \cdot \frac{100A_s}{bd} \cdot \frac{bd}{100A_s}$$

$$\therefore \quad \frac{t}{c} = \frac{nb}{2A_s} \cdot \frac{100A_s}{bd} \cdot \frac{1}{p} = \frac{50n_1}{p} \qquad \ldots\ldots(2,3)$$

where p = the percentage of reinforcement = $\dfrac{A_s}{bd} \times 100$. Equating (2,2) and (2,3) to eliminate t and c, which are not yet known,

$$m\left(\frac{1-n_1}{n_1}\right) = \frac{50n_1}{p}$$

$$\therefore \quad 50n_1{}^2 = mp - mpn_1$$

$$\therefore \quad n_1{}^2 + \frac{mp}{50}n_1 - \frac{mp}{50} = 0$$

$$\therefore \quad n_1 = -\left(\frac{mp}{100}\right) \pm \sqrt{\left(\frac{mp}{100}\right)^2 + \left(\frac{mp}{50}\right)}$$

Only the positive value of n_1 is required, therefore

$$n_1 = -\frac{mp}{100} + \sqrt{\left(\frac{mp}{100}\right)^2 + 2\left(\frac{mp}{100}\right)} \qquad \dots(2,4)$$

This equation locates the neutral axis.

Now if the external bending moment applied to the section is M, this is resisted by the internal couple formed by the equal and opposite forces C and T, and if a is the distance between the lines of actions of these two forces, then

$$M = Ca = Ta \qquad \dots(2,5)$$

and a is described as *the moment arm* or *lever arm*. From Fig. 11(iii) it can be seen that

$$a = a_1 + a_2 = \tfrac{2}{3}n + (d - n) = d - \frac{n}{3} \qquad \dots(2,6)$$

To determine the concrete stress, from equation (2,5),

$$C = \frac{M}{a}$$

and $C = \dfrac{c}{2} \cdot nb$ (as before)

$$\therefore \quad \frac{c}{2} \cdot nb = \frac{M}{a}$$

$$\therefore \quad c = \frac{2M}{anb} \qquad \dots(2,7)$$

To determine the steel stress, from equation (2,5),

$$T = \frac{M}{a}$$

and

$$T = A_s t \text{ (as before)}$$

therefore

$$A_s t = \frac{M}{a}$$

$$t = \frac{M}{a A_s} \qquad \dots(2,8)$$

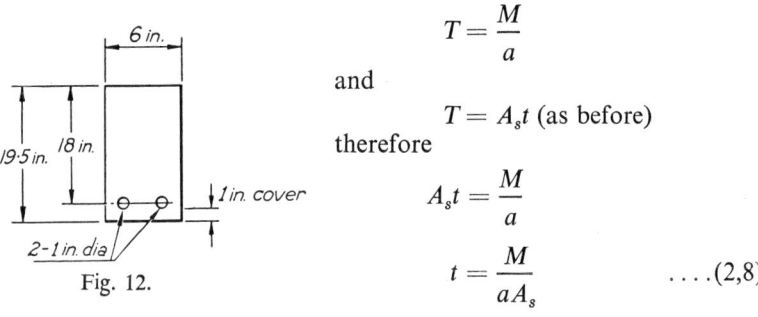

Fig. 12.

EXAMPLE 2.2.1

The section shown in Fig. 12 is subjected to a bending moment of 500,000 lb in. (i.e. 500 kip. in., using units popular with engineers of the U.S.A.). Determine the maximum stress in the concrete and the stress in the reinforcement, if the modular ratio is assumed to be 15.

$$A_s = 2 \times \frac{\pi}{4} \times 1^2 = 1\text{·}571 \text{ sq. in.}$$

$$p = \frac{1\text{·}571}{6 \times 18} \cdot 100 = 1\text{·}454\%$$

From equation (2,4),

$$n_1 = -\left(\frac{15 \times 1\text{·}454}{100}\right) + \sqrt{\left(\frac{15 \times 1\text{·}454}{100}\right)^2 + 2\left(\frac{15 \times 1\text{·}454}{100}\right)}$$

$$= 0\text{·}478$$

$$n = 0\text{·}478 \times 18 = 8\text{·}6 \text{ in.}$$

From equation (2,6),

$$a = 18 - \frac{8\text{·}6}{3} = 15\text{·}13 \text{ in.}$$

From equation (2,7),

$$c = \frac{2 \times 500{,}000}{15\text{·}13 \times 8\text{·}6 \times 6} = \underline{1{,}281 \text{ lb/sq. in.}}$$

From equation (2,8),

$$t = \frac{500{,}000}{15\text{·}13 \times 1\text{·}571} = \underline{21{,}000 \text{ lb/sq. in.}}$$

EXAMPLE 2.2.2

Determine the moment of resistance of the section shown in Fig. 12, assuming that the maximum permissible concrete stress is 1,500 lb/sq. in. (say a 1:1:2 mix according to B.S. C.P. 114). The maximum permissible steel stress is 30,000 lb/sq. in. (using say high-tensile steel), and the modular ratio is 15.

As in Example (2.2.1),

$$A_s = 1\text{·}571 \text{ sq. in.}$$
$$p = 1\text{·}454\%$$
$$n_1 = 0\text{·}478$$
$$n = 8\text{·}6 \text{ in.}$$
$$a = 15\text{·}13 \text{ in.}$$

Therefore, from equation (2,7), the moment of resistance, if the compressive strength of the concrete were the criterion, is given by

$$M = \frac{canb}{2}$$

$$= \frac{1{,}500 \times 15\text{·}13 \times 8\text{·}6 \times 6}{2} = \underline{586{,}000 \text{ lb in.}}$$

From equation (2,8), the moment of resistance, if the tensile strength of the steel were the criterion, is given by

$$M = taA_s$$

$$= 30,000 \times 15 \cdot 13 \times 1 \cdot 571 = \underline{712,500 \text{ lb in.}}$$

Therefore according to the assumptions of this design the moment of resistance of the beam is limited by the compressive strength of the concrete to 586,000 lb in.

EXAMPLE 2.2.3

State three assumptions upon which the usual solution of simple reinforced concrete beams depends.

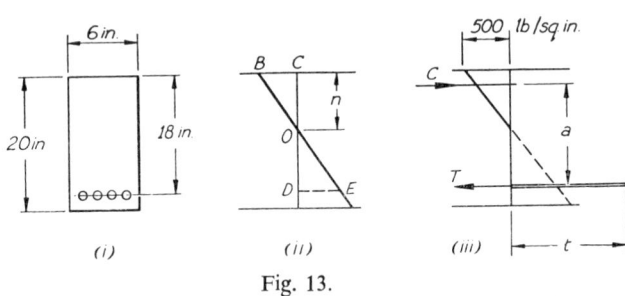

Fig. 13.

A concrete beam 6 in. wide and 20 in. deep overall is reinforced on the tension side by four steel rods, $\frac{7}{8}$ in. diameter, the centre of the rods being 2 in. from the lower edge of the beam. The maximum allowable stress in the concrete is 500 lb/sq. in. Find the tensile stress in the steel and the moment of resistance of the section. Assume $E_s/E_c = 15$.

The three assumptions can be stated thus:

1. Plane sections subjected to bending remain plane after bending.
2. Stress is proportional to strain for both the steel and the concrete.
3. The concrete is assumed to be cracked in tension.

The problem is represented by Fig. 13. Assumption (1) means that the distribution of strain is as represented in Fig. 13(ii), therefore

$$\frac{BC}{CO} = \frac{DE}{DO}$$

From assumption (2) this equation can be expressed as

$$\frac{500/E_c}{n} = \frac{t/E_s}{(18 - n)}$$

$$\therefore \quad 500 \times (18 - n) = nt \cdot \frac{E_c}{E_s} = \frac{nt}{15}$$

$$\therefore \quad 7{,}500(18 - n) = nt \qquad \qquad \ldots (2{,}9)$$

Now
$$C = T$$

From assumption (3),
$$\frac{500}{2} \cdot 6n = A_s t$$

now
$$A_s = 4 \cdot \frac{\pi}{4} \cdot \left(\frac{7}{8}\right)^2 = 2\cdot4 \text{ sq. in.}$$

$$\therefore \quad 1{,}500n = 2\cdot4t \qquad \qquad \ldots (2{,}10)$$

Eliminating t between equations (2,9) and (2,10),

$$\frac{7{,}500(18 - n)}{1{,}500n} = \frac{n}{2\cdot4}$$

therefore

$$5(18 - n)2\cdot4 = n^2$$
$$n^2 + 12n - 216 = 0$$

$$n = -\left(\frac{12}{2}\right) + \sqrt{\left(\frac{12}{2}\right)^2 + 216}$$

$$n = 9\cdot9 \text{ in.}$$

and therefore
$$a = 18 - \frac{9\cdot9}{3} = 14\cdot7 \text{ in.}$$

Therefore from equation (2,10),

$$t = \frac{1{,}500 \times 9\cdot9}{2\cdot4} = \underline{6{,}190 \text{ lb/sq. in}}$$

The moment of resistance of the section

$$= Ta = A_s ta$$
$$= 2\cdot4 \times 6{,}190 \times 14\cdot7$$
$$= \underline{218{,}000 \text{ lb in.}}$$

2.3 To design a rectangular section to resist a specified bending moment

Fig. 11(i) shows the section under consideration, and, using the same notation as above (for equation 2,2), the problem is to determine suitable values for b, d, and A_s. Fig. 11(ii) illustrates the distribution of strain, and Fig. 11(iii) the corresponding distribution of stress.

It is assumed that plane sections remain plane; hence the distribution of strain is linear; therefore, from Fig. 11(ii)

$$\frac{BC}{CO} = \frac{DE}{DO} \qquad \dots (2,1)$$

Now according to Hooke's Law,

$$\text{the strain } BC = \frac{c}{E_c}, \qquad \text{and}$$

$$\text{the strain } DE = \frac{t}{E_s},$$

Hence substituting these values of BC and DE in (2,1),

$$\frac{c/E_c}{n} = \frac{t/E_s}{(d-n)}$$

$$\frac{t}{c} = \frac{E_s}{E_c}\left(\frac{d-n}{n}\right) = m\left(\frac{1-n_1}{n_1}\right) = r$$

where $r = t/c$,

$$\therefore \quad n_1 r = m - m n_1$$

$$\therefore \quad n_1 = \frac{m}{r+m} = \frac{1}{\left(\dfrac{r}{m}\right)+1} \qquad \dots (2,11)$$

Now,

$$a = a_1 + a_2 = \tfrac{2}{3}n + (d-n) = d - \frac{n}{3}$$

$$\therefore \quad a_1 = 1 - \frac{n_1}{3} \qquad \dots (2,12)$$

The externally applied bending moment must equal the resistance of the internal couple formed by the forces C and T, i.e.

$$M = Ca = Ta$$

Firstly taking:

$$M = Ca$$

this gives:

$$M = \frac{c}{2} . nba$$

$$M = \frac{c}{2} . n_1 a_1 b d^2$$

$$M = Q b d^2 \qquad \dots (2,13)$$

$$\therefore \quad b d^2 = M/Q. \qquad \dots (2,14)$$

From this equation suitable corresponding values of b and d can be chosen.

Where

$$Q = \frac{cn_1a_1}{2} \qquad \dots(2,15)$$

Secondly taking $\qquad M = Ta,$

this gives $\qquad M = A_s ta$

$$M = A_s ta_1 d \qquad \dots(2,16)$$

$$A_s = \frac{M}{ta_1 d} \qquad \dots(2,17)$$

This equation allows the area of the tensile reinforcement to be computed.

EXAMPLE 2.3.1

Design a section to resist a bending moment of 1,000,000 lb in., using mild steel reinforcement and a 1:2:4 mix of concrete, all in accordance with B.S. C.P. 114 (1957), i.e. $p_{st} = 20,000$ lb/sq. in., $p_{cb} = 1,000$ lb/sq. in. and $m = 15$.

$$r = \frac{20,000}{1,000} = 20$$

From equation (2,11),

$$n_1 = \frac{1}{\frac{20}{15} + 1} = 0.428$$

From equation (2,12),

$$a_1 = 1 - \frac{0.428}{3} = 0.857$$

From equation (2,15),

$$Q = \frac{1,000 \times 0.428 \times 0.857}{2} = 183.3$$

From equation (2,14),

$$bd^2 = \frac{1,000,000}{183.3} = 5,450$$

If say d is chosen as 21 in., then $b = 12.37$ in. Suppose, therefore, that it is decided to make $b = 12$ in., then $d = 21.3$ in. Then from equation (2,17),

$$A_s = \frac{1,000,000}{20,000 \times 0.857 \times 21.3} = 2.74 \text{ sq. in.}$$

Hence use say two 1 in. diameter and two $\frac{7}{8}$ in. diameter mild steel bars. According to the British Code of Practice the minimum 'cover' of concrete to this reinforcement is 1 in. The centroid of the tensile reinforcement will therefore be approximately $1\frac{1}{2}$ in. above the soffit of the beam. Hence the overall depth of the beam is 21·3 in. plus $1\frac{1}{2}$ in. equals 22·8 in., say 23 in. The breadth of the beam must be checked to ascertain that the reinforcement bars are not too near together. The British Code of Practice requires the side 'cover' of concrete to be at least 1 in. Hence if the bars are equally spaced the distance between each pair of bars

$$= \frac{\text{breadth} - 2 \times (\text{side covers}) - \text{total diameters of bars}}{\text{number of spaces between bars}}$$

$$= \frac{12\text{ in.} - 2\text{ in.} - (2 \times \frac{7}{8}\text{ in.} + 2 \times 1\text{ in.})}{3} = 2\text{·}083\text{ in.}$$

This is satisfactory as it is greater than 1 in. which would be specified by the British Code of Practice.

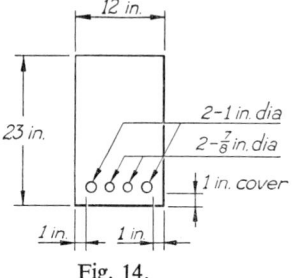

Fig. 14.

The concrete and steel sizes have been chosen slightly greater than strictly necessary, to suit practical considerations. Hence if the section shown in Fig. 14 is analysed in the same way as Example (2.2.1), the concrete stress will be slightly less than 1,000 lb/sq. in. and the steel stress will be slightly less than 20,000 lb/sq. in. This would be a useful exercise for the student.

EXAMPLE 2.3.2

A reinforced concrete cantilever beam projects 14 ft from a rigid wall. The beam is of rectangular section, 14 in. wide, and the effective depth from the centre of the reinforcement is 17 in. The beam itself has a weight of 280 lb per ft of length. The maximum stress in the concrete is not to exceed 1,000 lb/sq. in., and that in the steel is not to exceed 18,000 lb/sq. in.

If the modular ratio is 14, find the distance of the neutral axis from the lower compression edge, and also a suitable area for the reinforcement. What point load may be supported from the extremity of the beam?

The section is not fully defined and for economy A_s will be chosen so that the maximum concrete and steel stresses specified are realized simultaneously.

The distribution of strain is linear:

$$\frac{1,000/E_c}{n} = \frac{18,000/E_s}{(17 - n)}$$

$$\therefore \quad 14(17 - n) = 18n$$

$$n = \frac{14 \times 17}{32} = 7 \cdot 44 \text{ in.}$$

The longitudinal compressive force in the concrete must balance the longitudinal tensile force in the steel:

$$\therefore \quad \frac{1,000}{2} \times 14 \times 7 \cdot 44 = A_s \times 18,000$$

$$\therefore \quad A_s = 2 \cdot 895 \text{ sq. in.}$$

$$a = 17 - \frac{7 \cdot 44}{3} = \underline{14 \cdot 52 \text{ in.}}$$

The moment of resistance $= Ca = Ta$
$$= 2 \cdot 895 \times 18,000 \times 14 \cdot 52$$
$$= 757,000 \text{ lb in.}$$

Let the point load required $= W$ lb

The maximum bending moment $= W \times 14 + \dfrac{280 \times 14^2}{2}$

$$= (14W + 27,400) \text{ lb ft}$$
$$= (168 \times W + 328,800) \text{ lb in.}$$

therefore $\quad 168W + 328,800 = 757,000$

$$W = \frac{428,000}{168} = \underline{2,545 \text{ lb}}$$

EXAMPLE 2.3.3

Design a section to resist a bending moment of 500,000 lb in. The breadth is 12 in. and the effective depth 21 in. Assume a modular ratio of 15, and permissible concrete (in bending) and steel stresses of 1,000 and 20,000 lb/sq. in. respectively.

From equation (2,11),

$$n_1 = \frac{1}{\left(\frac{20}{15}\right) + 1} = 0 \cdot 4286$$

From equation (2,12),

$$a_1 = 1 - \frac{0 \cdot 4286}{3} = 0 \cdot 8571$$

From equation (2,15),

$$Q = \frac{1,000 \times 0.4286 \times 0.8571}{2} = 183.6$$

If the section were designed to make full use of the permissible stresses, then from equation (2,13),

$$M = 183.6 \times 12 \times 21^2 = 973,000 \text{ lb in.}$$

The section is therefore larger than the minimum requirement, hence the concrete will not be fully stressed. The reinforcement will however be fully stressed to keep its quantity to a minimum. Let the concrete stress at the extreme fibre be denoted by c. From equation (2,11),

$$n_1 = \frac{1}{\dfrac{20,000}{15c} + 1} \qquad \dots\dots(2,18)$$

From equation (2,16),

$$500,000 = A_s \times 20,000 \times a_1 \times 21$$

Substituting for a_1 from equation (2,12), this becomes,

$$1.191 = A_s\left(1 - \frac{n_1}{3}\right) \qquad \dots\dots(2,19)$$

Equating the longitudinal compressive and tensile forces,

$$\frac{c}{2} \times n \times 12 = A_s \times 20,000$$

$$cn_1 = 158.6A_s \qquad \dots\dots(2,20)$$

Thus equations (2,18), (2,19), and (2,20) are three equations relating three unknowns namely c, n_1, and A_s. Eliminating c and A_s between these equations gives the following cubic equation for n_1:

$$2.353n_1^3 - 7.06n_1^2 - n_1 + 1 = 0 \qquad \dots\dots(2,21)$$

The root required lies between 0 and 1 and by guessing an initial value the equation (2,21) can be solved by trial and error or by say Newton's Approximation

$$\therefore \quad n_1 = 0.327$$

Substituting this value in equation (2,19),

$$A_s = 1.337 \text{ sq. in., say four } \tfrac{5}{8} \text{ in. dia. and one } \tfrac{3}{8} \text{ in. dia. bars}$$

If these values are substituted in equation (2,20),

$$c = 649 \text{ lb/sq. in.}$$

N.B. Designers often simplify this design by assuming that the moment arm corresponds to the permissible stresses, (this of course is not true but it is a conservative assumption). In this instance a_1 would be assumed to be the 0·8571 computed above, then from equation (2,16),

$$500,000 = A_s \times 20,000 - 0·8571 \times 21$$

$\therefore \quad A_s = 1·388$ sq. in. say two $\frac{5}{8}$ in. dia. and one 1 in. dia. bars

There is now a greater proportion of steel than before but design time has been saved. If only one beam is to be made to this design, the designer's labour might be the criterion; if say, the beam is precast and there are to be many repeats then the saving in steel may be the more important factor. The design time can be reduced by the use of simple graphs or tables.*

2.4 Moment of inertia

Moment of Inertia is common jargon for the correct term, namely, the *Second Moment of Area*.

Referring to Fig. 15(i), NA is the neutral axis of any section subjected to bending. δA_c is a small portion of area of the concrete at a distance y from the neutral axis, and δA_s is a small portion of area of the steel at a distance y_1 from the neutral axis.

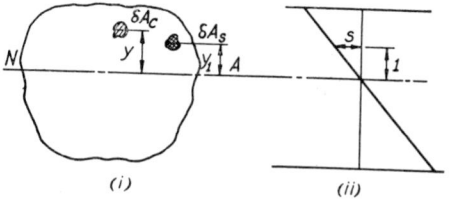

Fig. 15.

The distribution of strain is linear (as assumed previously) and is therefore as shown in Fig. 15(ii). Let the strain be of magnitude s at unit distance from the neutral axis.

$\therefore \quad$ the strain for portion $\delta A_c = s \cdot y$

$\therefore \quad$ the stress for portion $\delta A_c = s \cdot y \cdot E_c$

The force for portion $\delta A_c = s \cdot y \cdot E_c \cdot \delta A_c$. Similarly, the force for portion $\delta A_s = s \cdot y_1 \cdot E_s \cdot \delta A_s$. Therefore, the moment of resistance of the section $= M$

$$= \Sigma (syE_c \, \delta A_c) \cdot y + \Sigma (sy_1 E_s \, \delta A_s) \cdot y_1$$

$$= sE_c \left\{ \Sigma \delta A_c \cdot y^2 + \Sigma \frac{E_s}{E_c} \cdot \delta A_s \cdot y_1^2 \right\}$$

$$\therefore \quad M = sE_c \{ \Sigma \delta A_c \cdot y^2 + \Sigma m \, \delta A_s \cdot y_1^2 \} \qquad \dots.(2,22)$$

* For example: Wilby, C. B., "Graphs for Effecting Steel Economies in R.C. Beams and Slabs." The Association of Engineering and Shipbuilding Draughtsmen, Pamphlet for Session 1959–60.

The area of steel δA_s can be regarded as equivalent to an area of concrete $m . \delta A_s$; in other words, $m . \delta A_s$ is the *equivalent area* of the area of reinforcement δA_s.

The elastic analysis now considers the beam to be comprised only of concrete (the steel being expressed as its equivalent area of concrete) having a moment of inertia (i.e. second moment of area) $= I$. (The analysis could alternatively have been considered as a homogeneous steel section, the concrete being expressed as its elastically equivalent area in steel; this however is not normally done, probably because concrete comprizes the major portion of the section).

$$\therefore \quad I = \sum \delta A_c . y^2 + \sum m . \delta A_s . y_1{}^2 \qquad \ldots(2,23)$$

$$M = sE_cI \qquad \ldots(2,24)$$

Applying this formula to the rectangular beam shown in Fig. 11, s can be expressed as $\dfrac{BC}{CO}$ or as $\dfrac{DE}{DO}$

i.e. as $\dfrac{c/E_c}{n}$ or as $\dfrac{t/E_s}{(d-n)}$

in terms of c,

$$M = \frac{c}{E_c n} . E_c I = \frac{cI}{n} \qquad \ldots(2,25)$$

or in terms of t

$$M = \frac{t}{E_s(d-n)} . E_c I = \frac{tI}{m(d-n)} \qquad \ldots(2,26)$$

Fig. 11(iv) expresses the section elastically in terms of concrete; the area of steel A_s being substituted by its *equivalent area* of concrete $m . A_s$ concentrated at the same depth from the neutral axis.

The moment of inertia of the shaded areas in Fig. 11(iv) about the neutral axis

$$= I = \frac{bn^3}{3} + (mA_s)(d-n)^2 \qquad \ldots(2,27)$$

EXAMPLE 2.4.1

The problem stated in Example (2.2.1) can be alternatively solved as follows:

As computed before,

$$A_s = 1\cdot571 \text{ sq in.}$$
$$p = 1\cdot454\%$$
$$n_1 = 0\cdot478$$
$$n = 8\cdot6 \text{ in.}$$

From equation (2,27),

$$I = \frac{6 \times 8 \cdot 6^3}{3} + (15 \times 1 \cdot 571)(18 - 8 \cdot 6)^2$$

$$= 1,278 + 2,080 = 3,358 \text{ in.}^4$$

From equation (2,25),

$$c = \frac{Mn}{I} = \frac{500,000 \times 8 \cdot 6}{3,358}$$

$$= 1,281 \text{ lb/sq. in.}$$

From equation (2,26),

$$t = m \cdot \frac{M(d - n)}{I} = \frac{15 \times 500,000(18 - 8 \cdot 6)}{3,358}$$

$$= 21,000 \text{ lb/sq in.}$$

Compare these results with those of the Example (2.2.1).

2.5 A method of tabulating the computations for n and I

This method is illustrated in Table 4; the example illustrated concerns the rectangular section shown in Fig. 11. In the table, A is the equivalent area, x is the distance of the centroid of any such area from any chosen axis. In this particular case XX in Fig. 11(i) has been chosen as the axis for convenience. I_G is the moment of inertia of the portion in question about its centroid.

TABLE 4

Portion	Area	A	x	Ax	Ax^2	I_G
Concrete	bn	bn	$0 \cdot 5n$	$0 \cdot 5bn^2$	$0 \cdot 25bn^3$	$bn^3/12$
Steel	A_s	mA_s	d	$mA_s d$	$mA_s d^2$	0
		$bn + mA_s$		$0 \cdot 5bn^2 + mA_s d$	$0 \cdot 25bn^3 + mA_s d^2$	$bn^3/12$

The depth of the neutral axis n of the whole section from the axis XX is obtained by taking moments about XX

$$\therefore \quad \Sigma Ax = n \Sigma A$$

$$n = \frac{\Sigma Ax}{\Sigma A} \quad \quad \dots(2,28)$$

The moment of inertia of the whole section about the axis XX

$$= I_x = \Sigma A \cdot x^2 + \Sigma I_G \quad \quad \dots(2,29)$$

If I is the moment of inertia of the whole section about the neutral axis NA, then

$$I_x = n^2 \sum A + I \qquad \ldots (2,30)$$

From equations (2,29) and (2,30)

$$I = \sum A \cdot x^2 + \sum I_G - n^2 \sum A \qquad \ldots (2,31)$$

Applying equation (2,28) to the example considered in Table 4,

$$n = \frac{0 \cdot 5bn^2 + mA_s d}{bn + mA_s} \qquad \ldots (2,32)$$

This can be proved to be the same result as equation (2,4), as follows:

$$0 \cdot 5bn^2 + mA_s n - mA_s d = 0$$

$$n_1{}^2 + \frac{2}{bd} \cdot mA_s n_1 - \frac{2}{bd} \cdot mA_s = 0$$

$$n_1{}^2 + 2m \frac{p}{100} n_1 - 2m \cdot \frac{p}{100} = 0$$

$$\therefore \quad n_1 = -\frac{mp}{100} + \sqrt{\left(\frac{mp}{100}\right)^2 + 2\left(\frac{mp}{100}\right)} \qquad \ldots (2,33)$$

Applying equation (2,31) to Table 4,

$$I = 0 \cdot 25bn^3 + mA_s d^2 + \frac{bn^3}{12} - n^2(bn + mA_s)$$

$$\therefore \quad I = -\tfrac{2}{3} \cdot bn^3 + mA_s(d^2 - n^2) \qquad \ldots (2,34)$$

This can be proved to be the same result as equation (2,27) as follows:
Equating (2,27) and (2,34),

$$\frac{bn^3}{3} + mA_s(d - n)^2 = -\tfrac{2}{3} \cdot bn^3 + mA_s(d^2 - n^2)$$

$$bn^3 = mA_s(d^2 - n^2 - d^2 - n^2 + 2dn)$$

$$\frac{bn^2}{2} = mA_s(d - n)$$

From equation (2.2), $\dfrac{t}{c} = m\dfrac{(d - n)}{n}$

$$\frac{bn^2}{2} = \frac{t}{c} \cdot nA_s$$

$$\therefore \quad \frac{c}{2} \cdot nb = A_s t$$

i.e. the longitudinal compression = the longitudinal tension, which must be true as there are no externally applied longitudinal forces.

EXAMPLE 2.5.1

The problem stated in Example (2.2.1) (see also Example 2.4.1) can alternatively be solved by the method illustrated by Table 4.

Table 5 is derived in the same way as Table. 4

TABLE 5

Portion	Area	A	x	Ax	Ax^2	I_G
Concrete	$6n$	$6n$	$0 \cdot 5n$	$3n^2$	$1 \cdot 5n^3$	$6n^3/12$
Steel	$1 \cdot 571$	$23 \cdot 57$	18	$424 \cdot 2$	$7,630$	0
	$6n + 1 \cdot 571$	$6n + 23 \cdot 57$		$3n^2 + 424 \cdot 2$	$1 \cdot 5n^3 + 7,630$	$0 \cdot 5n^3$
						$2n^3 + 7,630$

Then using equation (2,28),

$$n = \frac{3n^2 + 424 \cdot 2}{6n + 23 \cdot 57}$$

$$3n^2 + 23 \cdot 57n - 424 \cdot 2 = 0$$

$$n^2 + 7 \cdot 857n - 141 \cdot 4 = 0$$

$$n = -3 \cdot 928 \pm \sqrt{3 \cdot 928^2 + 141 \cdot 4}$$

$$= -3 \cdot 93 \pm 12 \cdot 54$$

$$= 8 \cdot 61 \text{ in.}$$

From equation (2,31),

$$I = 2n^3 + 7,630 - n^2(6n + 23 \cdot 57)$$

$$= 1,280 + 7,630 - 5,570$$

$$= 3,340 \text{ in.}^4$$

The problem is then continued in the same way as Example (2.4.1).

2.6 To evaluate the concrete and reinforcement stresses for a fully defined rectangular section with compression reinforcement subjected to a given bending moment

The analysis can be attempted in a fashion similar to that in §2.2, or alternatively by computing the moment of inertia in a similar way to that in §2.4 or §2.5.

Considering the analagous method to §2.2 Fig. 16(i) shows the section under investigation. Fig. 16(ii) illustrates the distribution of strain when a bending moment is applied, and Fig. 16(iii) gives the corresponding distribution of stress.

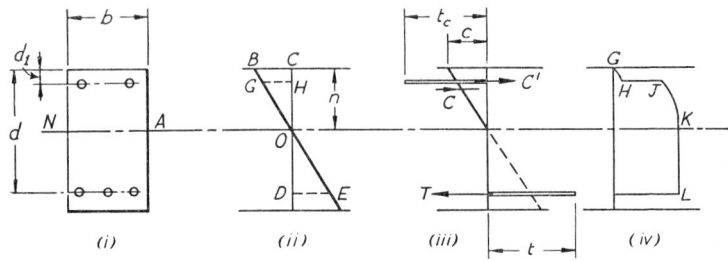

Fig. 16.

From Fig. 16(ii),

$$\frac{BC}{CO} = \frac{DE}{DO}$$

Applying Hooke's Law, this becomes,

$$\frac{c/E_c}{n} = \frac{t/E_s}{(d-n)}$$

therefore

$$c = \frac{tn}{m(d-n)} \qquad \dots(2,35)$$

Also from Fig. 16(ii)

$$\frac{GH}{HO} = \frac{DE}{DO}$$

Applying Hooke's Law, this becomes:

$$\frac{t_c/E_s}{(n-d_1)} = \frac{t/E_s}{(d-n)}$$

$$\therefore \quad t_c = \frac{t(n-d_1)}{(d-n)} \qquad \dots(2,36)$$

The longitudinal compression must equal the longitudinal tension, i.e.

$$C + C' = T \qquad \dots(2,37)$$

now $C =$ the compressive force imposed on the concrete

$= b \cdot n \cdot \dfrac{c}{2}$ minus the effect of the concrete displaced by the compression reinforcement.

The strain GH (see Fig. 16(ii)) $= \dfrac{t_c}{E_s}$

$\therefore$ The stress in the concrete at the depth of the compression reinforcement

$$= E_c \cdot \left(\frac{t_c}{E_s}\right) = \frac{t_c}{m}$$

$$\therefore \quad C = b \cdot n \cdot \frac{c}{2} - A_{sc} \cdot \frac{t_c}{m}$$

where A_{sc} = the area of the compression reinforcement (which is equal to the area of concrete displaced by this reinforcement) now C' = the compressive force imposed on the compression reinforcement = $A_{sc} \cdot t_c$. Therefore equation (2,37) becomes

$$b \cdot n \cdot \frac{c}{2} - A_{sc} \cdot \frac{t_c}{m} + A_{sc} \cdot t_c = A_s \cdot t$$

Substituting for c and t_c from equations (2,35) and (2,36),

$$\frac{bn}{2} \cdot \frac{tn}{m(d-n)} - A_{sc} \cdot \frac{t(n-d_1)}{(d-n)} \cdot \left(\frac{1}{m} - 1\right) = A_s t$$

$$bn^2 + 2A_{sc}(m-1)(n-d_1) - 2mA_s(d-n) = 0$$

$$bn^2 + 2n\{A_{sc}(m-1) + mA_s\} - 2\{A_{sc}(m-1)d_1 + mA_s d\} = 0$$

$$\ldots.(2,38)$$

This quadratic equation can be solved for n. It can also be expressed in a form similar to equation (2,4), if desired, as follows:

Divide equation (2,38) throughout by bd^2, then

$$n_1^2 + 2n_1\left\{\frac{A_{sc}}{bd} \cdot (m-1) + \frac{mA_s}{bd}\right\} - 2\left\{\frac{A_{sc}}{bd} \cdot (m-1) \cdot \frac{d_1}{d} + \frac{mA_s}{bd}\right\} = 0$$

$$\therefore \; n_1^2 + 2n_1\left\{\frac{p'}{100} \cdot (m-1) + \frac{mp}{100}\right\} - 2\left\{\frac{p'}{100} \cdot (m-1) \cdot \frac{d_1}{d} + \frac{mp}{100}\right\} = 0$$

$$\ldots.(2,39)$$

where $p' = \dfrac{A_{sc}}{bd} \cdot 100$ = the percentage of compression steel.

After the depth of the neutral axis has been determined from either equation (2,38) or equation (2,39), the stresses are then computed as follows:

Taking moments about the tension steel,

$$M = \left(bn \cdot \frac{c}{2}\right)\left(d - \frac{n}{3}\right) - \left(A_{sc} \cdot \frac{t_c}{m}\right)(d - d_1) + (A_{sc}t_c)(d - d_1)$$

$$M = \frac{bnc}{2}\left(d - \frac{n}{3}\right) + A_{sc}t_c(d - d_1)\left(\frac{m-1}{m}\right) \qquad \ldots.(2,40)$$

If c is required, then t_c must be expressed in terms of c; from equations (2,35) and (2,36),

$$t_c = c \cdot \frac{m(d-n)}{n} \cdot \frac{(n-d_1)}{(d-n)} = cm \cdot \frac{(n-d_1)}{n} \qquad \dots (2,41)$$

equation (2,40) becomes

$$M = \frac{bnc}{2} \cdot \left(d - \frac{n}{3}\right) + A_{sc} \cdot \frac{cm(n-d_1)}{n} \cdot (d-d_1)\left(\frac{m-1}{m}\right)$$

$$\therefore \quad c = \frac{M}{\dfrac{bn}{2}\left(d - \dfrac{n}{3}\right) + A_{sc}(m-1)\left(1 - \dfrac{d_1}{n}\right)(d-d_1)} \qquad \dots (2,42)$$

After obtaining c, from this equation, t and t_c can be computed from equations (2,35) and (2,36)

EXAMPLE 2.6.1

Suppose the beam described in Example (2.2.1) were to have two $\frac{1}{2}$ in. dia. bars as compression reinforcement, these bars having 1 in. cover of concrete. Determine the concrete and steel stresses.

$$A_{sc} = 0 \cdot 393 \text{ sq in.}$$
$$d_1 = 1 \text{ in. cover} + \tfrac{1}{4} \text{ in.} = 1\tfrac{1}{4} \text{ in.}$$

Using equation (2,38)

$$6n^2 + 2n\{0 \cdot 393 \times 14 + 15 \times 1 \cdot 571\}$$
$$- 2\{0 \cdot 393 \times 14 \times 1 \cdot 25 + 15 \times 1 \cdot 571 \times 18\} = 0$$
$$\therefore \quad n^2 + 9 \cdot 69n - 143 \cdot 7 = 0$$
$$n = 8 \cdot 08 \text{ in.}$$

From equation (2,42),

$$c = \frac{500,000}{\dfrac{6 \times 8 \cdot 08}{2} \cdot \left(18 - \dfrac{8 \cdot 08}{3}\right) + 0 \cdot 393 \times 14 \times \left(1 - \dfrac{1 \cdot 25}{8 \cdot 08}\right)(18 - 1 \cdot 25)}$$

$$= 1{,}112 \text{ lb/sq in.}$$

From equation (2,35),

$$t = \frac{cm(d-n)}{n}$$

$$= \frac{1{,}112 \times 15 \times (18 - 8 \cdot 08)}{8 \cdot 08}$$

$$= 20{,}550 \text{ lb/sq in.}$$

From equation (2.41),

$$t_c = 1{,}112 \times 15 \times \frac{(8 \cdot 08 - 1 \cdot 25)}{8 \cdot 08}$$

$$= 14{,}130 \text{ lb/sq in.}$$

It is instructive to compare these results with those of Example (2.2.1). The inclusion of the compression steel can be seen to reduce the depth of the neutral axis, and the stresses in the concrete and in the tension reinforcement.

Alternatively, once the depth of the neutral axis has been determined from equation (2,38), the moment of inertia can be evaluated in a similar fashion to §2.4 above.

Thus

$$I = \frac{bn^3}{3} - A_{sc}(n - d_1)^2 + mA_{sc}(n - d_1)^2 + mA_s(d - n)^2$$

$$I = \frac{bn^3}{3} + (m - 1)A_{sc}(n - d_1)^2 + mA_s(d - n)^2 \qquad \dots(2,43)$$

Then

$$c = \frac{M}{I} \cdot n \qquad \dots(2,44)$$

is comparable to equation (2,25),

$$t = m \cdot \frac{M}{I} \cdot (d - n) \qquad \dots(2,45)$$

is comparable to equation (2,26);
and similarly

$$t_c = m \cdot \frac{M}{I} \cdot (n - d_1) \qquad \dots(2,46)$$

EXAMPLE 2.6.2

Consider again Example (2.6.1).

As computed in the solution of Example (2.6.1),

$$n = 8 \cdot 08 \text{ in.}$$

Applying equation (2,43):

$$I = \frac{6 \times 8 \cdot 08^3}{3} + (15 - 1) \times 0 \cdot 393 \times (8 \cdot 08 - 1 \cdot 25)^2$$

$$+ 15 \times 1 \cdot 571 \times (18 - 8 \cdot 08)^2$$

$$= 1{,}056 + 256 \cdot 4 + 2{,}320$$

$$= 3{,}632 \text{ in.}^4$$

Using equation (2,44),

$$c = \frac{500,000}{3,632} \times 8\cdot08$$

$$= 1,113 \text{ lb/sq in.}$$

Using equation (2,45),

$$t = 15 \times \frac{500,000}{3,632} \times (18 - 8\cdot08) = \underline{20,470 \text{ lb/sq in.}}$$

Using equation (2,46),

$$t_c = 15 \times \frac{500,000}{3,632} \times (8\cdot08 - 1\cdot25)$$

$$= \underline{14,110 \text{ lb/sq in.}}$$

A further alternative is to use the tabular method described in (d) above. The equivalent area of the concrete is $(bn - A_{sc})$, and the equivalent area of the compression steel is mA_{cs}. To simplify the determination of the centroids of these areas the rectangular area (bn) is considered and then an area of $(-A_{sc} + mA_{sc})$ at the location of the compression reinforcement. Table 6 gives the necessary tabulation except that to facilitate printing, the columns are not totalled.

TABLE 6

Portion	A	x	Ax^2	Ax^2	I_G
Compression zone	bn	$0\cdot5n$	$0\cdot5bn^2$	$0\cdot25bn^3$	$bn^3/12$
Compression steel	$A_{sc}(m-1)$	d_1	$A_{sc}(m-1)d_1$	$A_{sc}(m-1)d_1^2$	0
Tension steel	mA_s	d	mA_sd	mA_sd^2	0

Therefore from equation (2,28),

$$n = \frac{\sum A \cdot x}{\sum A} = \frac{0\cdot5bn^2 + A_{sc}(m-1)d + mA_sd}{bn + A_{sc}(m-1) + mA_s} \quad \dots (2,47)$$

When the section is fully defined this quadratic equation can be solved to determine n.

From equation (2,31),

$$I = \sum A \cdot x^2 + \sum I_G - n^2 \sum A$$

$$= 0\cdot25bn^3 + A_{sc}(m-1)d_1^2 + mA_sd^2 + \frac{bn^3}{12}$$

$$-n^2(bn + A_{sc}(m-1) + mA_s) \quad \dots (2,48)$$

This equation enables I to be calculated. Then the stresses are determined from equations (2,44), (2,45), and (2,46).

EXAMPLE 2.6.3

Solve the problem of Example (2.6.1) by the tabular method just outlined.

The numerical values of this problem are inserted in Table 6 to give Table 7.

TABLE 7

Portion	A	x	Ax	Ax^2	I_G
Compression zone	$6n$	$0 \cdot 5n$	$3n^2$	$1 \cdot 5n^3$	$0 \cdot 5n^3$
Compression steel	$5 \cdot 5$	$1 \cdot 25$	$6 \cdot 88$	$8 \cdot 6$	0
Tension steel	$23 \cdot 5$	$18 \cdot$	$423 \cdot$	$7,610$	0
	$6n + 29$		$3n^2$ $+ 429 \cdot 9$	$1 \cdot 5n^3$ $+ 7,619$	$0 \cdot 5n^3$

Then $n\Sigma A = \Sigma Ax$

$$6n^2 + 29n = 3n^2 + 429 \cdot 9$$

$$n^2 + 9 \cdot 67n - 143 \cdot 3 = 0$$

$$n = 8 \cdot 08 \ (\text{or} \ -17 \cdot 75)$$

Now from equation (2,31),

$$I = \Sigma Ax^2 + \Sigma I_G - n^2 \Sigma A$$
$$= (1 \cdot 5n^3 + 7,619) + (0 \cdot 5n^3) - n^2(6n + 29)$$
$$= -4n^3 + 7,619 - 29n^2$$
$$= -2,120 + 7,619 - 1,890$$
$$= 3,609 \text{ in.}^4$$

From equation (2,44),

$$c = \frac{M}{I} \cdot n = \frac{500,000}{3,609} \times 8 \cdot 08$$
$$= 1,120 \text{ lb/sq in.}$$

From equation (2,45),

$$t = m \cdot \frac{M}{I} \cdot (d - n)$$

$$\therefore \quad t = 15 \times \frac{500,000}{3,609} \times (18 - 8 \cdot 08)$$
$$= 20,600 \text{ lb/sq. in.}$$

From equation (2,46),

$$t_c = m \cdot \frac{M}{I} \cdot (n - d_1)$$

$$= 15 \times \frac{550,000}{3,609} \times (8 \cdot 08 - 1 \cdot 25)$$

$$= 14,180 \text{ lb/sq in.}$$

It is interesting to observe how the results of Examples (2.6.1), (2.6.2), and (2.6.3) agree, within the limits of the accuracy of a slide rule.

2.7 To design a rectangular section with compression reinforcement to resist a specified bending moment

Once again consider Fig. 16. From Fig. 16(ii)

$$\frac{BC}{CO} = \frac{DE}{DO}$$

Applying Hooke's Law, this becomes,

$$\frac{c/E_c}{n} = \frac{t/E_s}{(d - n)}$$

$$\therefore \quad n_1 = \frac{m}{r + m} = \frac{1}{\left(\dfrac{r}{m}\right) + 1} \qquad \ldots (2,49)$$

Taking moments about the centroid of the tension steel,

$$M = \frac{c}{2} \cdot bn\left(d - \frac{n}{3}\right) - A_{sc} \cdot \left(\frac{t_c}{m}\right) \cdot (d - d_1) + A_{sc}t_c(d - d_1)$$

$$= \frac{c}{2} \cdot n_1 a_1 bd^2 + A_{sc}t_c(d - d_1)\left(1 - \frac{1}{m}\right)$$

$$M = Qbd^2 + (m - 1)A_{sc} \cdot \frac{t_c}{m} \cdot (d - d_1)$$

$$A_{sc} = \frac{M - Qbd^2}{(m - 1) \cdot \dfrac{t_c}{m} \cdot (d - d_1)} \qquad \ldots (2,50)$$

From Fig. 16(ii),

$$\frac{GH}{BC} = \frac{n - d_1}{n}$$

$$\frac{t_c/E_s}{c/E_c} = \frac{n - d_1}{n}$$

$$\frac{t_c}{m} = c \cdot \left(\frac{n - d_1}{n}\right) \qquad \ldots (2,51)$$

From (2,50) and (2,51)

$$A_{sc} = \frac{M - Qbd^2}{(m-1)c\left(\dfrac{n-d_1}{n}\right)(d-d_1)} \qquad \ldots .(2,52)$$

The total compression must equal the total tension,

$$\therefore \quad \frac{c}{2} . bn - \frac{t_c}{m} . A_{sc} + t_c A_{sc} = t A_s$$

$$A_s = \frac{cbn}{2t} + \frac{t_c A_{sc}}{t} . \left(\frac{m-1}{m}\right) \qquad \ldots .(2,53)$$

EXAMPLE 2.7.1

Suppose that the section designed in Example (2.3.1) concerned one locality of a continuous beam of a constant rectangular shape, namely 12 in. wide by 23 in. deep (see Fig. 14). At another section of this beam the bending moment is 1,500,000 lb in. Determine suitable quantities of compression and tension reinforcement for this section, assuming the maximum permissible compressive stress in bending = 1,000 lb/sq in., the maximum permissible tensile steel stress = 20,000 lb/sq in., the maximum permissible compressive steel stress = 18,000 lb/sq in. and the modular ratio = 15.

As the section is being designed (i.e. is not fully defined), the values of n_1, a_1, and Q depend only upon the value of r and are thus independent of whether or not compression reinforcement is to be used.

Therefore from the solution to Example (2.3.1),

$$n_1 = 0\cdot428, \ a_1 = 0\cdot857, \text{ and } Q = 183\cdot3$$

assume $d = 21$ in.,

$$n = 0\cdot428 \times 21 = 9\cdot0 \text{ in.}$$

assume $d_1 = 1\frac{1}{2}$ in.

∴ from equation (2,52),

$$A_{sc} = \frac{1,500,000 - 183\cdot3 \times 12 \times 21^2}{14 \times 1,000\left(\dfrac{9\cdot0 - 1\cdot5}{9\cdot0}\right)(21 - 1\cdot5)}$$

$$= 2\cdot32 \text{ sq in.}$$

Use say three 1 in. dia. M.S. bars as compression reinforcement (with 1 in. cover of concrete).

From equation (2,51),

$$t_c = 15 \times 1,000 \times \frac{(9\cdot0 - 1\cdot5)}{9\cdot0} = \underline{12,500 \text{ lb/sq in.}}$$

This is within the 18,000 lb/sq in. specified as the maximum permissible stress for the steel in compression.

From equation (2,53),

$$A_s = \frac{1,000 \times 12 \times 9 \cdot 0}{2 \times 20,000} + \frac{12,500 \times 2 \cdot 32}{20,000} \cdot \left(\frac{14}{15}\right)$$

$$= 4 \cdot 051 \text{ sq in.}$$

Use say four 1 in. dia. and one $1\frac{1}{4}$ in. dia. M.S. bars as tensile re-inforcement. These will need $1\frac{1}{8}$ in. of cover according to the British Code of Practice. This means that the effective depth of the reinforce-ment will be approximately 23 in. $- 1\frac{1}{8}$ in. $- \frac{1}{2}$ in. $= 21\frac{3}{8}$ in., which is satisfactory as it is greater than the 21 in. used above.

It would now be instructive for the student to analyse this section in accordance with §2.6.

EXAMPLE 2.7.2

Suppose that the T-beam designed in Example (2.9.1) is continu-ous and has to resist a moment of 2,400,000 lb in. over a support. Determine the areas of high tensile compressive and tensile re-inforcement required by the section at this location. Assume the permissible stress of the steel to be 23,000 lb/sq in. in compression and 30,000 lb/sq in. in tension.

The flange of the T-beam is in tension at this support. The stem of the beam acts in compression. The problem is therefore that of a rectangular beam of breadth 11 in.

$$r = \frac{30,000}{1,000} = 30,$$

$\therefore$ from equation (2,11), $n_1 = \left(\frac{1}{\frac{30}{15} + 1}\right) = 0 \cdot 3333$

$$n = 6 \cdot 67 \text{ in.}$$

From equation (2,12), $\quad a_1 = 1 - \frac{0 \cdot 333}{3} = 0 \cdot 889$

$$\therefore \quad a = 17 \cdot 78 \text{ in.}$$

From equation (2,15), $\quad Q = \frac{1,000 \times 0 \cdot 333 \times 0 \cdot 889}{2} = 148 \cdot 2$

From equation (2,52), assuming $d_1 = 1 \cdot 5$ in., and $d = 20$ in.,

$$A_{sc} = \frac{2,400,000 - 148 \cdot 2 \times 11 \times 20^2}{14 \times 1,000 \times \dfrac{(6 \cdot 67 - 1 \cdot 5)}{6 \cdot 67} \times (20 - 1 \cdot 5)}$$

$$= 8 \cdot 70 \text{ sq. in.}$$

From equation (2,51),

$$t_c = 15 \times 1,000 \times \left(\frac{6.67 - 1.5}{6.67}\right) = \underline{11,620 \text{ lb/sq in.}}$$

This does not make much use of the high tensile steel in compression. From equation (2,53),

$$A_s = \frac{1,000 \times 11 \times 6.67}{2 \times 30,000} + \frac{11,620 \times 8.70}{30,000} \times \left(\frac{14}{15}\right)$$

$$= 1.22 + 3.14 = \underline{4.36 \text{ sq in.}}$$

This is a case where more compression steel is required than tension steel. The beam can be reinforced in this fashion, but designers usually employ the 'Steel Beam Theory' under such circumstances, see §2.10.

2.8 To evaluate the concrete and reinforcement stresses for a fully defined T-section subjected to a given bending moment

In an *in-situ* reinforced concrete building, floor slabs are supported by beams, and as the whole construction is monolithic, each beam can include part of the slab in its structural strength, hence T-shaped beams are common in practice. They have very economical sections for resisting bending moments because the slab, which acts as a wide flange, gives a large concrete area where the stresses are greatest. The width of slab which can be considered in the strength of the beam is given by various Codes of Practice.[3,13] Because of the economy of T-beams, as mentioned above, precast and *in-situ* beams are sometimes made this shape in preference to a rectangular shape even if they are not supporting reinforced concrete slabs. The wide flange is often useful in decreasing any reduction of the permissible concrete stress due to bending required because of lateral instability, see Table 14 of reference 3.

The analysis of a T-section can be effected in a similar fashion to that in §2.2, or alternatively by computing the moment of inertia in a similar way to that in §2.4 or §2.5.

Considering the method analogous to that in §2.2, Fig. 17(i) shows the section under consideration. Fig. 17(ii) illustrates the distribution of strain when a bending moment is applied, and Fig. 17(iii) gives the corresponding distribution of stress.

When the neutral axis lies within the depth of the slab, the analysis becomes one of a rectangular beam of breadth B (see §2.2), because the assumption that the concrete does not resist tensile stresses means that the cross-sectional area of concrete below the neutral axis is irrelevant to the analysis. The following deals with the case when the neutral axis is below the soffit of the slab.

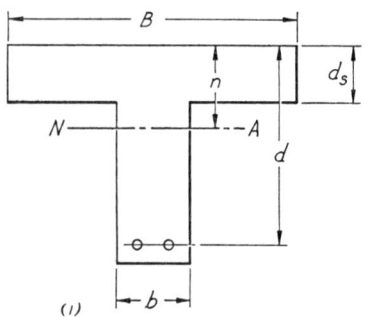

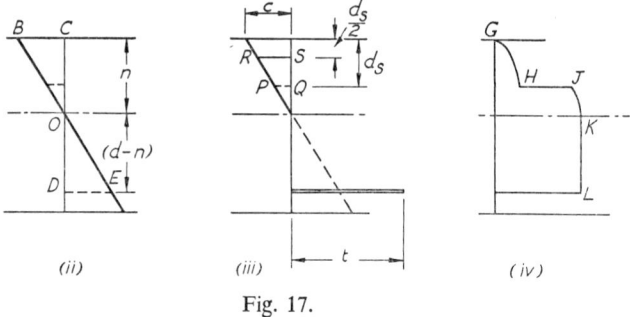

(ii) (iii) (iv)

Fig. 17.

From Fig. 17(ii),

$$\frac{BC}{CO} = \frac{DE}{OD}$$

$$\therefore \frac{c/E_c}{n} = \frac{t/E_s}{(d-n)}$$

$$\therefore \frac{t}{c} = \frac{m(d-n)}{n} = \frac{m(1-n_1)}{n_1} \qquad \ldots(2,54)$$

From Fig. 17(iii),

$$\frac{PQ}{(n-d_s)} = \frac{c}{n}$$

$$\therefore PQ = c \cdot \left(\frac{n-d_s}{n}\right)$$

The longitudinal compression must equal the longitudinal tension. (N.B. for ease of computation the compression zone is considered to be Bn less $(B-b)(n-d_s)$)

$$\therefore Bn \cdot \frac{c}{2} - (B-b)(n-d_s) \cdot \left(\frac{PQ}{2}\right) = A_s t$$

where A_s is the area of the tension reinforcement

$$\therefore \quad Bn \cdot \frac{c}{2} - (B - b)(n - d_s) \cdot \frac{c}{2} \cdot \left(\frac{n - d_s}{n}\right) = A_s t$$

$$\therefore \quad Bn^2 - (B - b)(n - d_s)^2 = 2nA_s \cdot \frac{t}{c} \qquad \ldots(2,55)$$

Substituting for t/c from equation (2,54),

$$Bn^2 - (B - b)(n^2 + d_s^2 - 2nd_s) = 2A_s m(d - n)$$

$$bn^2 + 2n\{d_s(B - b) + A_s m\} - \{(B - b)d_s^2 + 2A_s md\} = 0 \quad \ldots(2,56)$$

This equation can be solved for n.

Taking moments about the tension steel, the bending moment applied to the section

$$= M = \left(Bn \cdot \frac{c}{2}\right)\left(d - \frac{n}{3}\right) - (B - b)(n - d_s) \cdot \frac{PQ}{2}$$

$$\times \{d - n + \tfrac{2}{3}(n - d_s)\}$$

$$\therefore \quad M = Bn \cdot \frac{c}{2}\left(d - \frac{n}{3}\right) - (B - b)c \cdot \frac{(n - d_s)^2}{2n} \cdot \{d - \frac{n}{3} - \tfrac{2}{3}d_s\}$$

$$\ldots(2,57)$$

This equation enables c to be computed, then the value of t can be determined from equation (2,54).

EXAMPLE 2.8.1

In Fig. 17, suppose that $B = 30$ in., $d_s = 5$ in., $d = 20$ in., and $b = 12$ in. If the tension reinforcement comprises one layer of five 1 in. diameter bars and the section is subjected to a bending moment of 1,200,000 lb in., determine the stress in the reinforcement, and the maximum stress in the concrete, (assume m to be 15).

From equation (2,56),

$$12n^2 + 2n\{5 \times (30 - 12) + 3 \cdot 92 \times 15\}$$

$$- \{(30 - 12) \times 5^2 + 2 \times 3 \cdot 92 \times 15 \times 20\} = 0$$

$$n^2 + 24 \cdot 82n - 233 \cdot 3 = 0$$

$$n = 7 \cdot 29 \text{ in.}$$

N.B. if this had been less than 5 in. then the T-beam theory would not apply and the beam would be analysed as for a rectangular beam of breadth 30 in.

Then using equation (2,57),

$$1{,}200{,}000 = 30 \times 7 \cdot 29 \cdot \frac{c}{2} \cdot \left(20 - \frac{7 \cdot 29}{3}\right) - (30 - 12)c$$

$$\frac{(7 \cdot 29 - 5)^2}{2 \times 7 \cdot 29} \cdot \left\{20 - \frac{7 \cdot 29}{3} - \frac{2}{3} \times 5\right\}$$

$$\therefore \quad c = \underline{652 \ \text{lb/sq. in.}}$$

From equation (2,54),

$$\frac{t}{652} = \frac{15 \times (20 - 7 \cdot 29)}{7 \cdot 29}$$

$$t = \underline{17{,}070 \ \text{lb/sq. in.}}$$

Now consider the method analogous to that in §2.4. The depth of the neutral axis is computed as above and then referring to Fig. 17, the moment of inertia about the neutral axis is given by,

$$I = \frac{Bn^3}{3} - \frac{(B - b)(n - d_s)^3}{3} + A_s m(d - n)^2 \quad \ldots (2{,}58)$$

Then in a similar fashion to equation (2,25),

$$c = \frac{M}{I} \cdot n \qquad \ldots (2{,}59)$$

and comparably to equation (2,26),

$$t = m \cdot \frac{M}{I} \cdot (d - n) \qquad \ldots (2{,}60)$$

EXAMPLE 2.8.2

Repeat the Example (2.8.1) only using this latter method.

As before, $n = 7 \cdot 29$ in., then from equation (2,58),

$$I = \frac{30 \times 7 \cdot 29^3}{3} - \frac{(30 - 12)(7 \cdot 29 - 5)^3}{3}$$

$$+ 3 \cdot 92 \times 15 \times (20 - 7 \cdot 29)^2$$

$$= \underline{13{,}328 \ \text{in.}^4}$$

From equation (2,59),

$$c = \frac{1{,}200{,}000 \times 7 \cdot 29}{13{,}328} = \underline{656 \ \text{lb/sq. in.}}$$

From equation (2,60),

$$t = 15 \times \frac{1{,}200{,}000}{13{,}328} \times (20 - 7 \cdot 29) = \underline{17{,}170 \ \text{lb/sq. in.}}$$

These results compare favourably with those of Example (2.8.1).

With regard to the tabular method as expounded in §2.5; Table 8 illustrates the application of this method to the T-beam shown in Fig. 17. To aid printing, the columns of A, $A \cdot x$, $A \cdot x^2$ and I_G are not totalled.

EXAMPLE 2.8.3

Repeat the Example (2.8.1) only using this latter method.

The dimensions of this problem are inserted in Table 8 to give Table 9.

Then from equation (2,28),

$$12n^2 + 148 \cdot 8n = 6n^2 + 1,401$$

$$\therefore \quad n^2 + 24 \cdot 8n - 233 \cdot 5 = 0$$

$$n = 7 \cdot 3 \text{ in. (compare Example 2.8.1)}$$

From equation (2,31) and Table 9,

$$I = 3n^3 + 24,083 + n^3 + 187 \cdot 5 - n^2(12n + 148 \cdot 8)$$

$$= \underline{13,220 \text{ in.}^4} \text{ (compare Example 2.8.2)}$$

Then c and t can be evaluated in the same way as Example (2.8.2).

T-beams do not normally require compression reinforcement. The following example illustrates a method of analysing such sections.

EXAMPLE 2.8.4

In Fig. 17, suppose that $B = 30$ in., $d_s = 5$ in., and $b = 11$ in. The tension reinforcement is in two layers; the bottom layer comprising five 1 in. diameter bars at an effective depth of 20 in., the layer above comprising four 1 in. diameter bars at an effective depth of 18 in. This beam also contains two $\frac{3}{4}$ in. dia. bars as compression reinforcement, the centroid of this steel being $1\frac{3}{8}$ in. below the top of the beam. Assume $m = 15$, and determine the maximum stress in the concrete and the stresses in the reinforcements when the section is subjected to a bending moment of 2,000,000 lb in.

The tabular method expounded in §2.5 is applied as shown in Table 10.

Then from equation (2,28),

$$237 \cdot 5 + 5 \cdot 5n^2 + 17 + 848 + 1,180 = n\{95 + 11n$$

$$+ 12 \cdot 38 + 47 \cdot 1 + 59 \cdot 0\}$$

$$n^2 + 38 \cdot 8n - 416 = 0$$

$$n = \underline{8 \cdot 76 \text{ in.}}$$

TABLE 8

Portion	Area	x	Ax	Ax^2	I_G
Compression flanges	$(B-b)d_s$	$0.5\,d_s$	$0.5\,d_s^2(B-b)$	$0.25\,d_s^3(B-b)$	$\dfrac{(B-b)d_s^3}{12}$
Compression stem	bn	$0.5n$	$0.5\,bn^2$	$0.25\,bn^3$	$\dfrac{bn^3}{12}$
Tension steel	A_s	d	$A_s md$	$A_s md^2$	—

TABLE 9

Portion	Area	x	Ax	Ax^2	I_G
Compression flanges	90	2·5	225	562·5	187·5
Compression stem	$12n$	$0.5n$	$6n^2$	$3n^3$	n^3
Tension steel	3·92	20	1,176	23,520	—
	$12n+148.8$		$6n^2+1,401$	$3n^3+24,083$	$n^3+187.5$

TABLE 10

Portion	Area	A	x	Ax	Ax^2	I_G
Compression flanges	95	95	2·5	237·5	593·8	198
Compression stem	$11n$	$11n$	$0·5n$	$5·5n^2$	$2·75n^3$	$1·583n^3$
Compression steel	0·884	12·38	1·375	17·	23·4	—
Top layer tension steel	3·142	47·1	18	848·	15,260	—
Bottom layer tension steel	3·927	59·0	20	1,180	23,600	—

From equation (2,31),

$$\therefore \; I = 593 \cdot 8 + 2 \cdot 75 n^3 + 23 \cdot 4 + 15{,}260 + 23{,}600$$
$$+ \; 198 + 1 \cdot 583 n^3 - n^2 \{95 + 11n + 12 \cdot 38 + 47 \cdot 1 + 59 \cdot 0\}$$
$$= \; \underline{18{,}870 \; \text{in.}^4}$$

Therefore from equation (2.25), $c = \dfrac{2{,}000{,}000 \times 8 \cdot 76}{18{,}870} = \underline{928 \; \text{lb/sq. in.}}$

From equation (2,26), the stress in the bottom layer of the tension reinforcement:

$$= \frac{2{,}000{,}000 \times 15 \times (20 - 8 \cdot 76)}{18{,}870} = \underline{17{,}900 \; \text{lb/sq. in.}}$$

and the stress in the top layer of the tension reinforcement:

$$= \frac{2{,}000{,}000 \times 15 \times (18 - 8 \cdot 76)}{18{,}870} = \underline{14{,}700 \; \text{lb/sq. in.}}$$

From equation (2,46), the stress in the compression reinforcement:

$$= \frac{15 \times 2{,}000{,}000 \times (8 \cdot 76 - 1 \cdot 375)}{18{,}870}$$
$$= \underline{11{,}750 \; \text{lb/sq. in.}}$$

2.9   To design a T-section to resist a specified BM

This section deals with designs made to utilize fully the strengths of the materials, namely concrete and steel. Values of t, c, and m are chosen in accordance with the types of the materials proposed to be used.

Then equation (2,54) gives:

$$n_1 = \frac{m}{m + r} = \frac{1}{1 + \left(\dfrac{r}{m} \right)} \qquad \ldots . (2,61)$$

Referring to Fig. 17, for simplicity assume that only the flange of the T-beam resists compressive stresses. For further simplicity assume that the resultant compressive force exerted by this flange acts at its centre of area. These assumptions do not normally cause errors of any significance, and in any event they allow a preliminary estimate of the section to be made.

The moment arm is therefore given by,

$$a = d - \frac{d_s}{2} \qquad \ldots . (2,62)$$

Therefore taking moments about the line of action of the resultant compression in the flange,

$$M = A_s ta = A_s t \left(d - \frac{d_s}{2} \right)$$

$$A_s = \frac{M}{t \left(d - \frac{d_s}{2} \right)} \qquad \ldots (2,63)$$

The average compressive stress to which the flange may be subjected is represented by RS in Fig. 17(iii). From this diagram,

$$\frac{RS}{c} = \frac{n - \frac{d_s}{2}}{n} = \frac{n_1 d - \frac{d_s}{2}}{n_1 d}$$

$$\therefore \quad RS = c \left\{ \frac{n_1 d - \frac{d_s}{2}}{n_1 d} \right\} \qquad \ldots (2,64)$$

The total compression in the concrete flange of the T-beam is, therefore, given by:

$$C = (Bd_s)c \left\{ \frac{n_1 d - \frac{d_s}{2}}{n_1 d} \right\} \qquad \ldots (2,65)$$

Taking moments about the position of the tension steel,

$$M = Ca = Bd_s c \left\{ \frac{n_1 d - \frac{d_s}{2}}{n_1 d} \right\} \cdot \left(d - \frac{d_s}{2} \right)$$

$$\therefore \quad M = Bd_s c \left\{ 1 - \frac{d_s}{2 n_1 d} \right\} \cdot \left(d - \frac{d_s}{2} \right) \qquad \ldots (2,66)$$

This equation can be used for deciding the dimensions of the flange. Alternatively, if A_s has been obtained from equation (2,63), the total compression can be equated to the total tension to enable the dimensions of the flange to be chosen;

$$C = A_s t$$

therefore from (2.61), $\quad Bd_s c \left(1 - \frac{d_s}{2 n_1 d} \right) = A_s t \qquad \ldots (2,67)$

EXAMPLE 2.9.1

Design a T-beam to resist a bending moment of 2,000,000 lb in. Considerations of headroom and deflection limit the effective depth to 20 in. Assume the permissible stresses of the concrete (in compression due to bending) and steel (in tension) to be 1,000 and 30,000 lb/sq. in. respectively, and the modular ratio to be 15.

Assume $d_s = 5$ in., then from equation (2,63),

$$A_s = \frac{2,000,000}{30,000 \times (20 - 2 \cdot 5)} = 3 \cdot 81$$

therefore use five 1 in. dia. (high tensile) steel bars as tension reinforcement.

According to the British Code[3], it is necessary to have 1 in. spaces between these bars, and 1 in. side covers.

$$\therefore \quad b = 11 \text{ in.}$$

Now, $r = \dfrac{30,000}{1,000} = 30$

$\therefore$ from equation (2,61),

$$n_1 = \frac{15}{15 + 30} = 0 \cdot 3333$$

Then from equation (2,67),

$$B \times 5 \times 1,000 \left(1 - \frac{5}{2 \times 0 \cdot 3333 \times 20}\right) = 3 \cdot 81 \times 30,000$$

therefore $B = 36 \cdot 6$ in.

EXAMPLE 2.9.2

In accordance with clause 311(e) of reference (3), the breadth of the flange of a certain T-beam is limited to 6 ft for design purposes. The slab which forms the top flange of the T-beam is designed to span between the beams and requires to be 6 in. deep, and of a 1:2:4 mix. The maximum overall depth which can be permitted (consistent with the headroom desired) is 2 ft, and the beam is required to resist a bending moment of 1,500,000 lb in. The permissible steel stress in tension is 20,000 lb/sq. in. and the modular ratio is 15. Determine the tension steel required and check that the permissible stress of the concrete in compression does not exceed 1,000 lb/sq. in.

Thinking in terms of 1 in. dia. bars as tension steel with 1 in. cover,

$$d = 24 \text{ in.} - 1\tfrac{1}{2} \text{ in.} = 22 \cdot 5 \text{ in.}$$

From equation (2,63),

$$A_s = \frac{1,500,000}{20,000 \times (22 \cdot 5 - \frac{6}{2})} = 3 \cdot 84$$

therefore use five 1 in. dia. (mild steel) bars.

According to reference (3), the side covers and spaces between the bars require to be 1 in. (minimum).

$$\therefore \quad b = 11 \text{ in.}$$

For design purposes assume $c = 1,000$ lb/sq. in., then $r = 20$, and from equation (2,54),

$$n_1 = \frac{15}{15 + 20} = 0 \cdot 429$$

Therefore from equation (2,66), the moment of resistance of the concrete in compression is given by

$$M = 72 \times 6 \times 1,000 \cdot \left\{ 1 - \frac{6}{2 \times 0 \cdot 429 \times 22 \cdot 5} \right\} \left(22 \cdot 5 - \frac{6}{2} \right)$$

$$\underline{M = 5,800,000 \text{ lb in.}}$$

This is greater than necessary, so it is obvious that the maximum compressive stress in the concrete does not exceed 1,000 lb/sq. in.

2.10 Steel-beam theory

The assumptions of this theory are the same as those of the elastic theory except that the strength of the concrete is ignored in compression. In the early days of reinforced concrete construction, the quality of the concrete was often unreliable and not infrequently poor. Also the designer's fee was often proportional to the quantity of steel used in a reinforced concrete structure, the theory was conservative, simple to understand (being similar to the well established design of steel girders), and small sections could easily be obtained. Designs could therefore, be made rapidly and inexpensively by this method, but yet, because of the large amount of steel used, the design fee was relatively substantial. From these considerations it is understandable that the 'steel-beam theory' was often used in the early days of this industry, and even T-beams were sometimes designed by this method.

Subsequently, the steel-beam theory has been chiefly used for designing the compression reinforcement in a beam when the elastic method of design required the amount of such steel to be greater than the amount of the tension reinforcement (refer to Example 2.7.2). Designers who employ plastic theories have no such need of the steel-beam theory.

EXAMPLE 2.10.1

Solve Example (2.7.2) using the 'steel-beam' theory.

Thinking in terms of both the tension and compression reinforcement consisting of 1 in. diameter bars with 1 in. cover of concrete, the distance between the line of action of the compression force and the line of action of the tension force is equal to,

$$20 - 1\tfrac{1}{2} = 18\tfrac{1}{2} \text{ in.} = a$$

$$\therefore \quad A_{sc} = \frac{2,400,000}{23,000 \times 18\tfrac{1}{2}} = \underline{5 \cdot 64 \text{ sq. in.}}$$

and

$$A_s = \frac{2,400,000}{30,000 \times 18\tfrac{1}{2}} = \underline{4 \cdot 32 \text{ sq. in.}}$$

Comparing these results with those of Example (2.7.2), it will be appreciated that a substantial saving has been made in the amount of compression steel required.

2.11 Deflections

The deflection of a beam at its working load is often most important. Clients do not usually like deflections to be visible to the eye. Beams and slabs for example, can often be cast with cambered soffits so that deflections straighten but do not cause any noticeable sag. Deflections due to superimposed loads, if not limited to reasonable amounts, can cause damage to internal partitions, floor finishes, and windows, and give the client a sense of insecurity. It is, therefore, necessary to be able to compute deflections at working loads.

In §2.4, a moment of inertia was determined for a beam considering the beam to be comprised only of concrete from an elastic analysis point of view, the steel being replaced by an 'equivalent area' of concrete. Such moments of inertia can, therefore, be used for computing deflections, providing the corresponding Young's Moduli refer to the concretes involved.

EXAMPLE 2.11.1

If the beam described in Example (2.8.1) were used to support a uniformly distributed load over a span of 20 ft, determine the maximum deflection which could be experienced (assume $E_s = 30,000,000$ lb/sq. in.)

If the uniformly distributed load inclusive of its self weight $= w$ lb/ft,

then

$$\frac{w \times 20^2}{8} = \frac{1,200,000}{12} \text{ lb ft}$$

$$\therefore \quad w = 2,000 \text{ lb/ft.}$$

The maximum deflection $\quad = \dfrac{5}{384} \cdot \dfrac{wl^4}{E_c I}$

where l is the span, E_c is Young's Modulus for the concrete, and I is the moment of inertia of the *equivalent concrete section*.
From Example (2.8.2),

$$I = 13,328 \text{ in.}^4$$

$$E_c = \frac{E_s}{m} = \frac{30,000,000}{15} = 2,000,000 \text{ lb/sq. in.}$$

therefore the maximum deflection $= \dfrac{5 \times 2,000 \times 20^4 \times 12^3}{384 \times 2,000,000 \times 13,328}$

$$= \underline{0 \cdot 2701 \text{ in.}}$$

Chapter 3

THE PLASTIC ANALYSIS OF REINFORCED CONCRETE SECTIONS IN BENDING

3.1 Plastic analysis

A material is in a *plastic* condition when stresses cause permanent deformations, that is when stress is no longer directly proportional to strain (as in Hooke's Law). A section of a beam experiences such conditions when realizing its ultimate moment of resistance. The plastic method of design, the assumptions of which are described in §1.16, predicts the ultimate moment of resistance, and this is required to equal the bending moment derived from the working loads multiplied by a suitable *load factor*. Many scientists feel that this is a better conception of design than the method based on an elastic analysis (see Chapter 2); the elastic analysis ensures that the stresses at working loads are limited to certain desirable amounts. These stresses are proportioned to the ultimate stresses of the materials by factors of safety; the determination of such factors of safety takes account of the size of cracks at working loads. In practice, such cracks are sometimes a more important criterion to a client than the magnitude of the load factor. This must be considered when using plastic design methods. A structure designed by elastic methods will be found to have many different load factors for its various sections. Plastic designs therefore usually achieve a more efficient use of materials when the ultimate strengths of the members are the main consideration; and most authorities now accept such methods.

3.2 Plastic design in bending

This part of the chapter, and subsequently §3.3 to §3.9 have been written assuming that the reinforcement is mild steel. Other steels used as reinforcement are dealt with in §3.10.

The term *balanced design* refers to the situation when the beam is designed to fail simultaneously in flexural compression and tension. *Under-reinforced* sections will fail in flexural tension and *over-reinforced* sections will fail in flexural compression. An *under-reinforced* section fails owing to yielding of the tensile reinforcement; this causes the cracks to open so that the depth of the beam available to resist flexural compression is reduced, and final collapse occurs by the crushing of the compression zone. This is not however a *flexural compression failure*, since the failure has actually been precipitated by the failure of the tensile reinforcement and the final failure in apparent flexural compression is a secondary effect; it could be described as part of the disintegration of the beam after failure.

Fig. 5 shows a typical relationship between stress and strain for concrete in compression. As described in §1.10, this will vary in shape according to the speed of loading, the strength of the concrete, and other factors. Nevertheless, considerable plasticity is experienced towards failure, i.e. stress is not linearly proportional to strain near failure and large strains occur without proportional increases in stress. It is assumed that plane sections of the beam remain plane after bending (see §1.16), meaning that the distribution of strain due to bending is linear, as explained previously; see Fig. 8. The strain is therefore proportional to the distance from the neutral axis. Curves such as those illustrated in Fig. 5 can therefore be plotted on the axis Of and Oy as

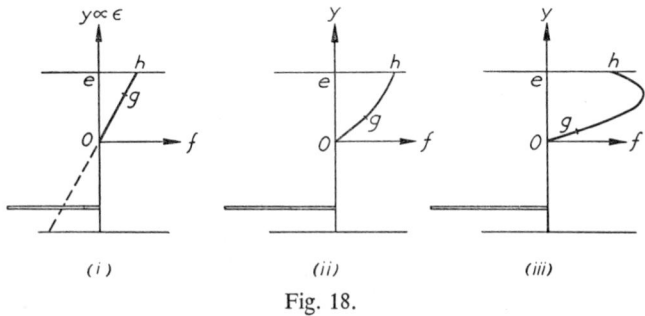

Fig. 18.

shown in Fig. 18. For example, Fig. 18(i) illustrates the elastic stress distribution for working stresses. For higher loads the stress distribution becomes as shown in Fig. 18(ii), and just before failure the stress distribution will be as shown in Fig. 18(iii). The point denoted by g is at the same position on all of Figs. 5, 18(i), (ii) and (iii), illustrating that different scales are used for the strains plotted on the axes Oy in Fig. 18(i), (ii), and (iii). The diagrams $ehgO$ in Fig. 18 are termed *stress blocks*.

For estimating the ultimate moments of resistance of beams, the shape of the stress block just prior to failure must be known. This is assessed empirically, and there are numerous ideas on the subject. Two of the earliest proposals were made by R. M. v. Thullie in 1897 and W. Ritter in 1899. Shapes suggested for the stress block just prior to failure have included parabolas, cubic parabolas, trapeziums, ellipses, and many unusual shapes; some theories have even been made on the assumption that part of the concrete below the neutral axis resists tensile stresses. This latter idea is not justified by experiments, because the cracks penetrate too far into the compression zone. H. Kempton Dyson suggested an elliptical stress block in 1922 and V.P. Jensen proposed a trapezoidal stress block in 1943. Probably the most famous work is by C. S. Whitney, who in 1937 suggested considering the stress block as equivalent to a rectangular shape. This leads to a simple theory which has often been found to be more accurate than other methods, e.g. see reference (10). The current British and A.C.I. Codes of Practice use Whitney's theories as the bases of their recommendations.

3.3 Plastic design of under-reinforced rectangular sections

The distribution of stress is shown in Fig. 19. A general shape is considered for the stress block; the average compressive stress of which

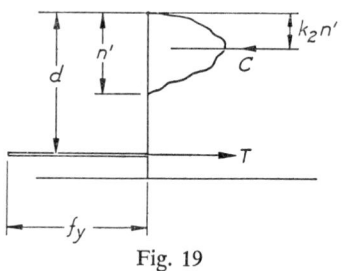

Fig. 19

is equal to c_1, and the centre of gravity is at a depth of $k_2 \cdot n'$. Equating longitudinal forces,

$$C = T$$

$$c_1 n' b = A_s f_y$$

$$\therefore \ n' = \frac{A_s f_y}{c_1 b} \qquad \ldots(3,1)$$

Taking moments about the line of action of C,

$$M_u = T(d - k_2 n')$$

Substituting for n' from equation (3,1) this becomes,

$$M_u = T\left(d - \frac{k_2 A_s f_y}{c_1 b}\right)$$

$$\therefore \ M_u = A_s f_y d\left(1 - \frac{k_2 p f_y}{c_1 \cdot 100}\right) \qquad \ldots(3,2)$$

Whitney and the 1956 A.C.I. Code specify $c_1 = 0 \cdot 85 f_c'$ and $k_2 = 0 \cdot 5$. The 1957 British Code of Practice specifies $c_1 = \frac{2}{3}(\frac{2}{3} \cdot u_w) = \frac{4}{9} \cdot u_w$, and $k_2 = 0 \cdot 5$. For the convenience of designers the British Code derives an expression for the moment of resistance at working loads; it recommends a load factor of 2, $u_w = 3p_{cb}$, and $f_y = 2p_{st}$, and therefore from equation (3,2),

$$2M_r = A_s \cdot 2p_{st} d\left(1 - \frac{0 \cdot 5 \cdot p 2 p_{st}}{\frac{4}{9} \cdot 3 p_{cb} \cdot 100}\right)$$

$$M_r = A_s p_{st} d\left\{1 - 0 \cdot 75 \cdot \frac{p_{st}}{p_{cb}} \cdot \frac{p}{100}\right\} \qquad \ldots(3,3)$$

3.4 *Balanced* plastic design of rectangular sections

Equations (3,1) and (3,2) apply, but the amount of steel required to achieve the *balanced design* condition, where failure occurs simultaneously in flexural tension and compression, is not known, and has to be determined experimentally.

Whitney considers that for balanced design $n' = 0.537d$. Substituting this and his previously mentioned values of c_1 and k_2 in equation (3,1),

$$0.537d = \frac{A_s f_y}{0.85 f_c' b}$$

therefore
$$p = 45.65 \cdot \frac{f_c'}{f_y} \qquad \ldots (3,4)$$

and from equations (3,2) and (3.4),

$$M_u = \frac{45.65}{100} \cdot \frac{f_c'}{f_y} \cdot f_y bd^2 \left(1 - \frac{0.5}{0.85 f_c'} \cdot \frac{45.65}{100} \cdot \frac{f_c'}{f_y} \cdot f_y \right)$$

$$\therefore \quad M_u = \frac{f_c'}{3} \cdot bd^2 \qquad \ldots (3,5)$$

The 1956 A.C.I. Code specifies that for balanced design,

$$p = 40 \cdot \frac{f_c'}{f_y} \qquad \ldots (3,6)$$

and that the value 40 is to be reduced at the rate of 2·5 per 1,000 lb/sq. in. concrete cylinder strength in excess of 5,000 lb/sq. in. When the concrete cylinder strength is less than 5,000 lb/sq. in. for example, the value of p given in equation (3,6) can be substituted in equation (3,2) to give,

$$M_u = 0.3056 f_c' bd^2 \qquad \ldots (3,7)$$

and the corresponding value of n' can be calculated from equations (3,6) and (3,1) to be 0·4706d.

The 1957 British Code of Practice recommends that for balanced design, $n' = 0.5d$, and substituting this in equation (3,1),

$$0.5d = \frac{A_s f_y}{\frac{4}{9} \cdot u_w b}$$

$$\therefore \quad p = 22.22 \times \frac{u_w}{f_y} \qquad \ldots (3,8)$$

Then substituting this in equation (3,2),

$$M_u = \frac{u_w}{6} \cdot bd^2 \qquad \ldots (3,9)$$

The British Code recommends that $M_r = 0.5M_u$, and that $u_w = 3p_{cb}$, hence equations (3,8) and (3,9) can be expressed as,

$$p = \tfrac{1}{3} \cdot \frac{p_{cb}}{p_{st}} \qquad \qquad \ldots\ldots(3,10)$$

$$M_r = \frac{p_{cb}}{4} \cdot bd^2 \qquad \qquad \ldots\ldots(3,11)$$

EXAMPLE 3.4.1 (compare Example 2.2.2)

Determine the moment of resistance at working loads of the section shown in Fig. 12, in accordance with the 1957 British Code of Practice recommendations concerning plastic design. The permissible concrete stress is 1,500 lb/sq. in. and the permissible steel stress is 30,000 lb/sq. in.

$$p = 1.454\% \text{ (see Example 2.2.2)}$$

For balanced design, from equation (3,8),

$$p = 22.22 \times \frac{u_w}{f_y} = 22.22 \times \frac{3 \times 1,500}{2 \times 30,000}$$
$$= 1.67\%$$

Hence the section is *under-reinforced*, therefore from equation (3,3),

$$M_r = 1.571 \times 30,000 \times 18 \times \left\{1 - \frac{0.75 \times 30,000 \times 1.454}{1,500 \times 100}\right\}$$

$$= \underline{664,000 \text{ lb in.}}$$

It is instructive to compare this result with the result of Example (2.2.2). Using the elastic analysis the strength of the concrete was the criterion, whereas with the plastic theory the strength of the steel is now the criterion. The British Code is such that for a fully defined section, the moment of resistance in flexural compression is very much greater when computed by the plastic theory than by the elastic theory, and the moment of resistance in flexural tension is slightly less when computed by the plastic theory than by the elastic theory.

EXAMPLE 3.4.2

Repeat Example (3.4.1) using the 1956 A.C.I. Building Code recommendations concerning plastic design in lieu of the 1957 British Code of Practice recommendations. Assume $f_c' = 0.84u_w$ and a load factor of 2, (N.B. this is assumed in order to compare the method with the British Code of Practice and is not in accordance with the A.C.I. requirements.)

As mentioned previously,

$$f_y = 2p_{st} = 60,000 \text{ lb/sq. in.}$$

$$u_w = 3p_{cb} = 3 \times 1,500 = 4,500 \text{ lb/sq. in.}$$

$$\therefore \ f_c' = 0.84 \times 4,500 = 3,780 \text{ lb/sq. in.}$$

For balanced design, from equation (3,6),

$$p = 40 \times \frac{3,780}{60,000} = 2.52\%$$

This is greater than 1·454%, hence the section is under-reinforced, therefore from equation (3,2),

$$M_u = 1.571 \times 60,000 \times 18 \left\{ 1 - \frac{0.5 \times 1.454 \times 60,000}{0.85 \times 3,780 \times 100} \right\}$$

$$= 1,468,000 \text{ lb in.}$$

therefore

$$M_r = \frac{1,468,000}{2} = 734,000 \text{ lb in.}$$

It is interesting to compare this result with the results of Examples (3.4.1) and (2.2.2). The moment of resistance, when flexural tension is the criterion, is slightly greater for this plastic theory than for the elastic theory. It will be appreciated, therefore, that the British Code is most conservative in predicting the ultimate moments of resistance in flexural compression. This is a deliberate policy to ensure that failures in bending will always occur in flexural tension, such failures being gradual, associated with large cracks and deflections and thus giving ample warnings to the occupants of buildings.

EXAMPLE 3.4.3

Repeat Example (3.4.1) using Whitney's Theory in lieu of the 1957 British Code of Practice recommendations. Assume a load factor of 2, and that $f_c' = 0.84u_w$.

As in Example (3.4.2)

$$f_y = 60,000 \text{ lb/sq. in.}$$

and

$$f_c' = 3,780 \text{ lb/sq. in.}$$

For balanced design, from equation (3,4),

$$p = 45.65 \times \frac{3,780}{60,000} = 2.88$$

This is greater than 1.454%, hence the section is under-reinforced, therefore (as in Example 3.4.2) from equation (3,2),

$$M_u = 1,468,000 \text{ lb in.}$$

$$\therefore \quad M_r = 734,000 \text{ lb in.}$$

EXAMPLE 3.4.4 (compare Example 2.3.1)

Design a section to resist a bending moment of 1,000,000 lb in., using mild steel reinforcement and a 1:2:4 mix of concrete, all in accordance with B.S. C.P.114 (1957), i.e. $p_{cb} = 1,000$ lb/sq. in., and $p_{st} = 20,000$ lb/sq. in.

From equation (3,11),

$$M_r = \frac{1,000}{4} \cdot bd^2 = 1,000,000$$

$$\therefore \quad bd^2 = 4,000$$

If say d is chosen as $19\frac{1}{2}$ in., then $b = 10\frac{1}{2}$ in., and from equation (3,10),

$$p = \frac{1}{3} \times \frac{1,000}{20,000} = \frac{1}{60}$$

$$\therefore \quad A_s = \frac{bd}{60} = \frac{10.5 \times 19.5}{60} = 3.42 \text{ sq in.}$$

Use say two $1\frac{1}{8}$ in. diameter and two 1 in. diameter bars, the minimum cover should be $1\frac{1}{8}$ in., according to the British Code of Practice, hence the overall depth will be approximately $19\frac{1}{2}$ in. $+ 1\frac{1}{8}$ in. $+ \frac{9}{16}$ in. $= 21.19$ in., say $21\frac{1}{4}$ in. N.B. It is interesting to make a comparison in cost between the beams designed in Examples (2.3.1) and (3.4.4) respectively. A particular cost analysis gave the following results:

(a) *In-situ construction;* the beam of Example (3.4.4) cost 5.2% less than the beam of Example (2.3.1).

(b) *Precast construction; manufacture and supply only;* the beam of Example (3.4.4) cost 11.4% less than the beam of Example (2.3.1).

(c) *Precast construction; manufacture, supply, unloading and erection;* the beam of Example (3.4.4) cost 13.9% less than the beam of Example (2.3.1).

In this instance the saving is greater for the precast construction than for the *in-situ* construction. This often occurs, chiefly because the saving in volume of the concrete makes valuable savings in the costs of handling, stacking, loading, transportation, unloading and erection, in the case of precast construction. It must however be borne in mind, concerning the above figures of costs, that costing is not the most precise of sciences, and care must be taken to avoid making unjustifiable generalizations. Different types of constructions are best judged by estimating the costs of the completed projects.

EXAMPLE 3.4.5 (compare Example 2.3.3)

Design a section to resist a bending moment of 500,000 lb in. The breadth is 12 in. and the effective depth 21 in. Use the plastic theory recommended by the British Code of Practice, and permissible concrete and steel stresses of 1,000 and 20,000 lb/sq. in. respectively.

From equation (3,11),

$$M_r = \frac{1,000}{4} \times 12 \times 21^2 = 1,325,000 \text{ lb in.}$$

This is greater than 500,000 lb in., hence the section is under-reinforced. From equation (3,3),

$$500,000 = A_s \cdot 20,000 \times 21 \left\{ 1 - 0 \cdot 75 \times \frac{20,000}{1,000} \cdot \frac{A_s}{12 \cdot 21} \right\}$$

$$A_s^2 - 16 \cdot 8 A_s + 20 \cdot 0 = 0$$

$$\therefore \quad A_s = 1 \cdot 288 \text{ and } 15 \cdot 51$$

The value of 15·51 corresponds to a value of n' from equation (3,1) equal to

$$\frac{15 \cdot 51 \times 2 \times 20,000}{\frac{4}{9} \times 3 \times 1,000 \times 12} = 38 \cdot 78,$$

which cannot occur as it is greater than the effective depth of the beam. The only acceptable value of A_s is therefore 1·288 sq. in.; use say two 1 in. diameter bars.

Comparing this with Example (2.3.3), it is seen that the plastic theory gives a less economical solution, when little use is being made of the strength of the concrete. Many beams in practice do not make full use of the concrete strength and therefore, in these instances, it can be more economical to use the elastic theory when designing in accordance with the British Code of Practice. If the two examples are repeated for a bending moment of 840,000 lb in., the areas of steel required are almost identical; and if the examples are again repeated for a bending moment of 973,000 lb in. (corresponding to balanced design for the elastic analysis), then the plastic design requires a slightly greater amount of reinforcement than the elastic design.

3.5 Plastic design of *under-reinforced* T-sections

For simplicity a rectangular stress block will be assumed; similar principles also apply to other shapes of stress block. Fig. 20 shows a T-section and the stress distribution at failure. Equating longitudinally,

$$C = T$$

$$\therefore \quad c_1[Bd_s + (n' - d_s)b] = A_s f_y$$

$$\therefore \quad n' = \frac{A_s f_y}{c_1 b} + d_s \left\{1 - \frac{B}{b}\right\} \qquad \ldots(3,12)$$

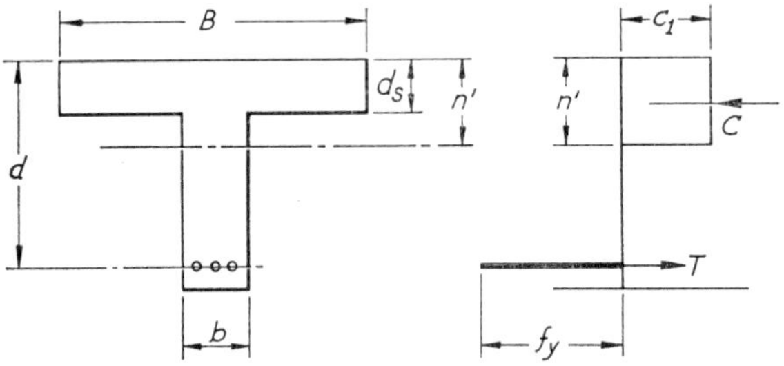

Fig. 20.

Taking moments about the line of action of T,

$$M_u = \text{moment due to flanges of area } (B - b) \cdot d_s \text{ plus}$$
$$\text{moment due to remainder of area } b \cdot n'$$

$$= c_1(B - b)d_s\left(d - \frac{d_s}{2}\right) + c_1 bn'\left(d - \frac{n'}{2}\right)$$

$$\therefore \quad M_u = c_1\left[(B - b)d_s\left(d - \frac{d_s}{2}\right) + bn'\left(d - \frac{n'}{2}\right)\right] \quad \ldots(3,13)$$

Whitney and the A.C.I. Code specify $c_1 = 0.85 f_c'$. The British Code of Practice specifies $c_1 = \frac{4}{9} \cdot u_w$. Both Codes of Practice recommend that B should not be given a greater value than $(12d_s + b)$.

The British Code suggests a simplification of the above by ignoring the portion of the stem (or rib) taking compression; the line of action of the resultant compressive force will, therefore, be at the centre of depth of the slab. This gives a moment arm of $\left(d - \frac{d_s}{2}\right)$ and,

$$\therefore \quad M_u = T\left(d - \frac{d_s}{2}\right) = A_s f_y \cdot \left(d - \frac{d_s}{2}\right) \qquad \ldots(3,14)$$

Unfortunately this slightly overestimates the value given in equation (3,13), and should not therefore be used for designs where the area of the slab is small in relation to the depth of the beam. (e.g. certain precast purlins and floor units).

3.6 *Balanced* plastic design of T-sections

Equations (3,12), (3,13), and (3,14) apply, but the amount of steel required to achieve the balanced design condition has to be determined experimentally.

Whitney considers that for balanced design $n' = 0.537d$, as in the case of a rectangular beam. Substituting this value of n' and his value of c_1 in equation (3,12),

$$0.537d = \frac{A_s f_y}{0.85 f_c' b} + d_s\left(1 - \frac{B}{b}\right)$$

$$\therefore\quad 0.537 . \frac{f_c'}{f_y} . \frac{b}{B} = \frac{p}{85} + \frac{b}{B} . \frac{d_s}{d} . \frac{f_c'}{f_y} . \left(1 - \frac{B}{b}\right)$$

$$\therefore\quad p = 85 . \frac{f_c'}{f_y}\left[\frac{d_s}{d} + \frac{b}{B} . \left(0.537 - \frac{d_s}{d}\right)\right] \quad \dots.(3,15)$$

Also by substitution in equation (3,13),

$$M_u = 0.85 f_c'\left[(B - b)d_s\left(d - \frac{d_s}{2}\right) + 0.393bd^2\right] \quad \dots.(3,16)$$

The A.C.I. Code specifies for balanced design:

$$\frac{A_s}{bd} - 0.85 . \frac{f_c'}{f_y} . \frac{(B - b)d_s}{bd} = 0.4 . \frac{f_c'}{f_y} \quad \dots.(3,17)$$

and that the coefficient of 0.4 is to be reduced at the rate of 0.025 per 1,000 lb/sq. in. concrete cylinder strength in excess of 5,000 lb/sq. in. Equation (3,17) can be expressed in a comparable form to equation (3,15), as,

$$p = 85 . \frac{f_c'}{f_y}\left[\frac{d_s}{d} + \frac{b}{B}\left(0.471 - \frac{d_s}{d}\right)\right] \quad \dots.(3,18)$$

From equations (3,18) and (3,12),

$$n' = 0.471d \quad \dots.(3,19)$$

Then by substitution in equation (3,13),

$$M_u = 0.85 f_c'\left[(B - b)d_s\left(d - \frac{d_s}{2}\right) + 0.36bd^2\right] \quad \dots.(3,20)$$

The British Code specifies that for balanced design, $n' = 0\cdot5d$. Substituting this and the relevant value of c_1 in equation (3,12),

$$0\cdot5d = \frac{9A_sf_y}{4u_wb} + d_s\left(1 - \frac{B}{b}\right)$$

$$\frac{9pf_y}{400u_w} = 0\cdot5 + \frac{d_s}{d}\left(\frac{B}{b} - 1\right)$$

$$\therefore \quad p = 44\cdot44 \cdot \frac{u_w}{f_y}\left[\frac{d_s}{d} + \frac{b}{B}\left(0\cdot5 - \frac{d_s}{d}\right)\right] \quad \ldots(3,21)$$

Then by substitution in equation (3,13),

$$M_u = \frac{4}{9} \cdot u_w\left[(B - b)d_s\left(d - \frac{d_s}{2}\right) + 0\cdot375bd^2\right] \quad \ldots(3,22)$$

Then by substituting $2M_r$ for M_u and $3p_{cb}$ for u_w, this can be expressed as,

$$M_r = p_{cb}Bd^2\left[\frac{b}{4B} + \frac{1}{3}\left(1 - \frac{b}{B}\right)\left\{2 \cdot \frac{d_s}{d} - \left(\frac{d_s}{d}\right)^2\right\}\right] \quad \ldots(3,23)$$

which the Code expresses as

$$M_r = \gamma \cdot p_{cb} \cdot Bd^2 \quad \ldots(3,24)$$

where $\quad \gamma = \frac{b}{4B} + \frac{1}{3}\left(1 - \frac{b}{B}\right)\left[2 \cdot \frac{d_s}{d} - \left(\frac{d_s}{d}\right)^2\right] \quad \ldots(3,25)$

EXAMPLE 3.6.1

A T-beam is such that $B = 30$ in., $d_s = 5$ in., $d = 20$ in. and $b = 12$ in. If the tensile reinforcement comprises one layer of five 1 in. diameter bars and the permissible concrete and steel stresses are 1,000 lb/sq. in. and 30,000 lb/sq. in. respectively, determine the permissible moment of resistance using the British Code of Practice.

$$p = \frac{3\cdot92}{30 \times 20} \cdot 100 = 0\cdot6533\%$$

From equation (3,21), p for balanced design

$$= 44\cdot44 \cdot \frac{3 \times 1,000}{2 \times 30,000}\left[\frac{5}{20} + \frac{12}{30}\left(0\cdot5 - \frac{5}{20}\right)\right]$$

$$= 0\cdot7777\%$$

Hence the section is *under-reinforced*, therefore applying the simplified equation (3,14), $\qquad M_u = 3\cdot92f_y \cdot (20 - \frac{5}{2})$

$$\therefore \quad 2M_r = 3\cdot92(2 \times 30,000)(17\cdot5)$$

$$M_r = 2,060,000 \text{ lb in.}$$

The solution above only applies if the section is acting as a T-beam. If for example n' is less than d_s the problem is that of a rectangular beam. It is therefore necessary to confirm the above by evaluating n'; from equation (3,12):

$$n' = \frac{3 \cdot 92 \times (2 \times 30,000)}{\frac{4}{9}(3 \times 1,000)12} + 5\{1 - \tfrac{30}{12}\}$$

$$= 7 \cdot 2$$

which is greater than d_s, so that the above calculation is correct.

Alternatively, M_r can be evaluated by the more accurate equation (3,13):

$$2M_r = \tfrac{4}{9} \times 3 \times 1,000\left[(30 - 12)5(20 - \tfrac{5}{2}) + 12 \times 7 \cdot 2\left(20 - \frac{7 \cdot 2}{2}\right)\right]$$

$$\therefore \quad M_r = 1,995,000 \text{ lb in.}$$

N.B. An elastic analysis (compare Example 2.8.1) gives the moment of resistance as 1,840,000 lb in., the concrete being the criterion. If the steel were the criterion, the moment of resistance would be 2,110,000 lb in.

EXAMPLE 3.6.2

Repeat Example (3.6.1) using the A.C.I. Code and assuming $f_c' = 0 \cdot 84 u_w$.

As before $p = 0 \cdot 6533\%$; then from equation (3,18) p, for balanced design,

$$= 85 \times \frac{0 \cdot 84 \times 3 \times 1,000}{2 \times 30,000}\left[\tfrac{5}{20} + \tfrac{12}{30}(0 \cdot 471 - \tfrac{5}{20})\right]$$

$$= 1 \cdot 209\%$$

Hence the section is under-reinforced. From equation (3,12),

$$n' = \frac{3 \cdot 92 \times 2 \times 30,000}{0 \cdot 85 \times 0 \cdot 84 \times 3 \times 1,000 \times 12} + 5\{1 - \tfrac{30}{12}\}$$

$$= 1 \cdot 65$$

This is less than d_s, hence the beam is behaving as a rectangular beam and the T-beam theory does not apply, so commence the problem again, considering a rectangular beam of breadth 30 in. Applying equation (3,2),

$$2M_r = 3 \cdot 92 \times 2 \times 30,000$$

$$\times 20\left\{1 - \frac{0 \cdot 5 \times 2 \times 30,000 \times 3 \cdot 92}{0 \cdot 85 \times 0 \cdot 84 \times 3 \times 1,000 \times 30 \times 20}\right\}$$

$$\therefore M_r = 2,140,000 \text{ lb in.}$$

7

It is interesting to compare this calculation with Example (3.6.1); the British Code is seen to be more conservative with respect to the strength in flexural compression. This is a deliberate policy of the British Code of Practice as described previously (see §3.4).

3.7 Plastic design of under-reinforced rectangular sections containing compression steel

It might be said that compression reinforcement is only required in a beam when the balanced design condition applies. Whilst this is often true, there are also cases where compression steel is available even though not required to assist flexural compression. This can sometimes occur at the supports of continuous beams. In such circumstances the compression reinforcement can increase the moment of resistance of the

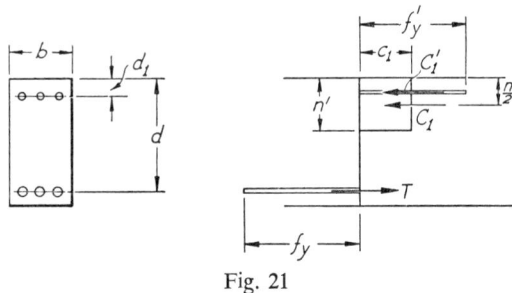

Fig. 21

section, which sometimes makes for economies in the tensile reinforcement. Fig. 21 shows the stress distribution at failure, assuming a rectangular stress block.

Equating longitudinal forces,

$$C_1 + C_1' = T$$

$$c_1 b n' + A_{sc}(f_y' - c_1) = A_s f_y$$

$$\therefore \quad n' = \frac{1}{b}\left[A_s \cdot \frac{f_y}{c_1} + A_{sc}\left(1 - \frac{f_y'}{c_1}\right)\right] \qquad \ldots(3,26)$$

Taking moments about the line of action of T,

$$M_u = C_1\left(d - \frac{n'}{2}\right) + C_1'(d - d_1)$$

$$= c_1 b n'\left(d - \frac{n'}{2}\right) + A_{sc}(f_y' - c_1)(d - d_1) \qquad \ldots(3,27)$$

EXAMPLE 3.7.1

A rectangular reinforced concrete beam is such that $b = 6$ in., $d = 18$ in., $d_1 = 1\frac{1}{4}$ in., the compressive reinforcement comprises two $\frac{1}{2}$ in. diameter bars, and the tensile reinforcement comprises two 1 in. diameter bars. Assume that $f_y' = 36,000$ lb/sq. in., $f_y = 40,000$ lb/sq. in. and $f_c' = 3,150$ lb/sq. in. Determine the ultimate moment of resistance of the section, using Whitney's Theory.

From Whitney's Theory, see earlier, $c_1 = 0.85 f_c' = 2,680$ lb/sq. in. Substituting in equation (3,26),

$$n' = \frac{1}{6}\left[1.571 \times \frac{40,000}{2,680} + 0.393\left(1 - \frac{36,000}{2,680}\right)\right]$$

$$= 3.09$$

This is less than (0.537×18) which would be the depth of the neutral axis for *balanced design*, see later §3.8, hence the beam is under-reinforced. Therefore, substituting in equation (3,27),

$$M_u = 2,680 \times 6 \times 3.09\left(18 - \frac{3.09}{2}\right)$$

$$+ 0.393(36,000 - 2,680)(18 - 1.25)$$

$$= 1,038,000 \text{ lb in.}$$

In this instance, if the compression steel were ignored and equation (3,2) applied, $M_u = 1,008,000$ lb in. Hence if the compression steel were ignored and the section had to resist a bending moment of 1,038,000 lb in., then extra tensile reinforcement would need to be provided.

The above solution is often simplified as follows: equating longitudinal forces,

$$C + C' = T$$

$$\therefore \quad c_1 bn' + A_{sc}f_y' = A_s f_y$$

$$n' = \frac{A_s f_y - A_{sc} f_y'}{c_1 b} \qquad \ldots (3,28)$$

Taking moments about the line of action of T,

$$M_u = C\left(d - \frac{n'}{2}\right) + C'(d - d_1)$$

$$= c_1 bn'\left(d - \frac{n'}{2}\right) + A_{sc}f_y'(d - d_1) \qquad \ldots (3,29)$$

EXAMPLE 3.7.2

Repeat Example (3.7.1) only using the above simplification.

From equation (3,28),

$$n' = \frac{1.571 \times 40,000 - 0.393 \times 36,000}{2,680 \times 6}$$

$$= 3.04$$

From equation (3,29),

$$M_u = 2{,}680 \times 6 \times 3\cdot04(18 - 1\cdot52) + 0\cdot393 \times 36{,}000(18 - 1\cdot25)$$
$$= 1{,}043{,}000 \text{ lb in.}$$

It is interesting to compare the results of this example with those of Example (3.7.1).

3.8 Balanced plastic design of rectangular sections with compression steel

Whitney considers that for balanced design $n' = 0\cdot537d$, and substituting this in equation (3,26) together with his value of c_1.

$$0\cdot537d = \frac{1}{b}\left[\frac{A_s f_y}{0\cdot85 f_c'} + A_{sc}\left(1 - \frac{f_y'}{0\cdot85 f_c'}\right)\right]$$

$$\therefore \quad p\cdot\frac{f_y}{f_c'} + p'\left(0\cdot85 - \frac{f_y'}{f_c'}\right) = 45\cdot65 \qquad \dots(3,30)$$

which relates p and p' for *balanced design*.
Then substituting in equation (3,27),

$$M_u = \tfrac{1}{3}\cdot f_c' b d^2 + A_{sc}(f_y' - 0\cdot85 f_c')(d - d_1) \qquad \dots(3,31)$$

The above can be simplified by substitution in equations (3,28) and (3,29) in lieu of equations (3,26) and (3,27); this gives,

$$pf_y - p'f_y' = 45\cdot65 f_c' \qquad \dots(3,32)$$

and
$$M_u = \tfrac{1}{3}\cdot f_c' b d^2 + A_{sc}f_y'(d - d_1) \qquad \dots(3,33)$$

The A.C.I. Code specifies that $p - p' \not> 40\cdot\dfrac{f_c'}{f_y}$ for *balanced design*, the coefficient 40 to be reduced at the rate of 2·5 per 1,000 lb/sq. in. concrete cylinder strength in excess of 5,000 lb/sq. in., and this assumes that $f_y = f_y'$. In the case when $f_c' \leqslant 5{,}000$ lb/sq. in.,

taking
$$p - p' = 40\cdot\frac{f_c'}{f_y} \text{ and } f_y = f_y',$$

then substituting in equations (3,28) and (3,29),

$$M_u = 0\cdot3056 f_c' b d^2 + A_{sc}f_y(d - d_1) \qquad \dots(3,34)$$

The British Code of Practice specifies that $n' = 0\cdot5d$, for balanced design, and substituting this in equation (3,28),

$$\frac{d}{2} = \frac{A_s f_y - A_{sc}f_y'}{\tfrac{4}{9}\cdot u_w b}$$

$$pf_y - p'f_y' = \frac{200}{9}\cdot u_w \qquad \dots(3,35)$$

and substituting in equation (3,29),

$$M_u = \frac{u_w}{6} \cdot bd^2 + A_{sc}f_y'(d - d_1) \qquad \dots(3,36)$$

The British Code expresses this as follows:

$$2M_r = \frac{3p_{cb}}{6} \cdot bd^2 + A_{sc} \cdot 2p_{sc}(d - d_1)$$

$$M_r = \frac{p_{cb}}{4} \cdot bd^2 + A_{sc} \cdot p_{sc}(d - d_1) \qquad \dots(3,37)$$

Similarly the British Code would express equation (3,35) as

$$p \cdot 2p_{st} - p' \cdot 2p_{sc} = \frac{200}{9} \cdot 3p_{cb}$$

$$\therefore \quad p \cdot p_{st} - p' \cdot p_{sc} = 33 \cdot 33 p_{cb} \qquad \dots(3,38)$$

The British Code also gives guidance upon limiting the stress in the compressive reinforcement. Tests show that the maximum strain which can occur in flexural compression is approximately $\frac{1}{3}\%$. Fig. 22 shows the distribution of strain in the compression zone; hence by similar triangles the strain at the level of the compressive reinforcement = $\left(\dfrac{n - d_1}{n}\right) \cdot \frac{1}{3}\%$, and applying Hooke's Law this corresponds to a stress of $\left(\dfrac{n - d_1}{n}\right) \cdot \frac{1}{300} \cdot 30{,}000{,}000 = 100{,}000\left(1 - \dfrac{d_1}{n}\right)$ lb/sq. in. The Code uses a load

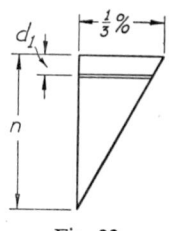

Fig. 22.

factor of 2, assumes $n' = n$ (see §3.9) for the purposes of this calculation, and therefore specifies that the permissible stress in the compression reinforcement must not exceed $50{,}000\left(1 - \dfrac{d_1}{n}\right)$ lb/sq. in. This rarely has any practical significance, because in the case of mild steel, it will only be of importance when

$$50{,}000\left(1 - \frac{d_1}{n'}\right) < 18{,}000$$

i.e. when $d_1 > 0 \cdot 64 n_1$

Similarly for high-tensile steel with a permissible stress in compression limited to 23,000 lb/sq. in., it will only be of importance when $d_1 > 0 \cdot 54 n_1$.

EXAMPLE 3.8.1

Repeat Example (2.7.1) using the plastic in lieu of the elastic method of design of the British Code of Practice.

From equation (3,11),

$$M_r = \frac{1,000}{4} \times 12 \times 21^2 = 1,323,000 \text{ lb in.}$$

Hence the beam needs compression reinforcement; assuming $d_1 = 1.5$ in. and applying equation (3,37):

$$1,500,000 = 1,323,000 + A_{sc} \cdot 18,000(21 - 1.5)$$

$$\therefore \quad A_{sc} = 0.504 \text{ sq. in.}$$

Then from equation (3,38),

$$\frac{A_s \times 100 \times 20,000}{12 \times 21} - \frac{50.4 \times 18,000}{12 \times 21} = 33.33 \times 1,000$$

$$\therefore \quad A_s = \underline{4.654 \text{ sq. in.}}$$

Comparing this with Example (2.7.1) it can be seen that the plastic theory has resulted in a substantial saving in compression steel but a relatively smaller increase in the tensile reinforcement. The total area of the compression and tension steel has been decreased by 19% in this instance, by the use of the plastic theory.

3.9 Depth of neutral axis

The neutral axis coincides with the extremity of the true stress block. However when 'equivalent' stress blocks are specified the neutral axes are not necessarily at the extremities of such stress blocks. For instance, the rectangular stress block specified by the British Code of Practice is not of the same depth as the neutral axis. Fig. 23(i) illustrates the conditions at failure, the depth of the neutral axis being n, and Fig. 23(ii) shows the 'equivalent' stress block assumed in design. The British Code is such that $n' = 0.85n$. When however it specifies a limitation to the compressive stress in the reinforcement (see §3.8) it assumes that $n' = n$ for simplicity of calculation and extra safety.

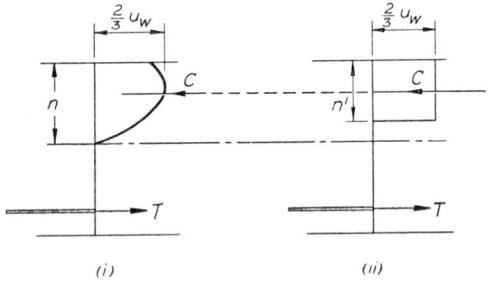

(i)   *(ii)*

Fig. 23

3.10   Plastic design using high-tensile steel

The method is the same as previous methods described in this chapter except that for the high-tensile steels recommended for use by the British Code of Practice C.P. 114 (1957), the 0·25% proof stress can be used in lieu of the yield stress. Such steels do not of course exhibit a clearly defined yield stress and the 0·25% proof stress specified by the Code is the stress at which the permanent deformation of the steel is 0·25% of its original gauge length, (see reference 11). Irrespective of the recommended yield stress, however, the Code specifies maximum permissible stresses (see Table 11 of reference 3) which should not be exceeded.

CHAPTER 4

COLUMNS AND WALLS

4.1 General

There has been no sudden change to plastic theories from elastic theories in the case of columns, because the plastic theory was used for axially loaded columns for a considerable period, when, inconsistently, the elastic theory was used for eccentrically loaded columns. The plastic theories are most advantageous for columns as the sections are chiefly in compression, and plastic theories make the most of reinforced concrete in compression; also the analyses are simplified. If however the concrete section is of an unusual shape that has not been considered by investigations which have established the plastic theories, then the elastic design is to be preferred. The elastic conditions should not be ignored even when plastic designs are used, because to a client the sizes of cracks and deflections at working loads are usually more important than the actual value of the load factor; after all, elastic theories have certainly proved to be safe over a long period of time.

4.2 Long columns

It is assumed that the reader is familiar with the phenomenon of the buckling of long slender columns. The conventional jargon is to term such columns *long columns* and the term *short column* signifies a column unaffected by buckling. The British Code of Practice defines a column as *long* when its *effective length* exceeds 15 times its least lateral dimension; whereas the A.C.I. Building Code uses a figure of 10 in lieu of 15.

The long columns empirical reduction coefficients are specified for various ratios of effective length to least lateral dimension, for example see Table 18 of reference (3). The design procedure is to assume the column to be short and to calculate the permissible axial load, or axial load and bending moment, or eccentric load; then the corresponding permissible value for the long column is obtained by multiplication with the appropriate reduction coefficient.

EXAMPLE 4.2.1

The effective length of a column is 24 times the magnitude of its least lateral dimension. Designed as a short column it is permissible for it to carry a load of 200,000 lb at an eccentricity of 10 inches. Determine the permissible load for the column.

Referring to Table 18 of reference (3), the reduction coefficient is 0·7. Hence the permissible load at an eccentricity of 10 inches

$$= 0·7 \times 200,000 = 140,000 \text{ lb}$$

Alternatively, this problem could have expressed the eccentric load as an axial load of 200,000 lb combined with a bending moment of 2,000,000 lb in. The answer in this case would have been expressed as an axial load of 140,000 lb combined with a bending moment of 1,400,000 lb in.

4.3 Elastic analysis for axially loaded short columns

The assumptions of this analysis are as discussed in §1.13. Fig. 24(i) shows the cross-section of a column, Fig. 24(ii) shows the distribution of

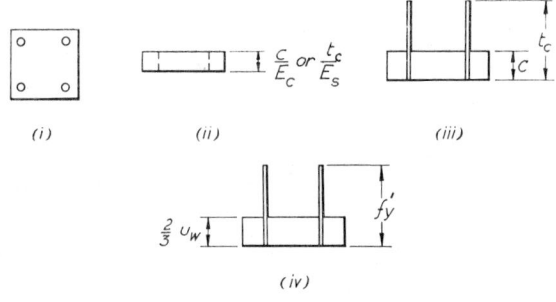

(i)   *(ii)*   *(iii)*

(iv)

Fig. 24.

strain across the section, in accordance with the assumptions that plane sections remain plane and that perfect adhesion occurs between the steel and the concrete. Fig. 24(iii) shows the corresponding distribution of stress across the cross-section. From Fig. 23(ii), the strain in the steel is equal to the strain in the concrete, therefore

$$\frac{t_c}{E_s} = \frac{c}{E_c}$$

$$\frac{t_c}{c} = \frac{E_s}{E_c} = m \qquad \qquad \dots.(4,1)$$

Resolving in the direction of the axial force,

$$\text{axial force} = P = cA_c' + t_cA_{sc} \qquad \dots.(4,2)$$

From equations (4,1) and (4,2):

$$P = c(A_c' + mA_{sc}) \qquad \dots.(4,3)$$

or

$$P = \frac{t_c}{m}(A_c' + mA_{sc}) \qquad \dots.(4,4)$$

If the section was supposed to be equivalent to a homogeneous concrete section, then the *equivalent area* of the concrete section from equation (4,3) would be $A_c' + mA_{sc}$ which can also be expressed as $(A - A_{sc}) + mA_{sc} = A + (m - 1)A_{sc}$

EXAMPLE 4.3.1

A short reinforced concrete column has a rectangular cross-section of 10 in. by 12 in. and is symmetrically reinforced with four $\frac{3}{4}$ in. diameter steel rods. If the permissible stress of the concrete in direct compression is 950 lb/sq. in., the permissible stress of the steel in compression is 18,000 lb/sq. in., and the modular ratio is 15, determine the axial load which the column can safely withstand.

$$A_{sc} = 1\cdot767 \text{ sq. in.}$$
$$A_c = 120 - 1\cdot767 = 118\cdot2 \text{ sq. in.}$$
$$A_c + mA_{sc} = 118\cdot2 + 15 \times 1\cdot767 = 144\cdot7 \text{ sq. in.}$$

From equation (4,3), if the strength of the concrete is the criterion,

$$P = 950 \times 144\cdot7 = 137,500 \text{ lb}$$

From equation (4,4), if the strength of the steel is the criterion:

$$P = \frac{18,000}{15} \times 144\cdot7 = 173,700 \text{ lb}$$

Hence the required answer $= \underline{137,500 \text{ lb.}}$

4.4 Plastic analysis for axially loaded short columns

The assumptions of this analysis are as discussed in §1.16. The British Code of Practice considers that the distribution of stress at failure is as shown in Fig. 24(iv). Generally, the concrete strains in a plastic fashion until the reinforcement yields; the crushing strength of the concrete in the column is considered to be two thirds of the cube strength. Hence resolving in the direction of the axial load,

$$\text{ultimate axial force} = P_u = A_c' \tfrac{2}{3} u_w + A_{sc} \cdot f_y' \quad ....(4,5)$$

As described in Chapter 3, the British Code likes to express formulae in terms of working loads and permissible stresses; with a load factor of 2, $P_u = 2P_0$; the code is such that $u_w = 3\cdot95p_{cc}$ and $f_y' = 0\cdot5p_{sc}$. Substituting these values in equation (4,5),

$$P_0 = 1\cdot317A_c' \cdot p_{cc} + A_{sc} \cdot p_{sc} \quad ....(4,6)$$

Then for simplicity and additional safety the British Code specifies equation (4,6) in the following form:

$$P_0 = A_c' \cdot p_{cc} + A_{sc} \cdot p_{sc} \quad ....(4,7)$$

The A.C.I. Code gives a similar equation to (4,5), thus

$$P_u = 0.85f_c' \cdot A_c' + f_y' \cdot A_{sc} \qquad \ldots.(4,8)$$

It also specifies that columns must always be designed to allow for a minimum eccentricity of loading of 0.10 times the depth of the column section; this figure is 0.05 in the case of columns with spiral reinforcement.

EXAMPLE 4.4.1

Repeat Example (4.3.1) by the method of §4.4.

Applying equation (4,7),

$$P_0 = 118.2 \times 950 + 1.767 \times 18,000$$
$$= 144,200 \text{ lb}$$

It is therefore more economical and simpler to use the plastic theory than the elastic theory for the design of a short axially loaded column, and hardly anyone would now use the elastic method for this purpose.

EXAMPLE 4.4.2

Design a short reinforced concrete column to safely support an axial load of 650,000 lb.

Suppose a $1:1\frac{1}{2}:3$ mix to be used in conjunction with mild steel reinforcement; therefore, referring to the British Code of Practice $p_{cc} = 950$ lb/sq. in., and $p_{sc} = 18,000$ lb/sq. in. Assuming say 2% of reinforcement, then $A_{sc} = \frac{2}{100}(A_c + A_{sc})$

therefore $\qquad A_{sc} = \frac{2}{98} \cdot A_c'$

Hence, applying equation (4,7):

$$650,000 = A_c'950 + \frac{2}{98}A_c' \cdot 18,000$$

therefore $\qquad A_c' = 493$ sq. in.

therefore the gross cross-sectional area $= 493 + \frac{2}{98} \times 493 = 504$ sq. in. If the column is to be square, the length of a side would need to be 22.5 in. Suppose it is decided to make this dimension 24 in., then applying equation (4,7),

$$650,000 = (24^2 - A_{sc})950 + A_{sc} \cdot 18,000$$

therefore $\qquad A_{sc} = 6.04$ sq. in.

Use say eight 1 in. diameter bars. Expressing this as a percentage of the gross cross-sectional area, this equals $\dfrac{6.283}{24^2} \times 100 = 1.095\%$. This lies between 0.8% and 4% and is therefore acceptable to the British Code of Practice.

Many designers would make the initial estimate of the size of the column more speedily and slightly less accurately as follows:

$$A_{sc} \simeq \tfrac{2}{100} \cdot A_c'$$

From equation (4,7),

$$650{,}000 = A_c' \times 950 + \tfrac{2}{100} \cdot A_c' \times 18{,}000$$

therefore $A_c' = 496$ sq. in.

therefore the cross-sectional area $\simeq 496 + \tfrac{2}{100} \times 496 = 506$ sq. in.

4.5 Elastic analysis for eccentrically loaded short columns

One of the assumptions made (see §1.13) is that concrete cannot resist tensile stresses, consequently as soon as the eccentricity of loading is sufficient to cause a resultant tension on one face of the column, then the concrete in this zone is neglected. For smaller eccentricities this concrete is counted in the structural strength as it is in compression. Hence two different theoretical analyses have to be considered:

Case 1: The concrete is entirely in compression. Fig. 25(i) represents the cross-section of a column, *CG* being a principal axis passing through the centroid of the equivalent concrete section. In determining this position the steel is taken as equivalent to *m* times its area if the nett area of the concrete section is considered, or, more usually, it is taken as equivalent to $(m - 1)$ times its area and the gross sectional area of the concrete is used. This will be appreciated by reference to equations (4,1), (4,3), and (4,5), and also to Chapter 2. The load *P* is to be carried at an eccentricity *e*. Fig. 25(ii) shows the distribution of strain and Fig. 25(iii) shows the distribution of stress. From Hooke's Law, the dimensions of the strain diagram are as follows:

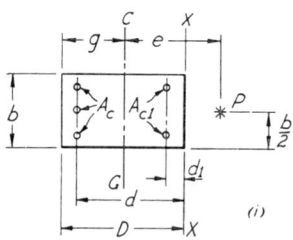

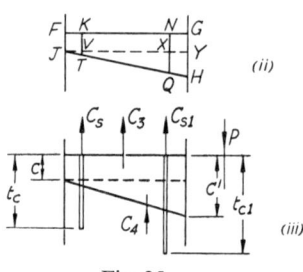

Fig. 25.

$$FJ = \frac{c}{E_c}$$

$$KT = \frac{t_c}{E_s}$$

$$NQ = \frac{t_{c1}}{E_s}$$

$$GH = \frac{c'}{E_c}$$

The distribution of strain is linear, hence by similar triangles in Fig. 25(ii):

$$\frac{HY}{YJ} = \frac{QX}{XJ} = \frac{VT}{VJ}$$

therefore

$$\frac{\dfrac{c'}{E_c} - \dfrac{c}{E_c}}{D} = \frac{\dfrac{t_{c1}}{E_s} - \dfrac{c}{E_c}}{D - d_1} = \frac{\dfrac{t_c}{E_s} - \dfrac{c}{E_c}}{D - d}$$

therefore

$$\frac{m}{D}(c' - c) = \frac{t_{c1} - mc}{D - d_1} = \frac{t_c - mc}{D - d} \qquad \dots(4,9)$$

Resolving vertically,

P = force on gross area of concrete — force on areas of concrete replaced by steel + force on steel

therefore

$$P = \left(\frac{c + c'}{2}\right)bD - \left[A_{c1}\left(\frac{t_{c1}}{m}\right) + A_c\left(\frac{t_c}{m}\right)\right] + A_{c1}.t_{c1} + A_c t_c$$

$$\dots(4,10)$$

Taking moments about the side remote from the load,

$P(e + g)$ = moments due to C_3 and C_4 — moments included due to concrete which is actually replaced by steel + moments due to C_s and C_{s1}

therefore

$$P(e + g) = cbD.\frac{D}{2} + \left(\frac{c' - c}{2}\right)bD.\frac{2}{3}D - A_{c1}\left(\frac{t_{c1}}{m}\right)(D - d_1)$$

$$- A_c\left(\frac{t_c}{m}\right)(D - d) + A_{c1}.t_{c1}(D - d_1) + A_c t_c(D - d) \qquad \dots(4,11)$$

When the section is defined and the force and its eccentricity are known, there are four unknowns namely c, c', t_c, and t_{c1}, and these can be determined from equations (4,9), (4,10), and (4,11). Usually in practice $A_c = A_{c1}$ and thus the formulae are simplified.

A much easier alternative to the above is by considering the equivalent concrete section. The method may be tabulated if desired. This method is analogous to that enunciated in §2.4 and §2.5, and is simply illustrated by the following well known formulae:

$$c' = \frac{P}{A} + \frac{Pe}{I}(D - g) \qquad \dots(4,12)$$

$$c = \frac{P}{A} - \frac{Pe}{I}.g \qquad \dots(4,13)$$

where A and I are the area and second moment of area respectively of the *equivalent* concrete cross-section. As explained previously if the gross concrete section is considered then the steel areas are multiplied by $(m - 1)$.

EXAMPLE 4.5.1

Given $b = 18$ in., $D = 20$ in., $A_c = 3\cdot98$ sq. in. (four $1\frac{1}{8}$ in. diameter bars), $A_{c1} = 4\cdot91$ sq. in. (four $1\frac{1}{4}$ in. diameter bars), and the axial load to be carried is 190,000 lb combined with a bending moment of 742,000 lb in. The line of action of the axial load passes through the centroid of the section. Calculate the concrete and steel stresses for this loading. Assume the modular ratio $= 15$, and the cover to the steel to be $1\frac{1}{2}$ in.

$$(m - 1)A_c = 14 \times 3\cdot98 = 55\cdot7 \text{ sq. in.}$$

$$(m - 1)A_{c1} = 14 \times 4\cdot91 = 68\cdot7 \text{ sq. in.}$$

$$d_1 = 1\cdot5 + 0\cdot5 \times 1\cdot25 = 2\cdot125 \text{ in.}$$

$$d = 20 - (1\cdot5 + 0\cdot5 \times 1\cdot125) = 17\cdot938 \text{ in.}$$

Table 11 is built up as described in Chapter 2.

TABLE 11

Portion	A	x	Ax	Ax^2	I_G
Gross concrete section	360·0	10	3,600	36,000	12,000
A_c	55·7	17·94	1,000	17,940	negligible
A_{c1}	68·7	2·125	146·1	310·5	negligible
	484·4		4,746	66,250	

$$\therefore \quad (D - g) = \frac{4,746}{484\cdot4} = 9\cdot79$$

$$\therefore \quad g = 10\cdot21 \text{ in.}$$

$$I = 66,250 - 484\cdot4 \times (D - g)^2$$
$$= 19,850 \text{ in.}^4$$

From equation (4,12),

$$c' = \frac{190,000}{484\cdot4} + \frac{742,000}{19,850} \times 9\cdot79$$

$$= 392 + 37\cdot4 \times 9\cdot79 = 758\cdot5 \text{ lb/sq. in.}$$

From equation (4,13),

$$c = 392 - 37\cdot4 \times 10\cdot21 = 10 \text{ lb/sq. in.}$$

Further,

$$t_{c1} = \left[\frac{190,000}{484 \cdot 4} + \frac{742,000}{19,850}(D - d_1 - g)\right] m.$$

$$= 10,182 \text{ lb/sq. in.}$$

$$t_c = \left\{\frac{190,000}{484 \cdot 4} - \frac{742,000}{19,850}[g - (D - d)]\right\} m.$$

$$= 1,312 \text{ lb/sq. in.}$$

A designer does not normally need to compute t_c and t_{c1} because he is only concerned that the permissible compressive stress of 18,000 lb/sq. in. (for mild steel) is not exceeded. The corresponding concrete stress at the positions of the steel reinforcement is therefore desired to be less than $\frac{18,000}{m} = 1,200$ lb/sq. in. Hence if

c and c' are less than 1,200 lb/sq. in., (generally this is so), then t_c and t_{c1} do not need to be calculated. In the case of high tensile steel, c and c' would have to exceed $\frac{23,000}{15} = 1,533$ lb/sq. in.

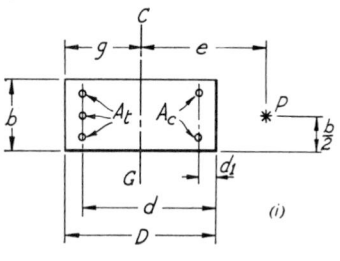

(i)

Case 2: In this case the bending moment is sufficiently high relative to the axial load, or in other words the eccentricity of loading is sufficiently great, for part of the section to be in tension. As the concrete is assumed not to resist tensile stresses (refer to §1.13) then the tension needs to be resisted by the reinforcement. Fig. 26(i) shows the section under consideration, Fig. 26(ii) the distribution of strain, and Fig. 26(iii)

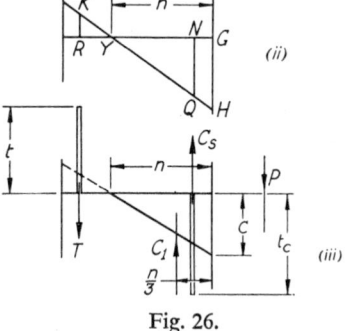

(ii)

(iii)

Fig. 26.

the corresponding distribution of stress. From Figs. 26(ii) and (iii), $GH = c/E_c$, $KR = t/E_s$, and $NQ = t_c/E_s$. By geometry, in Fig. 26(ii),

$$\frac{GH}{GY} = \frac{NQ}{NY} = \frac{KR}{RY}$$

$$\therefore \quad \frac{c/E_c}{n} = \frac{t_c/E_s}{n - d_1} = \frac{t/E_s}{d - n}$$

$$\therefore \quad \frac{c}{n} = \frac{t_c}{m(n - d_1)} = \frac{t}{m(d - n)} \qquad \dots(4,14)$$

Resolving vertically:

$$P = C_1 - \text{force on area of concrete } (A_c) \text{ replaced by steel} + C_s - T$$

$$= \frac{c}{2} \cdot nb - A_c(NQ)E_c + A_c t_c - A_t t$$

$$= \frac{cnb}{2} - A_c \cdot \frac{t_c}{E_s} \cdot E_c + A_c t_c - A_t t$$

$$= \frac{cnb}{2} + A_c t_c \left(1 - \frac{1}{m}\right) - A_t t \qquad \qquad \dots(4,15)$$

Taking moments about the line of action of T,

$$P\{(e + g) - (D - d)\} = C_1 \left\{d - \frac{n}{3}\right\} - \text{moment of force on area of}$$

$$\text{concrete } (A_c) \text{ replaced by steel} + C_s(d - d_1)$$

$$= \frac{e}{2} \cdot nb \left\{d - \frac{n}{3}\right\} - A_c \cdot \frac{t_c}{E_s} \cdot E_c(d - d_1)$$

$$+ A_c \cdot t_c(d - d_1)$$

$$P(e + g - D + d) = \frac{c}{2} \cdot nb \left\{d - \frac{n}{3}\right\} + A_c \cdot t_c \left(1 - \frac{1}{m}\right)(d - d_1)$$

$$\dots(4,16)$$

When the section is defined and the force and eccentricity are known, there are four unknowns namely c, t_c, t, and n; these can be determined from the equations (4,14), (4,15), and (4,16).

EXAMPLE 4.5.2

Using the notation of Fig. 26, if $b = 18$ in., $D = 20$ in., $A_t = 3\cdot98$ sq. in. (four $1\frac{1}{8}$ in. diameter bars), $A_c = 4\cdot91$ sq. in. (four $1\frac{1}{4}$ in. diameter bars), $(g + e) = 18$ in. Calculate the concrete and steel stresses if $P = 190{,}000$ lb. Assume the modular ratio $= 15$, and the cover to the steel $= 1\frac{1}{2}$ in.

As in the last example, $d_1 = 2\cdot125$ in., $d = 17\cdot94$ in. If this is computed, for example, as for Case (1), i.e. as Example (4.5.1), it is found that c is negative, hence as concrete is assumed not to resist tensile stresses Case (1) does not apply and Case (2) is applicable. From equation (4,14),

$$\frac{c}{n} = \frac{t_c}{15 \times (n - 2\cdot125)} = \frac{t}{15 \times (17\cdot94 - n)} \qquad \dots(4,17)$$

From equation (4,15),

$$190,000 = \frac{cn \times 18}{2} + 4 \cdot 91t_e\left(1 - \frac{1}{15}\right) - 3 \cdot 98t$$

$$\therefore \quad 190,000 = 9cn + 4 \cdot 58t_e - 3 \cdot 98t \qquad \ldots(4,18)$$

From equation (4,16),

$$190,000(18 - 20 + 17 \cdot 94) = \frac{c}{2} \cdot n \times 18\left(17 \cdot 94 - \frac{n}{3}\right)$$

$$+ 4 \cdot 91t_e\left(1 - \frac{1}{15}\right)(17 \cdot 94 - 2 \cdot 13)$$

$$3,030,000 = 9cn\left\{17 \cdot 94 - \frac{n}{3}\right\} + 72 \cdot 5t_e \qquad \ldots(4,19)$$

From equation (4,17),

$$t = \frac{15c}{n}(17 \cdot 94 - n) \quad \text{and} \quad t_e = \frac{15c}{n}(n - 2 \cdot 125)$$

Hence substituting for these values of t and t_e, equations (4,18) and (4,19) become

$$190,000n = 9cn^2 + 4 \cdot 58 \times 15c(n - 2 \cdot 125) - 3 \cdot 98 \times 15c(17 \cdot 94 - n)$$
$$\ldots(4,20)$$

$$3,030,000n = 9cn^2\left(17 \cdot 94 - \frac{n}{3}\right) + 72 \cdot 5 \times 15c(n - 2 \cdot 125) \quad \ldots(4,21)$$

By eliminating c between equations (4,20) and (4,21) the following cubic equation is obtained for n:

$$0 \cdot 19\left[9n^2\left(17 \cdot 94 - \frac{n}{3}\right) + 1 \cdot 088(n - 2 \cdot 13)\right]$$

$$= 3 \cdot 03[9n^2 + 68 \cdot 7(n - 2 \cdot 13) - 59 \cdot 7(17 \cdot 94 - n)]$$

$$\therefore \quad n^3 - 6 \cdot 02n^2 + 320n - 5,710 = 0$$

Solving this equation either by trial and error or by Newton's Approximation,

$$n = 13 \cdot 52 \text{ in.}$$

Substituting this in equation (4,21), it can be calculated that

$$c = 1,186 \text{ lb/sq. in.}$$

Hence from equation (4,17),

$$t = 5 \cdot 810 \text{ lb/sq. in.} \quad \text{and} \quad t_e = 14,950 \text{ lb/sq. in.}$$

8

As a check these results can be substituted in equations (4,18) and (4,19), and of course (4,17) although this is more likely to be satisfactory as it has just been used to determine t and t_c.

4.6 Plastic analysis for eccentrically loaded short columns

We now consider the case when part of the cross-section of the column has to resist tensile stresses and the section is *under-reinforced* with regard to the tensile reinforcement. Referring to the column section of Fig. 26(i), the distribution of strain for the *plastic theory* is linear as shown in Fig. 26(ii), but the corresponding distribution of stress is assumed by the British Code of Practice, to be as shown in Fig. 27. The

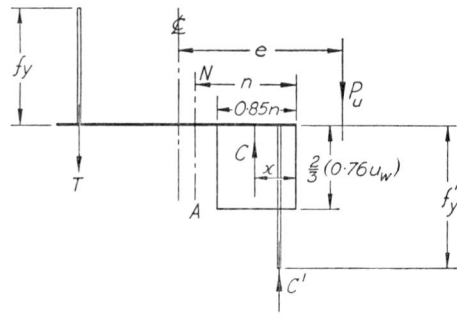

Fig. 27.

eccentricity e should be measured from the line of action which would be taken by a force P_0; for simplicity this is assumed to be the centre line of the column. Resolving the vertical forces shown in Fig. 27,

$$P_u = C + C' - T \qquad \ldots (4,22)$$

where C = force resisted by concrete = $(0{\cdot}85n)b[\tfrac{2}{3} \times 0{\cdot}76u_w]$ ignoring area of concrete displaced by compression steel. The Code multiplies the experimentally obtained $0{\cdot}76u_w$ by two thirds to make sure that a tension rather than a compression failure occurs.

$$C' = A_c f_y'$$

$$T = A_t f_y$$

$$P_u = P/2$$

using a load factor of 2.

The British Code expresses $\dfrac{0{\cdot}76u_w}{3} = p_{cc}$, $f'_y/2 = p_{sc}$, and $f_y/2 = p_{st}$.

Hence substituting these values in equation (4,22),

$$P = p_{cc} \cdot b(0{\cdot}85n) + A_c \cdot p_{sc} - A_t \cdot p_{st} \qquad \ldots (4,23)$$

Again referring to Fig. 24 and taking moments about the tension steel,

$$P_u\left(e + d - \frac{D}{2}\right) = C(d - x) + C'(d - d_1) \quad \ldots(4,24)$$

Now the computation of the force C ignored the area of concrete displaced by the compression reinforcement; hence $x = \frac{1}{2} \times 0.85n$. Consequently substituting this and the above in equation (4,24),

$$P\left\{e + d - \frac{D}{2}\right\} = p_{cc} \cdot b(0.85n)(d - 0.425n) + A_c p_{sc}(d - d_1)$$

$$\ldots(4,25)$$

For a fully defined section and a known eccentricity of loading, equations (4,23) and (4,25) can be solved for P and n. This applies to sections *under-reinforced* with regard to the tensile steel, and this applies for values of P less than the load P_b for *balanced design* when the concrete is giving its maximum possible contribution. It is found experimentally that the maximum concrete strain cannot exceed 0.33%,* hence for balanced design the distribution of strain as shown in Fig. 26(ii) will be such that GH is 0.0033, and from this diagram, by geometry,

$$\frac{0.0033}{n} = \frac{KR}{d - n}$$

Then from Fig. 27, $KR = f_y/E_s$, so that,

$$\frac{0.0033}{n} = \frac{f_y}{E_s(d - n)}$$

$$\therefore \quad n = \frac{d}{1 + \dfrac{300f_y}{E_s}} = \frac{d}{1 + \dfrac{600p_{st}}{E_s}} \quad \ldots(4,26)$$

N.B. For high-tensile reinforcement, E_s is specified by the Code as the secant Young's Modulus of the steel at a stress of $2p_{st}$; this however gives certain inconsistencies.[12] In the case of mild steel where $E_s = 30,000,000$ lb/sq. in., equation (4,26) becomes,

$$n = \frac{100,000d}{100,000 + 2p_{st}} \quad \ldots(4,27)$$

If the depth of the stress block, namely $0.85n$ (see Fig. 27) is denoted as Xd, then from equation (4,27),

$$X = \frac{0.85n}{d} = \frac{85,000}{100,000 + 2p_{st}} \quad \ldots(4,28)$$

* Higher strains have been measured but 0.33% is an accepted figure.

This enables the depth of the stress block to be determined for the *balanced design* condition. Hence substituting in equations (4,23) and (4,25),

$$P_b = p_{cc} \cdot bXd + A_c \cdot p_{sc} - A_t \cdot p_{st} \qquad \ldots.(4,29)$$

$$P_b \left\{ e_b + d - \frac{D}{2} \right\} = p_{cc} \cdot bXd^2(1 - 0.5X) + A_c \cdot p_{sc}(d - d_1)$$

$$\ldots.(4,30)$$

As mentioned before, if P is less than P_b the section is *under-reinforced*. Now if P is greater than P_b, referring to equation (4,29), the first term cannot increase because X is a maximum (from the above considerations concerning maximum strain in the concrete), the second term cannot increase, consequently the last term must decrease. In other words, the tension in the above tensile reinforcement must reduce, and the maximum value of P that the column can withstand is when the tension in this steel has not only been reduced but has been converted to the maximum compression it can carry, i.e. when the whole section is in compression and the load is equal to P_0, see equation (4,7). Consequently for values of P between P_b and the maximum value P_0 the British Code recommends the following empirical relationship:

$$P = \frac{P_0}{1 + \left(\dfrac{P_0}{P_b} - 1\right)\dfrac{e}{e_b}} \qquad \ldots.(4,31)$$

The limiting values of this expression are when $e = 0$, i.e. $P = P_0$, and when $e = e_b$, i.e. $P = P_b$.

EXAMPLE 4.6.1

The cross-section of a column is fully defined as follows: $b = 10$ in., $D = 15$ in., $d_1 = D - d = 2$ in., $A_t = A_c = 2.36$ sq. in. (three 1 in. diameter bars). If $p_{cc} = 760$ lb/sq. in., $p_{st} = 20,000$ lb/sq. in., $p_{sc} = 18,000$ lb/sq. in., and $E_s = 30,000,000$ lb/sq. in., determine the permissible load which can be carried at an eccentricity $e = 12$ in.

From equation (4,23),

$$P = 760 \times 10 \times 0.85n + 2.36 \times 18,000 - 2.36 \times 20,000$$

$$\therefore \quad P = 6,460n - 4,720 \qquad \ldots.(4,32)$$

From equation (4,25),

$$P(12 + 13 - \tfrac{15}{2}) = (6,460n)(13 - 0.425n) + 2.36 \times 18,000(13 - 2)$$

$$\therefore \quad P = 4,800n - 156.9n^2 + 26,740 \qquad \ldots.(4,33)$$

From equations (4,32) and (4,33),

$$n^2 + 10.59n - 200.5 = 0$$

$\therefore$ $n = 9.845$ in., ignoring the unrealistic negative solution.

For *balanced design* equation (4,27) gives,

$$n = \frac{100,000 \times 13}{100,000 + 2 \times 20,000} = 9.29 \text{ in.}$$

Hence P must exceed P_b in this instance and P is therefore given by equation (4,31). To evaluate this equation it is necessary to compute P_b; e_b, P_b can be obtained from equation (4,29) or more simply by substituting the above value of $n = 9.29$ in equation (4,32), which is the same process as was used for obtaining equation (4,29). Hence from equation (4,32),

$$P_b = 6,460 \times 9.29 - 4,720 = 55,280 \text{ lb.}$$

From equation (4,28),

$$X = 0.85 \times \frac{9.29}{13} = 0.606$$

From equation (4,30),

$$55,280(e_b + 5.5) = 760 \times 10 \times 0.606$$
$$\times 13^2(1 - 0.5 \times 0.606) + 2.36 \times 18,000(13 - 2)$$
$$\therefore \quad e_b = 12.77 \text{ in.}$$

From equation (4,7),

$$P_0 = (10 \times 15 - 2 \times 2.36) \times 760 + 2 \times 2.36 \times 18,000 = 195,400 \text{ lb.}$$

From equation (4,31),

$$P = \frac{195,400}{1 + \left(\dfrac{195,400}{55,280} - 1\right) \times \dfrac{12}{12.77}} = \underline{57,800 \text{ lb}}$$

It is of interest to use the elastic theory and determine the stresses which would occur for this loading. Such an analysis concerns Case (2) of §4.5, and the maximum concrete stress is approximately equal to 1,480 lb/sq. in. which, of course, is considerably greater than the 760 lb/sq. in. used by the plastic theory above. This illustrates the greater structural use which is made of the concrete by the plastic theory than by the elastic theory and hence the greater economy that can often be achieved in the design of columns.

4.7 Helical reinforcement

The majority of columns in Britain are reinforced with longitudinal bars tied to prevent buckling and also for fixing purposes at regular intervals by stirrups in accordance with the Code of Practice.[3] Columns of circular and octagonal sections are often reinforced with helices in lieu of stirrups. Helices are specified by Codes of Practice, and the efficient action of such helices in preventing the lateral bursting normally associated with failure, as well as the fact that any force in the steel of a helix has a longitudinal as well as a lateral component, allows helices to assist the longitudinal reinforcement structurally. If the volume of a helix is divided by the length of a column the result is known as the *equivalent area of the helical reinforcement* $= A_b$. Experiments show that if this is considered in the same way as longitudinal reinforcement, for axially loaded columns, it is twice as effective as such reinforcement, hence equation (4,7) becomes,

$$P_0 = A_c'p_{cc} + (A_{sc} + 2A_b)p_{sc} \qquad \ldots(4,34)$$

As mild steel is usually used for the helix, even if not for the longitudinal steel, then $p_{sc} = 18,000$ lb/sq. in. for the helical steel,

$$\therefore \quad P_0 = A_c'p_{cc} + A_{sc}p_{sc} + 36,000A_b \qquad \ldots(4,35)$$

Now the British Code is more conservative than this, using the area of the core A_k bounded by the helix in lieu of A_c', and using a figure of 27,000 in lieu of the above value of 36,000. Hence this Code gives,

$$P_0 = A_k p_{cc} + A_{sc}p_{sc} + 27,000A_b \qquad \ldots(4,36)$$

and further stipulates that $A_k \cdot p_{cc} + 27,000A_b \not> 0.5u_w \cdot A_c' \quad \ldots(4,37)$

The British Code[3] does not recommend any account being taken of helical reinforcement in the calculation of the strength of, or stresses in, eccentrically loaded columns. The American Code[13] agrees with this except for Case (1) of the elastic method of §4.5.

EXAMPLE 4.7.1

A circular column of 12 in. diameter is reinforced with eight $\frac{5}{8}$ in. diameter bars having $1\frac{1}{2}$ in. cover of concrete, and a helix to assist in the longitudinal strength in accordance with the British Code of Practice.[3] Determine the maximum safe working axial load by this Code, using the plastic method, and assuming $p_{cc} = 760$ lb/sq. in. and $p_{sc} = 18,000$ lb/sq. in.

$$A_k = \frac{\pi}{4} \times (12 - 1.5 - 1.5) = 63.7 \text{ sq. in.}$$

Referring to the Code, the diameter of the helical bar must not be less than $\frac{3}{16}$ in. or less than $\frac{1}{4} \times \frac{5}{8} = \frac{5}{32}$ in., so the diameter will be taken as $\frac{3}{16}$ in. The pitch of the helix must not exceed either 3 in. or $(12 - 1.5 - 1.5)/6 = 1.5$ in.; it should not be less than 1 in., nor $3 \times \frac{3}{16} = \frac{9}{16}$ in., so the pitch will be taken as 1·5 in. The diameter of the helix $= 12 - 1.5 - 1.5 - \frac{3}{16} = 8.813$ in.

$$A_b \frac{\pi}{4} \left(\frac{3}{16}\right)^2 (\pi 8.813)/1.5 = 0.509 \text{ sq. in.}$$

$$A_{sc} = 8 \frac{\pi}{4} \left(\frac{5}{8}\right)^2 = 2.45 \text{ sq. in.}$$

$$A_c' = \frac{\pi}{4} (12)^2 - 2.45 = 110.55 \text{ sq. in.}$$

$A_k p_{cc} + 27{,}000 A_b = 63.7 \times 760 + 27{,}000 \times 0.509 = 62{,}160 \text{ lb.}$

Referring to §4.4, $u_w = 3.95 p_{cc} = 3.95 \times 760 = 3{,}000 \text{ lb/sq. in.}$

$$\therefore \quad 0.5 u_w A_c' = 0.5 \times 3{,}000 \times 110.55 = 165{,}800 \text{ lb.}$$

Hence equation (4,37) is satisfied, because $62{,}160 \not> 165{,}800$
From equation (4,36) and the calculation above,

$$P_0 = 62{,}160 + 2.45 \times 18{,}000 = 106{,}260 \text{ lb.}$$

4.8   Design of eccentrically loaded columns

This is a matter of guessing a size from experience and checking the strength according to the elastic (§4.5) or plastic (§4.6) theories whichever is preferred. If, upon analysis, the original guess does not give adequate strength, the dimensions of the column and the amount of reinforcement are increased, and vice-versa. The second estimate of the size of the section is analysed, and if this is not satisfactory the process is repeated until the designer is satisfied. This will often be when the section is slightly in excess of the minimum requirements. A novice might require many attempts, but with experience it is soon possible to be correct after either the original guess or the first subsequent modification. Consequently it is desirable to be able to analyse sections rapidly, and either tables[15] or graphs[14] can be most useful to the practical designer.

The original guess for the size of the section can be assisted by designing for vertical load only, assuming a permissible concrete stress of about 60% of that specified. The total area of reinforcement corresponding to this can be assumed to be about 2% of the cross-sectional area of the column.

EXAMPLE 4.8.1

Design a column to resist a load of 57,800 lb at an eccentricity of 12 in., assuming $p_{st} = 20,000$ lb/sq. in., $p_{sc} = 18,000$ lb/sq. in., $p_{cc} = 760$ lb/sq. in., and $E_s = 30,000,000$ lb/sq. in. (cf. Example 4.6.1).

Estimate of cross-sectional area $= \dfrac{57,800}{0\cdot 6 \times 760} = 126\cdot 5$ sq. in. Say

$b = 10$ in. and $D = 13$ in., an estimate for the total steel in this section

$$= \frac{2}{100} \times 126\cdot 5 = 2\cdot 53$$

i.e. $A_t = A_c = 2\cdot 53$ sq. in.

It can be seen that this approximation is not a long way away from a possible solution given by the column defined in Example (4.6.1).

4.9   Reinforced concrete walls

In Britain *in-situ* reinforced concrete walls are almost invariably more expensive than brickwork walls, and also inferior as regards durability to industrial atmospheres, resistance to the penetration of dampness and thermal and acoustic resistance. Consequently in framed structures where walls are required chiefly for cladding rather than for structural purposes, brickwork is nearly always used in preference to *in-situ* concrete walls.

When walls are precast in Britain by highly organized and efficient methods, the same efficiency being used in erection, it is possible to be competitive in price with brickwork and have other very important advantages, namely, speed of erection, and freedom from the national shortage of bricks and bricklayers. The majority of the labour is classed as unskilled and consequently can be recruited reasonably easily in most localities, hence relieving local unemployment situations. One way of preventing staining due to industrial atmospheres is to use an exposed aggregate face where the exposed aggregate consists of white pots and the background concrete is preferably black or as dark as possible.

When walls are required to be load bearing, precast concrete walls are sometimes more economical than brickwork, e.g. for multi-story blocks of flats. If walls are required to resist horizontal and vertical forces then *in-situ* concrete walls are usually the most economical and reliable, e.g. retaining walls, or walls to bunkers and silos.

Load-bearing reinforced concrete walls are designed as columns, but if any structural reliance is made on the reinforcement, such reinforcement needs to have ties across the wall to prevent the bars buckling outwards. Such ties are highly undesirable in practice, causing much trouble to both the steelfixer and concretor. It is therefore usually more economical to design the wall as though it contained no reinforcement. It would not however be built without any reinforcement because differential settlement, shrinkage and temperature expansion or contraction could all cause cracking, which would be most noticeable on a concrete surface. Such small movements also cause hair cracks between the bricks of brickwork walls, but even if occasional bricks are cracked the cracks blend with the pattern of the wall and are not noticeable to the layman. Cracks in concrete surfaces tend to concentrate into a few of large size, rather than many of a small size, and ramble in various directions in an unsightly way. Consequently horizontal and vertical reinforcement is placed in both faces of a reinforced concrete wall, whether the wall is load-bearing or not, the horizontal reinforcement usually being nearer the surface than the vertical reinforcement. In practice, the vertical bars are usually made at least $\frac{1}{2}$ in. diameter (except in the case of very thin walls; see Example 4.9.1) as these have to support the horizontal reinforcement. The constructing of walls may be very difficult if light reinforcement fabrics are used.

EXAMPLE 4.9.1

A reinforced concrete load-bearing wall supports a maximum load of 4,000 lb/sq. in., inclusive of its self weight. The maximum laterally unsupported height is such that the *effective height* (comparable to *effective length* for a column = 13 ft. Determine a suitable thickness for the wall and recommend suitable reinforcement, assuming $p_{cc} = 760$ lb/sq. in., and $p_{sc} = 18,000$ lb/sq. in., all in accordance with the British Code of Practice.[3]

Ignoring buckling (as a long column) the necessary thickness = $\dfrac{4,000}{12 \times 760} = 0\cdot438$ in. The Code recommends a minimum thickness of 4 in. Hence the ratio of effective height to the least lateral dimension (cf. a long column) = $\dfrac{13 \times 12}{4} = 39$. Referring to Table 18 of the Code, the reduction coefficient for this value of 39 is equal to 0·3. Hence the load to be designed for = $\dfrac{4,000}{0\cdot3} = 13,333$ lb/ft. The necessary thickness is therefore = $\dfrac{13,333}{12 \times 760} = 1\cdot464$ in. Hence the 4 in. mentioned above is a satisfactory thickness. The total vertical reinforcement, according to the Code, must not be less than $\dfrac{0\cdot2}{100} \times 4 \times 12 = 0\cdot096$ sq.

in./ft run of wall. Hence per face this means 0·048 sq. in./ft, say $\frac{1}{4}$ in. diameter bars, at 12 in. centres. The total horizontal reinforcement can be 0·1 % of the cross-section = 0·048 sq. in./ft, hence per face this becomes 0·024 sq. in./ft, say $\frac{3}{16}$ in. diameter bars at 12 in. centres.

When a wall has to carry vertical loads eccentric to the plane of the wall, it is designed as an eccentrically loaded column, and to avoid cross ties, steel reinforcement is calculated to take tension but not compression. If there are also horizontal loads eccentric to the plane of the wall, then these are considered independently of the vertical loads. Moments in other planes are treated independently, but at places where compressive stresses superimpose on one another; these should be added together and should total less than the permissible concrete stress in compression. These remarks also apply to the walls of bunkers, silos and tanks.

4.10 Columns with high-tensile steel

The British Code uses the previous theories of this Chapter but specifies the permissible steel stresses to be as described in §3.10. As mentioned previously, reference (12) concerns the use of high-tensile steel in columns.

CHAPTER 5

SHEAR AND TORSION

5.1 Elastic theory for shear stresses

The assumptions of the elastic theory (see §1.13) resulted in an elastic theory for bending as described in Chapter 2. Using this theory of bending it is possible to compute the distribution of horizontal shear stresses, as is done by the classical elastic designs for homogeneous materials. It is basic knowledge that the shear force is equal to the rate of change of the bending moment along a beam, and for this to occur the beam has to withstand horizontal shearing stresses.

The section of a reinforced concrete beam shown in Fig. 28(i) is symmetrical about a vertical axis. The distributions of bending stresses for two sections distance δx apart are shown in Fig. 28(ii), the bending moments causing the distributions being M and $(M + \delta M)$ respectively. The horizontal shear stress will now be determined for a section AB. The concrete stress on the small element of area $b\, \delta y$ is given by

$$c' = \frac{M}{I} y \qquad \qquad \ldots. (5,1)$$

at one section of Fig. 28(ii) and at the other section by

$$c' + \delta c' = \left(\frac{M + \delta M}{I}\right) y \qquad \ldots. (5,2)$$

Subtracting these quantities,

$$\delta c' = \frac{\delta M}{I} y \qquad \qquad \ldots. (5,3)$$

Forces on strip at the two sections are

$$F' = c'b\, \delta y \qquad \qquad \ldots. (5,4)$$

$$F' + \delta F' = (c' + \delta c')b\, \delta y \qquad \ldots. (5,5)$$

Subtracting these quantities,

$$\delta F' = \delta c'b\, \delta y \qquad \qquad \ldots. (5,6)$$

Fig. 28(iii) shows the same two sections as Fig. 28(ii) and for clarity only the forces on the ends of the small elemental strip and the section $AB\, A'B'$ are shown. From this diagram it can be seen that the

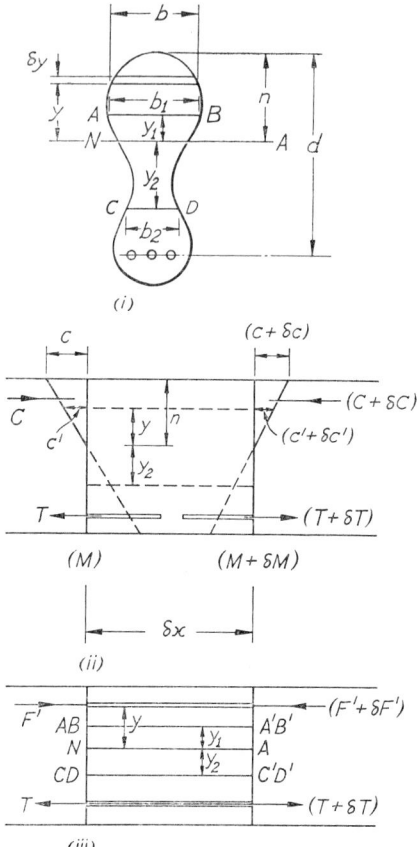

Fig. 28.

plane $AB\,A'B'$ has to resist shear stresses due to all such quantities as $(F' + \delta F') - F' = \delta F'$. Hence the total shear stress resisted by plane $AB\,A'B'$ is given by

$$q = \frac{\sum \delta F'}{b_1\,\delta x} \qquad \ldots\ldots(5,7)$$

Substituting from equations (5,6) and (5,3), equation (5,7) becomes

$$q = \frac{\sum \dfrac{\delta M}{I} \cdot yb\,\delta y}{b_1\,\delta x} \qquad \ldots\ldots(5,8)$$

Now from the well known theory of bending,

$$F = \frac{\delta M}{\delta x} \qquad \ldots\ldots(5,9)$$

Therefore from equations (5,8) and (5,9),

$$q = \frac{\sum \dfrac{F\,\delta x}{I} \cdot yb\,\delta y}{b_1\,\delta x} = \frac{F}{Ib_1} \sum by \cdot \delta y \qquad \ldots\ldots(5,10)$$

Or more precisely,

$$q = \frac{F}{Ib_1} \int_{y_1}^{n} by \cdot dy \qquad \ldots\ldots(5,11)$$

This is the horizontal shearing stress at a point distance y_1 from the neutral axis; from basic theory of elasticity it is also therefore the vertical shearing stress at this point. Equation (5,11) has been derived considering the rate of change of compressive stress in the concrete along the beam, and only concerns sections above the neutral axis. Considering a plane $CD\,C'D'$ at below the neutral axis, as shown on Fig. 28(ii) and (iii), the horizontal shear stress resisted by the plane, considering forces below the neutral axis, is given by

$$q = \frac{(T + \delta T) - T}{b_2\,\delta x} = \frac{1}{b_2}\frac{\delta T}{\delta x} \qquad \ldots\ldots(5,12)$$

Now (refer to equation 2,5),

$$M = Ta$$

and combining this with equation (5,9),

$$F = \frac{\delta M}{\delta x} = a \cdot \frac{\delta T}{\delta x} \qquad \ldots\ldots(5,13)$$

From equations (5,12) and (5,13),

$$q = \frac{F}{ab_2} \qquad \ldots\ldots(5,14)$$

This equation is independent of y_2, hence the shear stress (vertical or horizontal) is constant below the neutral axis.

Equations (5,11) and (5,14) are expressions which apply to any section which is singly reinforced and symmetrical about its vertical axis. Applying these to a rectangular section as shown in Fig. 11(i),

$$b_1 = b_2 = b$$

Equation (5,11) therefore becomes

$$q = \frac{F}{I} \int_{y_1}^{n} y \cdot dy \qquad \ldots\ldots(5,14a)$$

$$= \frac{F}{2I} (n^2 - y_1^2) \qquad \ldots\ldots(5,14b)$$

This gives a parabolic distribution of stress above the neutral axis and the maximum value is at the neutral axis when $y_1 = 0$, and therefore,

$$\text{max.}\, q = \frac{Fn^2}{2I} \qquad \ldots(5,15)$$

Now from equations (2,7) and (2,25),

$$M = Ca = \frac{c}{2} \cdot nba \qquad \ldots(5,16)$$

$$M = c\,\frac{I}{n} \qquad \ldots(5,17)$$

Eliminating M between equations (5,16) and (5,17),

$$\frac{n^2}{2I} = \frac{1}{ba} \qquad \ldots(5,18)$$

Substituting this in equation (5,15),

$$\text{max.}\, q = \frac{F}{ab} \qquad \ldots(5,19)$$

Below the neutral axis, applying equation (5,14),

$$q = \frac{F}{ab} \qquad \ldots(5,20)$$

The distribution of shear stress is therefore as shown in Fig. 11(v). Now concrete is much stronger in compression and shear than it is in tension. Consequently the principal tensile stresses often known as the *diagonal tensile stresses* are the criterion as regards failure due to shearing forces. If the principal tensile stresses due to combining the stresses shown in Figs. 11(iii) and 11(v) are computed, above the neutral axis the shear stresses are less, and also the compressive stresses result in the principal tensile stresses being smaller than at the neutral axis. Below the neutral axis there are no tensile stresses in addition to the shear stresses, hence the maximum diagonal tensile stresses occur at points at and below the neutral axis. The maximum diagonal tensile stresses thus result only from the maximum shear stresses, and are therefore equal in magnitude to the shear stresses and inclined at 45° to the horizontal, for vertical and horizontal shear stresses. This inclination results in the word *diagonal* of the expression diagonal tensile stresses.

The British Code of Practice recommends permissible 'shear stresses', which are more precisely permissible diagonal tensile stresses, for various grades of concrete.

EXAMPLE 5.1.1

Suppose in Example (2.2.1) that the beam carries a uniformly distributed load and is simply supported over a span of 20 ft. Determine the maximum diagonal tensile stress, and if the permissible shear stress is 106 lb/sq. in., state whether shear reinforcement is required.

Let w lb/ft = the total uniformly distributed load (including self weight).

$$\frac{w \times 20^2 \times 12}{8} = 500,000$$

$$\therefore \quad w = 833 \text{ lb/ft}$$

Maximum shear force $= 833 \times \frac{20}{2} = 8,330$ lb

From equations (5,19) and (5,20),

$$\text{max. } q = \frac{8,330}{15\cdot13 \times 6} = 91\cdot8 \text{ lb/sq. in.}$$

This is less than 106, hence no shear reinforcement is required.

Consider a T-section, for example the section shown in Fig. 17(i). Applying equation (5,11) for sections within the depth of the top flange

$$q = \frac{F}{IB} \int_{y_1}^{n} By \cdot dy = \frac{F}{2I}(n^2 - y_1^2) \qquad \ldots.(5,21)$$

This represents a parabolic curve and q will be a maximum for this zone when y_1 is the minimum value of $(n - d_s)$. Applying equation (5,11) to sections within the portion of the stem (or rib) above the neutral axis,

$$q = \frac{F}{Ib}\left\{ \int_{(n-d_s)}^{n} By \cdot dy + \int_{y_1}^{(n-d_s)} by \cdot dy \right\}$$

$$= \frac{F}{2Ib}\left\{ B[n^2 - (n - d_s)^2] + b[(n - d_s)^2 - y_1^2] \right\}$$

$$= \frac{F}{2Ib}\left\{ B(2nd_s - d_s^2) + b(n^2 - 2nd_s + d_s^2 - y_1^2) \right\}$$

$$= \frac{F}{2I}\left\{ \left(\frac{B}{b} - 1\right) d_s(2n - d_s) + n^2 - y_1^2 \right\} \qquad \ldots.(5,22)$$

This is a parabolic curve and q will be a maximum for this zone when y_1 is the minimum value of zero. For sections below the neutral axis, apply equation (5,14),

$$q = \frac{F}{ab} \qquad \ldots.(5,23)$$

This can be proved to be the same as the value of equation (5,22) when $y_1 = 0$, i.e. at the neutral axis. The distribution of shear stress given by equations (5,21), (5,22), and (5,23) is illustrated in Fig. 17(iv).

EXAMPLE 5.1.2

Suppose in Example (2.8.1) that the maximum shear force to be resisted by the beam is 20,000 lb. If Fig. 14(iv) illustrates the distribution of the shear stresses, calculate the shear stresses represented by points H, J, K, and L on this figure, for the maximum shear force.

For point H apply equation (5,21), putting $y_1 = (n - d_s)$,

Therefore $\quad q = \dfrac{20,000}{2 \times 13,328}(7{\cdot}29^2 - 2{\cdot}29^2) = 35{\cdot}8$ lb/sq. in.

The value of I was obtained from Example (2.8.2). Now for point J apply equation (5,22), putting $y_1 = (n - d_s)$,

$$q = \frac{20,000}{2 \times 13,328}\{(\tfrac{30}{12} - 1)5(2 \times 7{\cdot}29 - 5) + 7{\cdot}29^2 - 2{\cdot}29^2\}$$

$$= 89{\cdot}7 \text{ lb/sq. in.}$$

For point K or L apply equation (5,23),
Therefore

$$q = \frac{20,000}{\left(20 - \dfrac{7{\cdot}29}{3}\right)12} = 94{\cdot}8 \text{ lb/sq. in.}$$

Now consider a rectangular beam with compression reinforcement, for example, of the section shown in Fig. 16(i). As explained in Chapter 2 the compression reinforcement can be considered as an equivalent area of concrete of $(m - 1)A_{sc}$ and this can be used in conjunction with the gross area of concrete above the neutral axis. For a section above the compression reinforcement, applying equation (5,11),

$$q = \frac{F}{Ib}\int_{y_1}^{n} by \, . \, \mathrm{d}y$$

$$= \frac{F}{2I}(n^2 - y_1^2) \qquad \qquad \ldots (5,24)$$

For a section between the neutral axis and the position of the compression reinforcement, applying equation (5,11) and remembering that the integral is the area moment about the neutral axis when the compression steel is considered,

$$q = \frac{F}{Ib}\left\{\int_{y_1}^{n} by\,dy + (m-1)A_{sc}(n-d_1)\right\}$$

$$= \frac{F}{Ib}\left\{\frac{b}{2}(n^2 - y_1^2) + (m-1)A_{sc}(n-d_1)\right\} \quad\ldots(5,25)$$

At the neutral axis $y_1 = 0$, and equation (5,25) gives

$$q = \frac{F}{Ib}\left\{\frac{b}{2}n^2 + (m-1)A_{sc}(n-d_1)\right\} \qquad\ldots(5,26)$$

This can be proved to be the same as

$$q = \frac{F}{ab} \qquad\ldots(5,27)$$

For sections below the neutral axis, equation (5,14) gives the same result as equation (5,27). The distribution of shear stress obtained from the above calculation is shown in Fig. 16(iv).

EXAMPLE 5.1.3

Suppose that in Example (2.6.1) the maximum shear force to be resisted by the beam is 8,330 lb. Assuming Fig. 16(iv) illustrates the distribution of the shear stresses, calculate the shear stresses represented by points H, J, K, and L on this figure, for the maximum shear force.

For point H, apply equation (5,24), putting $y_1 = (n-d_1)$, and using the value of I obtained in Example (2.6.2),

$$q = \frac{8,330}{2 \times 3,632}[8\cdot08^2 - (8\cdot08 - 1\cdot25)^2]$$

$$= 21\cdot37 \text{ lb/sq. in.}$$

For point J, apply equation (5,25), putting $y_1 = (n-d_1)$,

$$q = \frac{8,330}{3,632 \times 6}\left\{\frac{6}{2}[8\cdot08^2 - (8\cdot08 - 1\cdot25)^2] + (15-1)\right.$$

$$\left. \times 0\cdot393 \times (8\cdot08 - 1\cdot25)\right\}$$

$$= 35\cdot8 \text{ lb/sq. in.}$$

For points K or L, apply equation (5,26):

$$q = \frac{8,330}{3,632 \times 6}\left\{\frac{6}{2} \times 8\cdot08^2 + (15-1) \times 0\cdot393 \times (8\cdot08 - 1\cdot25)\right\}$$

$$= 89\cdot2 \text{ lb/sq. in.}$$

9

5.2 Shear reinforcement

When the permissible shear stresses are exceeded, shear reinforcement must be provided. This usually takes the form of either stirrups or bent-up bars, or both can be used simultaneously, the shear resistances of the two systems being simply added together, irrespective of the rather contrary actions assumed to be involved by the respective systems. It is crudely assumed that the two systems can be superimposed upon one another, experience showing that such results are certainly safe and usually conservative.

It is almost invariably found that, when shear reinforcement accords with most codes of practice, the design is conservative; for example, it is quite common for the ultimate shearing strength of a beam to be seven times the permissible shearing strength given by the British Code of Practice [see references (16) and (17)]. This very safe state of affairs does not always apply to beams without shear reinforcement. The British Code of Practice (3) relates the permissible shear stress to the permissible compressive stress of the concrete, thus the permissible shear stress for a 1:1:2 mix is 130 lb/sq. in. and, if good workmanship can be proved for such as mix, the permissible shear stress is 152·5 lb/sq. in. The Code allows higher strength mixes to be designed which have even greater permissible shear stresses, no ceiling value being specified. This is much different to the A.C.I. Building Code[13] which does not recommend permissible shear stresses in excess of 90 lb/sq. in. The experimental evidence cited in reference (18) illustrates that the permissible shear stress should be limited to 106 lb/sq. in., except for rectangular beams with more than 0·17% of longitudinal compression reinforcement, when the permissible shear stress should then be limited to 79 lb/sq. in. It is also recorded that the higher permissible shear stresses recommended by the British Code of Practice can often result in unsatisfactory factors of safety. In special circumstances, with long continuous structures, it is possible that shrinkage and temperature stresses can cause longitudinal tensile stresses and if these are not assessed then the permissible shear stresses referred to above need to be even lower. If an approximate evaluation of such tensile stresses can be made then these values can be used in conjunction with the shear stresses for computing the maximum diagonal tensile stresses, which should not exceed the relevant permissible shear stresses.

When the diagonal tensile stresses to be resisted are greater than the permissible 'shear' stress of the concrete, then the British and most other European codes of practice recommend all the shear being resisted by web reinforcement, either using stirrups or bent-up bars. The A.C.I. Code, on the other hand, only requires the shear in excess of the permissible amount on the concrete to be resisted by web reinforcement.

5.3 Stirrups as shear reinforcement

Stirrups are almost invariably vertical as this has many practical advantages but they can of course be inclined if desired. The method of design recommended by the British and many other Codes of Practice is to equate the vertical component of the total force P, in all arms of the

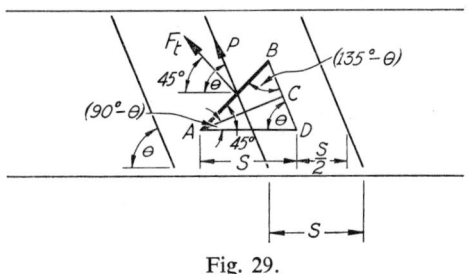

Fig. 29.

stirrup, to the vertical component of the force F_t, due to the diagonal tensile stresses, assumed to be uniform over an area such as that represented by AB in Fig. 29.

Therefore
$$F_t \sin 45° = P \sin \theta \qquad \dots(5,28)$$

If the beam is rectangular with a uniform breadth of b, then

$$F_t = qb \cdot AB \qquad \dots(5,29)$$

From triangle ABD in Fig. 29,

$$\frac{AB}{\sin \theta} = \frac{S}{\sin (135° - \theta)} \qquad \dots(5,30)$$

Hence from equations (5,28), (5,29), and (5,30),

$$\frac{qbS \sin \theta}{\sin (135° - \theta)} \cdot \sin 45° = P \sin \theta \qquad \dots(5,31)$$

Then from equation (5,27),

$$\frac{FS \sin 45°}{a \sin (135° - \theta)} = P \qquad \dots(5,32)$$

Therefore
$$P = \frac{FS \sin 45°}{a \sin (45° + \theta)} \qquad \dots(5,33)$$

Therefore
$$P = \frac{FS}{a (\sin \theta + \cos \theta)} \qquad \dots(5,34)$$

If the stirrups are vertical, $\theta = 90°$,

Therefore
$$P = \frac{FS}{a} \qquad \dots(5,35)$$

If the stirrups are inclined so that $\theta = 45°$, then

$$P = \frac{FS}{a\sqrt{2}} \qquad \dots (5,36)$$

Equation (5,34) can be used to determine the inclination of the stirrups to give the minimum quantity of stirrup reinforcement for any particular shearing resistance. The total cross-sectional area of all the arms of a stirrup is given by $\dfrac{P}{p_{st}}$; this occurs in an area of concrete of $(AC)b$, see Fig. 29, hence the percentage of stirrup or web reinforcement is given by

$$r = \frac{100P}{p_{st}} \bigg/ (AC)b \qquad \dots (5,37)$$

Now from triangle ACD,

$$AC = S \sin \theta \qquad \dots (5,38)$$

Substituting for P from equation (5,34) and for AC from equation (5,38) in equation (5,37):

$$r = \frac{100F}{p_{st}ab \sin \theta(\sin \theta + \cos \theta)} \qquad \dots (5,39)$$

For a given beam, a and b are constants, and for a given type of reinforcement p_{st} is constant; hence for a given value of F, r is related to θ as in equation (5,39). Therefore for a minimum value of r, the following quantity must be a maximum:

$$\sin \theta(\sin \theta + \cos \theta)$$

The differential of this with respect to θ is therefore equated to zero:

$$\cos \theta(\sin \theta + \cos \theta) + (\cos \theta - \sin \theta) \sin \theta = 0$$

$$\therefore \quad \cos^2 \theta - \sin^2 \theta = -2 \sin \theta \cos \theta$$

$$\therefore \quad \cos 2\theta = -\sin 2\theta$$

$$\therefore \quad \tan 2\theta = -1$$

$$\therefore \quad 2\theta = 135°$$

$$\therefore \quad \theta = 67\tfrac{1}{2}° \qquad \dots (5,40)$$

Hence this value of θ gives a minimum value of r. This all depends of course upon the reliability of equation (5,34); see §5.5.

EXAMPLE 5.3.1

Suppose in Example (2.2.1) that the beam carries a uniformly distributed load and is simply supported over a span of 16 ft 6 in.

Design any shear reinforcement which might be necessary assuming the following data:

$$\text{permissible shear stress} = 106 \text{ lb/sq. in.}$$

$$p_{st} = 20,000 \text{ lb/sq. in.}$$

Let w lb/ft = the total uniformly distributed load (including self weight)

Therefore $\qquad \dfrac{w16{\cdot}5^2}{8} \times 12 = 500,000$

Therefore $\qquad\qquad\qquad w = 1,222 \text{ lb/ft}$

$$\text{Maximum shearing force} = 1,222 \times \frac{16{\cdot}5}{2} = 10,100 \text{ lb}$$

From equations (5,19) and (5,20),

$$\text{max.} \, q = \frac{10,100}{15{\cdot}13 \times 6} = 111 \text{ lb/sq. in.}$$

This is greater than 106, hence shear reinforcement needs to be provided to take all the shear so that the design is in accordance with the British Code of Practice. If vertical stirrups are to be used, applying equation (5,35),

$$P = \frac{10,100S}{15{\cdot}13}$$

The cross-sectional area of all the arms of a stirrup

$$= \frac{P}{20,000} = \frac{10,100S}{20,000 \times 15{\cdot}13} = 0{\cdot}03335S$$

If stirrups with two arms each of $\tfrac{3}{8}$ in. diameter are assumed then

$$2 \times \frac{\pi}{4} \times \left(\frac{3}{8}\right)^2 = 0{\cdot}03335S$$

Therefore $\qquad\qquad S = 6{\cdot}64 \text{ in., say } 6\tfrac{1}{2} \text{ in.}$

5.4 Bent-up bars as shear reinforcement

Bars belonging to the main tensile reinforcement are bent-up at points such as C and E in Fig. 30(i). Alternatively independent shear bars may be used as illustrated in Fig. 30(ii). The method of design propounded in the early days of reinforced concrete and still recommended by the British and other Codes of Practice can be referred to as the 'truss-analogy' theory. A beam is considered to be a statically determinate truss as illustrated in Fig. 30(i). The longitudinal tension reinforcement is analogous to tension members such as AC and CE in Fig. 30(i); the concrete resisting longitudinal compression (due to bending) is analogous to compression members such as BD and DF; the bent-up bars are analogous to inclined tension members such as BC and DE, and the inclined compression members such as AB, CD and EF, required to

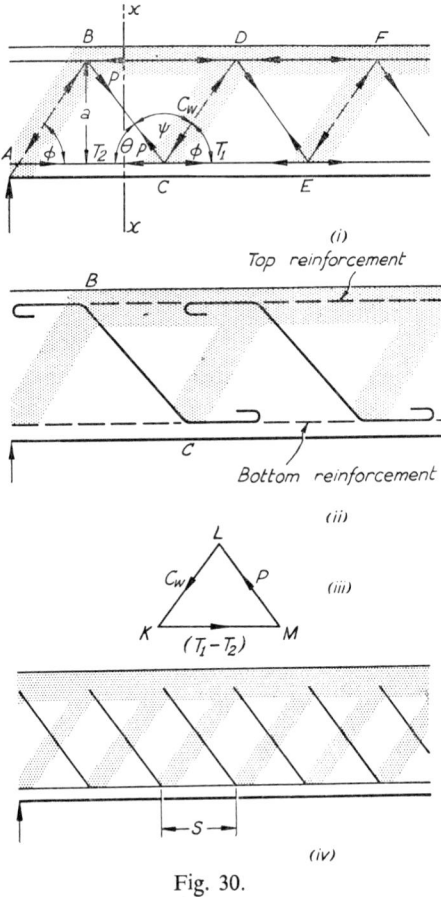

Fig. 30.

complete the truss analogy, are provided by the concrete of the web. The forces in the analogous truss members AC, BC, DC, and EC are as shown, namely T_2, P, C_w, and T_1 respectively. A vector diagram is drawn for these forces in Fig. 30(iii); as the bending moment increases for sections further away from the supports, T_1 will be greater than T_2, and their difference is represented by the vector KM; forces C_w and P are represented by the vectors LK and LM respectively. If the area of tensile reinforcement which is analogous to member CE is A_s, and the area of the bars bent-up is αA_s, and if the bent-up bars are required to develop their full permissible shearing stress p_{ss}, then $P = \alpha A_s p_{ss}$. At the same time, if the stresses in the members CA and CE are not to exceed the permissible tensile stress of the reinforcement p_{st}, they are designed so that $T_1 = A_s p_{st}$ and $T_2 = (A_s - \alpha A_s)p_{st}$. Hence referring to Fig. 30(iii) the vector $LM = \alpha A_s p_{ss}$ and the vector $KM = A_s p_{st} - (A_s - \alpha A_s)p_{st} = \alpha A_s p_{st}$. In the case of mild steel reinforcement, $p_{ss} = p_{st}$, and therefore $LM = KM$; consequently in the vector diagram LKM,

$$\phi = \psi \qquad \qquad \dots(5,41)$$

For high tensile steel,[6] the British Code gives $p_{ss} = 20,000$ lb/sq. in. and $p_{st} = 30,000$ lb/sq. in.; hence $LM = 20,000\ \alpha A_s$ and $KM = 30,000\ \alpha A_s$, and from the vector diagram,

$$\frac{\sin \phi}{\sin \psi} = \frac{LM}{KM} = \frac{2}{3} \qquad \qquad \dots(5,42)$$

The inclined compression members are assumed to be sufficiently strong for all requirements. By Ritter's Method of Sections, assume the truss to be cut at the section xx shown in Fig. 30(i). Then resolving vertically for, say, the left-hand side of this section,

$$P \sin \theta = \text{shear force at } xx = F \qquad \dots(5,43)$$

The principle of the superposition of trusses can be applied. For example, the system shown in Fig. 30(iv), where $S = \dfrac{AC}{2}$ is assumed to be twice as strong as the system of Fig. 30(i); hence from equation (5,43),

$$F = 2P \sin \theta \qquad \qquad \dots(5,44)$$

The inclined bars shown in Figs. 30(i) and (iv) are sometimes described as being in *single-shear* and *double-shear* respectively.

Extending this principle of superposition for any value of S in Fig. 30(iv), equation (5,44) becomes

$$F = \frac{AC}{S} \cdot P \sin \theta \qquad \qquad \dots(5,45)$$

providing $S < AC$. The theory does not apply to inclined bars farther apart than in the single-shear system of Fig. 30(i); now from triangle ABC,

$$AC = a(\cot \phi + \cot \theta) \qquad \qquad \dots(5,46)$$

Hence equation (5,45) becomes

$$F = \frac{Pa}{S} \sin \theta\, (\cot \phi + \cot \theta) \qquad \qquad \dots(5,47)$$

Providing $\qquad\qquad S < a(\cot \phi + \cot \theta) \qquad \qquad \dots(5,48)$

Applying equation (5,47) to mild steel reinforcement and hence using the equation (5,41), also from triangle *KLM* in Fig. 30(iii),

$$\theta + \phi + \psi = 180° \qquad \qquad \dots(5,49)$$

Therefore, from equation (5,41),

$$\phi = 90° - \frac{\theta}{2} \qquad \qquad \dots(5,50)$$

Substituting this in equation (5,47),

$$F = \frac{Pa}{S} \sin \theta \left(\tan \frac{\theta}{2} + \cot \theta \right)$$

$$= \frac{Pa}{S} \left(2 \sin^2 \frac{\theta}{2} + \cos \theta \right)$$

$$\therefore \quad F = \frac{Pa}{S} \qquad \qquad \dots(5,51)$$

Apply equation (5,47) to high-tensile reinforcement and hence using the equation (5,42),

$$\sin \phi = \tfrac{2}{3} \sin \psi$$

Therefore from equation (5,49),

$$\sin \phi = \tfrac{2}{3} \sin (180° - \theta - \phi)$$

$$\therefore \quad 1\cdot5 \sin \phi = \sin \theta \cos \phi + \cos \theta \sin \phi$$

$$\therefore \quad \cot \phi = \frac{1\cdot5 - \cos \theta}{\sin \theta} \qquad \qquad \dots(5,52)$$

Substituting this in equation (5,47),

$$F = \frac{Pa}{S} (1\cdot5 - \cos \theta + \cos \theta) = 1\cdot5 \frac{Pa}{S} \qquad \dots(5,53)$$

EXAMPLE 5.4.1

In the design of a beam, several $\frac{3}{4}$ in. diameter mild steel bars are available for bending-up, one at a time, at 45° to the horizontal to act as shear reinforcement. Design this system to resist a shear force of 10,100 lb, assuming that the lever arm of the beam is 15·13 in., and that the permissible stress of the steel in tension is 20,000 lb/sq. in.

$$P = \frac{\pi}{4} \times \left(\frac{3}{4} \right)^2 \times 20,000 = 8,830 \, \text{lb}$$

The shear resistance of the system in single-shear is given by equation (5,43):

$$F = 8,830 \sin 45° = 6,240 \, \text{lb}$$

This is insufficient, hence the inclined bars need to be closer together. Applying equation (5,51),

$$S = \frac{8,830 \times 15\cdot13}{10,100}$$

$$= 13\cdot23 \text{ in.}$$

EXAMPLE 5.4.2

In the design of a beam, several $\frac{3}{4}$ in. diameter high-tensile steel bars are available for bending-up, one at a time, at 30° to the horizontal to act as shear reinforcement. Design this system to resist a shear force of 10,100 lb, assuming that the lever arm of the beam is 15·13 in., and that the permissible stress of the steel in tension is 30,000 lb/sq. in. for bending and 20,000 lb/sq. in. in diagonal tension.

$$P = \frac{\pi}{4} \times \left(\frac{3}{4}\right)^2 \times 20,000 = 8,830 \text{ lb}$$

The shear resistance of the system in single-shear is given by equation (5,43),
$$F = 8,830 \sin 30° = 4,415 \text{ lb}$$

This is insufficient, hence the inclined bars need to be closer together. From equation (5,53),

$$S = \frac{1\cdot5 \times 8,830 \times 15\cdot13}{10,100}$$

$$= 19\cdot85 \text{ in.}$$

Equations (5,51) and (5,53) can be used to determine the inclination of the bars to give the minimum quantity of inclined bar reinforcement for any particular shearing resistance [cf. §5.3, equation (5,40)]. Equations (5,37) and (5,38) apply equally to inclined bars as to inclined stirrups, hence using these two equations and equation (5,51),

$$r = \frac{100F}{p_{st} \cdot ba \sin \theta} \qquad \dots (5,54)$$

If F, p_{st}, b, and a are constants, then r is a minimum when $\sin \theta$ is a maximum, i.e. when, $\theta = 90°$. $\qquad \dots (5,54A)$

The same result is obtained for high-tensile reinforcement by using equations (5,37), (5,38), and (5,53). Examples where $\theta = 90°$ in practice are not known to the authors, but according to this theory θ is preferably as great as possible. The theory however is not very practical as it does not consider bond lengths or the possible positions where longitudinal steel can be curtailed in the span, and over the supports in the case of continuous beams. For example, in the case of shear bars, as illustrated in Fig. 30(ii), for any particular diameter of shear bar, the total length of such a bar will be constant, say l (depending on the bond length) and similarly to the above it can be proved that,

$$r = \frac{100Fl}{p_{st} \cdot abD} \qquad \qquad \dots .(5,55)$$

This expression is independent of the angle θ; in this instance, the percentage of web reinforcement is the same for any value of θ; this differs from equation (5,54). It is therefore difficult to generalize, for inclined bars, about which inclination gives the smallest amount of reinforcement. The inclinations most commonly used in Britain are 45°, 30° and sometimes 60°. Consideration of curtailments of longitudinal steel and bond lengths available for anchoring inclined bars often decides the system which can best be used.

Inclined bars tend to make for complex reinforcement details, especially over supports of internal columns where continuous beams cross one another. This increases the costs of reinforcement fixing and concreting. It is therefore not uncommon practice to resist as much shear as is practical with vertical stirrups (the maximum limit often being $\frac{3}{8}$ in. diameter stirrups at 3 in. centres in normal building work) and take any excess shear near the support by a system of bent-up bars in single-shear. Bars in double-shear or closer centres are sometimes very troublesome in detailing adjacent to the supports.

5.5   Brief discussion on design of beams in shear

It is possibly true to say that the design of beams in shear is the least satisfactory of all the theories relating to the design of reinforced concrete. When a beam reinforced with stirrups is tested, it is not unusual for its ultimate shearing strength to be 10 times (see references 16 and 17) the permissible shearing strength computed in accordance with the British Code of Practice.[3]   When however beams with plain webs are tested, it is even possible for the ultimate shearing strength to be less than the permissible shearing strength (see references 18 and 22) of the British Code of Practice.[3]   This situation for plain webbed beams is probably aggravated by shrinkage and temperature movement in the case of long continuous structures, and a structural failure, possibly due to such effects, was reported in the U.S.A. in 1956. The design of beams in shear is therefore an important subject and a reliable design method would lead to substantial economies in web reinforcement and ease the detailing and concreting difficulties caused by the familiar large amounts of such reinforcements used in Europe. The British Code, for example, never utilizes percentages of vertical stirrups of less than 0·5% whereas tests show[16,17] that much smaller percentages are still effective for resisting shear. In 1907 Talbot[19] recommended the formula of equation

(5,19) for the computation of diagonal tensile stresses, and Mörsch[20] recommended the formulae of equations (5,35) and (5,43) for the design of shear reinforcement. Hence the design methods recommended by the present British Code of Practice were subtantiated by Talbot and Mörsch in 1907, and consequently this Code does not take into account or make recommendations from any of the many subsequent works on this subject.[21]

The classical theories expounded in §5.3 and §5.4 can soon be realized to be extremely illogical and contrary to experimental evidence. For example, why equate the vertical components of P and F_t in equation (5,28)? As F_t is the principal force to be resisted it would seem more logical to determine the resistance the stirrup can offer in the direction of this principal force, i.e. equate F_t to $P \cos (\theta - 45°)$; then the stirrups would be most efficient when in the direction of the principal tensile stresses, which seems quite sensible. This gives the same result as equation (5,36) but the right-hand side of equation (5,35) becomes doubled. Hence for vertical stirrups, which are most commonly used in practice, this idea would be more conservative and this is undesirable as most tests show that equation (5,35) is already too conservative for modern designs. The illogicality, just mentioned, of equation (5,28) and hence of equation (5,34), as well as the invariable lack of any reasonable agreement of equation (5,34) with experimental evidence, can hardly substantiate the further use of equation (5,34) in the theory to evaluate equation (5,40).

The truss-analogy of §5.4 seems logical as a single-shear system but it is difficult to believe the principle of superposition of such systems, resulting in equation (5,51) and (5,53), can actually happen internally in a reinforced concrete beam. The distribution of cracks at failure obtained by most experiments are absolutely inconsistent with the system of analogous trusses. The equations (5,43), (5,51), and (5,53) of the truss-analogy do not agree with equation (5,34), yet all these equations relate to the same requirement, namely the design of shear reinforcement. As would be expected therefore, neither does equation (5,40) agree with equations (5,54A) and (5,55).

There are several other theories for deriving the same formulae as in §5.3 and §5.4. Many of these are expounded by Paduart;[25] (this reference gives a useful history of the subject which should be read in conjunction with a later historical review by Hognestad[21]).

However illogical and inaccurate the equations of §5.3 and §5.4 are considered to be, they have resulted in structures which are safe in shear, even if conservative, over a long period of time, and must be obeyed implicitly if designs are to be in accordance with the British and many other Codes of Practice.

Beams with plain webs are discussed in §5.2. Now with regard to the design of shear reinforcement, the criticism of the British Code is only its conservatism, which often results in detailing difficulties, in steel congestion near supports, and sometimes in bad concreting at such places. References (16) and (17) suggest a simple method of design which is consistently conservative, but much less conservative than the British Code. Possibly the most accurate method of predicting the ultimate shearing strength of a beam with web reinforcement is given by reference (23); this applies to concretes with cylinder strengths less than 6,000 lb/sq. in. The method has been applied to concretes with higher strengths and the formula modified for such concretes.[24] The mechanism of the method[23] is open to criticism but, judging by experimental evidence, the theory certainly seems to result in the choice of most suitable factors for the expression of the empirical formula expounded.

5.6 Stirrups and bent-up bars

Stirrups and bent-up bars can assist one another in resisting shear. Their shear resistances, calculated as described in §5.3 and §5.4, are simply added together. This is theoretically very illogical, as the different internal effects, described in §5.3 and §5.4, are thus assumed to be superimposed. Experimental and practical experience however shows that the simple addition of such systems is, if anything, conservative.

5.7 Anchorage of web reinforcement

Sometimes an arm of a stirrup is regarded as adequately anchored if it is simply hooked over a longitudinal bar, irrespective of whether it has sufficient bond length to develop its full working stress. This does not appear to be satisfactory[26] and good practice should ensure that the arms of stirrups have sufficient bond length on either side of the neutral axis. According to theory however, the maximum diagonal tensile stress is not only at the neutral axis but occurs equally at all positions below the neutral axis; hence the stirrups are theoretically fully stressed at all points below the neutral axis. Experience has established that it is satisfactory to assume that maximum stress in a stirrup occurs only at the neutral axis and to anchor accordingly, as described above. This sometimes means, in shallow beams, that smaller diameter stirrups have to be used or that the stirrups have to be of a shape as shown in Fig. 31(i) in lieu of the more common shape shown in Fig. 31(ii).

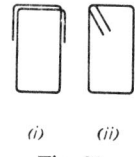

(i)   (ii)

Fig. 31.

With inclined bars, a consideration of the truss-analogy theory indicates that any such bar is fully stressed for the full depth of the lever arm of the beam. This means that the bond length to anchor a fully stressed bar would need to commence at each extremity of the lever arm of the beam. However, the usual practice, which has proved to be conservative, is to consider an inclined bar to be fully stressed only at the neutral axis, the necessary bond length therefore being provided on either side of this point. The bends at positions such as B and C in Fig. 30(ii) are often counted as having extra anchorage value in accordance with clause 310(e) of the British Code of Practice.[3]

5.8 Bond stresses due to shear

The theory expounded concerning shear stresses (§5.1) naturally assumes perfect adhesion of the concrete to the tensile reinforcement, and therefore involves bond stresses being developed between the steel and the concrete. Referring to Fig. 28(ii), the change of force in the tensile reinforcement between the sections shown is $(T + \delta T) - (T) = \delta T$. This can only be resisted by bond stresses which act on the contact area between the steel and the concrete of $\sigma \, \delta x$. Hence the bond stress at this locality is given by

$$c_{lb} = \frac{\delta T}{\sigma \, \delta x} = \frac{1}{\sigma} \frac{dT}{dx} \qquad \ldots (5,56)$$

Now

$$F = \frac{dM}{dx} = \frac{d}{dx} (Ta) = a \cdot \frac{dT}{dx} \qquad \ldots (5,57)$$

Hence from equations (5,56) and (5,57),

$$c_{lb} = \frac{F}{a\sigma} \qquad \ldots (5,58)$$

Such stresses are known as *local bond stresses* by the British Code[3] and permissible values are recommended for various types of concrete. Designs need to ensure that such permissible local bond stresses are nowhere exceeded and this is the only requirement in this connection; such bond stresses are local effects and do not for instance require any anchorage.

EXAMPLE 5.8.1

The maximum tensile reinforcement in a beam consists of four $1\frac{1}{8}$ in. diameter bars. The maximum shear force immediately adjacent to a support is 16,000 lb. If the lever arm of the beam is 20 in. and the permissible local bond stress is 200 lb/sq. in., what is the least number of the reinforcement bars which must continue through to the support?

Applying equation (5,58),
$$200 = \frac{16,000}{20 \times \sigma}$$

Therefore $\sigma = 4$ in.

the circumference of one $1\frac{1}{8}$ in. diameter bar $= \pi \times 1\frac{1}{8} = 3\cdot54$ in.

No. of bars required to continue through to support $= \dfrac{4}{3\cdot54} = 2,$
to nearest integer.

5.9 Torsion

Torques are usually calculated assuming a structure to be elastic and uncracked. This is neither true at working nor ultimate loads. However there is no reliable alternative to this procedure and as many structures very seldom experience their full working loads, the elastic and un-cracked condition will often apply to a substantial proportion of the life of the structure. The monolithic nature of *in-situ* construction means that most sections inevitably experience torques, even if only very small, at some time or other. The experience of the designer usually enables him to provide for minor torques when detailing the reinforcement. For example, the external beams to a floor might be given nominal stirruping of say $\frac{3}{8}$ in. diameter at 9 in. centres as opposed to say $\frac{1}{4}$ in. diameter at 12 in. centres for the internal beams (assuming the possibility of torques on the internal beams is negligible, i.e. a low ratio of live to dead load). This practice is obviously satisfactory in that torsional failures are ex-tremely rare but this is not the only criterion, as the majority of struc-tures are never overloaded. When torques are not minor a scientific method of design is essential. Torsion failures are very inconsistent and this leads to divergent views upon design by various experts. In practice, torques often occur simultaneously with shear forces and bending moments, thus complicating the problem still further, especially as the design of members in shear is a difficult problem in itself. Many Codes of Practice ignore the problem of torsion entirely. This is unfortunate as one cannot ignore torsion in certain structural members and the designer in these instances has to make his own choice of a design method. In this respect it is good practice to design structural systems so that torsion is always a subsidiary and negligible effect.

In practice it is preferable to resist torsion by vertical stirrups. Experi-ments indicate however that spirals with the wires inclined at 45° to the longitudinal axis of the beam are more effective in resisting torsion. Longitudinal bars are not very effective in torsion, but when large torques have to be resisted by very small sections (bad practice of course) spirals and longitudinal bars can be used, even in addition to vertical stirrups.[27]

Sections entirely in compression

The shear stresses due to torsion for a member with a *circular cross-section* can be assessed in accordance with elementary Strength of Materials theory. With regard to the section shown in Fig. 32, the *equivalent* area of the reinforcement $= (m_s - 1)A_s$, the polar moment of inertia of this being $(m_s - 1)A_s R_s^2$. The polar moment of inertia of the concrete $= \dfrac{\pi R^4}{2}$. Hence the total polar moment of inertia is

$$J = \frac{\pi R^4}{2} + (m_s - 1)A_s R_s^2 \qquad \ldots\ldots(5,59)$$

The maximum shear stress due to a torque is at the extreme fibre and is given by

$$q_T = \frac{M_T R}{J} \qquad \ldots\ldots(5,60)$$

The shear stresses due to torsion for a member with a *rectangular cross-section* can only be assessed as above if plane sections remain plane. Plane cross-sections, however, warp under these conditions and St. Vernant showed that the distribution of extreme fibre stress is parabolic

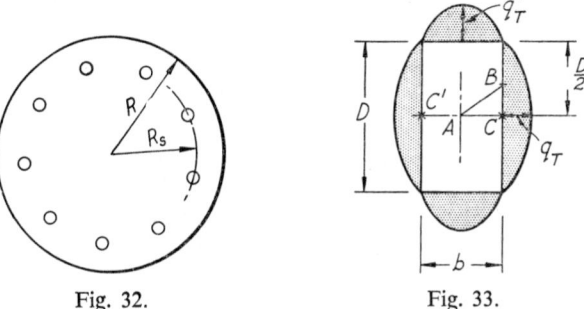

Fig. 32.   Fig. 33.

along the sides as shown in Fig. 33. For each section such as *AB* in Fig. 33, the stress varies linearly from a maximum at *B* to zero at *A*. The maximum shear stress due to torsion occurs at points *C* and *C'*, half way along the longer sides. This maximum stress is given by

$$q_T = \left(3 + \frac{2 \cdot 6}{0 \cdot 45 + \dfrac{D}{b}}\right)\frac{M_T}{Db^2} \qquad \ldots\ldots(5,61)$$

Similarly, the maximum shear stress on the shorter side is less than this, and is given by

$$q_T' = \left(3 + \frac{2 \cdot 6}{0 \cdot 45 + \dfrac{b}{D}}\right)\frac{M_T}{bD^2} \qquad \ldots\ldots(5,62)$$

Equations (5,61) and (5,62) only apply within the range of $D < 1.5b$. The generalized expression for these equations is given in reference (28).

The effect of longitudinal reinforcement in reducing the above stresses is usually only slight and it is far simpler (and this gives extra safety) to ignore its effect. For those interested in considering such reinforcement, see references (28), (29), and (27).

To *reinforce against torsion*, the most effective method according to tests is by the use of *helical binding*. This is very impractical and is rarely used in Britain. Apart from the obvious practical disadvantages, there is also the difficulty caused in detailing at points of contra-torsion (where the direction of torsion reverses), i.e. in changing the direction of the helices at such points. If the torque is too great to be resisted by vertical stirrups (see below)—this is not good practice, as mentioned earlier—helices can be considered.[27,29,30]

Torsion often occurs in conjunction with bending moments and shearing forces. Stirrups can be provided to resist both torques and shearing forces, both of these causing shearing stresses which are additive. Bending moments have some influence on the resistance to torsion but may be ignored as most tests indicate that bending moments slightly increase torsional resistances.[30]

Vertical stirrups are the most practical way of resisting torsion, and are designed as follows: (a) determine q_T from equation (5.61), (b) add q_T to the maximum shear stress due to the shearing force from equation (5,19) and this total must not exceed $3p_{cs}$, (c) deduct from this total the permissible shear stress (i.e. diagonal tensile stress) of the concrete, and the remainder is designed to be resisted by stirrups using the method described in §5.3. For these purposes p_{cs} can be assumed to be $0.03f_c' = 0.0252u_w$, (say), and must not be greater than 90 lb/sq. in. Designs on this basis sometimes give fewer stirrups for torsion and shear, than is required by the British Code of Practice for shear only. In these circumstances, in Britain, the greater of the two amounts should be taken, although the smaller amount would actually be satisfactory and would probably be acceptable in the U.S.A. This difference occurs because of the very conservative design of shear reinforcement recommended by the British Code of Practice.

Alternatively to the above design, bent-up bars can carry some or all of the shearing force, the remaining shear stress, after deduction of the effect of the bent-up bars from (c) above, being resisted by stirrups. It is felt however that when torsion is present, as much torsion and shearing force should be taken on stirrups as possible.

Longitudinal reinforcement, as mentioned earlier, is only slightly effective in resisting torsion; little is lost and a lot gained in simplicity by ignoring its effect. For those interested, it resists torsion by reducing the value of q_T in equation (5,61) as explained in references (28) and (29). If, however, longitudinal reinforcement is ignored for resisting torsion, a nominal amount must still be used to anchor the corners of the stirrups, say a minimum of one $\frac{1}{2}$ in. diameter bar at each corner of a stirrup. Indeed, Turner and Davis[23] do not consider stirrups to be effective in resisting torsion without such longitudinal reinforcement.

Rectangular sections cracked in bending

The design is the same as described above except that the uncracked area only is considered in the computation of q_T in equation (5,61), i.e. D is taken as n (see Fig. 11) or $1 \cdot 5b$, whichever is the least. This value of q_T is assumed to occur at the neutral axis and it is added to the shearing stress due to the shearing force as in (b) above. This is an empirical and conservative, if not logical, procedure.

T- and L- sections cracked in bending

According to Baker[31] the contribution of the slab portion to the torsional resistance is negligible. For simplicity, such beams can therefore be treated as rectangular. The slight increase in the torsional resistance due to the slab portions of T- and L-beams can be determined from the work by Turner and Davis,[32] reported by Reynolds.[15]

EXAMPLE 5.9.1

Suppose in Example (5.3.1) that the section subjected to the maximum shear stress of 111 lb/sq. in. is also required to resist a torque of 10,000 lb in. Design suitable reinforcement for torsion and shear.

From Example (5.3.1) (and Example (2.2.1) which refers to the same member), $n = 8 \cdot 6$ in., $a = 15 \cdot 13$ in., $b = 6$ in., $c = 1,281$ lb/sq. in., and $p_{st} = 20,000$ lb/sq. in.

Now $n = 8 \cdot 6$ in. and $1 \cdot 5b = 9$ in.; hence applying equation (5,61),

$$q_T = \left(3 + \frac{2 \cdot 6}{0 \cdot 45 + \dfrac{8 \cdot 6}{6}}\right) \frac{10,000}{8 \cdot 6 \times 6^2} = 141 \cdot 4 \text{ lb/sq. in.}$$

Also $u_w = 3 \times 1,281 = 3,843$ lb/sq. in.

$\therefore \quad p_{cs} = 0 \cdot 0252 \times 3,843 = 96 \cdot 8$ lb/sq. in.

which is greater than 90. Hence use $p_{cs} = 90$ lb/sq. in.

Using vertical stirrups as reinforcement, the stirrups need to resist a shear stress of

$$(141 \cdot 4 + 111) - 90 = 162 \cdot 4 \text{ lb/sq. in.}$$

This is satisfactory as it is less than $3 \times 90 = 270$ lb/sq. in.

Equating this to $\dfrac{F}{ab}$ [see equation (5,19)],

$$\frac{F}{6a} = 162\cdot4$$

$$\therefore \quad \frac{F}{a} = 162\cdot4 \times 6 = 974\cdot4$$

From equation (5,35),

$$P = 974\cdot4S$$

Using $\tfrac{3}{8}$ in. diameter (2 arm) stirrups,

$$P = 2 \times \frac{\pi}{4} \times (\tfrac{3}{8})^2 \times 20,000 = 4,420 \text{ lb}$$

$$\therefore \quad 4,420 = 974\cdot4S$$

$$\therefore \quad S = 4\cdot53 \text{ in., } \quad \text{say } 4\tfrac{1}{2} \text{ in.}$$

EXAMPLE 5.9.2

Repeat Example (5.9.1) using a torque of 20,000 lb in. in lieu of 10,000 lb in.

$$q_T = 2 \times 141\cdot4 = 282\cdot8 \text{ lb/sq. in.}$$

Shear stress to be resisted by reinforcement

$$= (282\cdot8 + 111) - 90 = 303\cdot8 \text{ lb/sq. in.}$$

Similarly to above,

$$S = 4\cdot53 \times \frac{162\cdot4}{303\cdot8} = 2\cdot422 \text{ in.}$$

This is rather close for the stirrups; suppose also it is not desired to make S less than 3 in. The resistance contributed by the concrete, namely 90 lb/sq. ft, can be proportioned between the torsion and the shear, thus:

Torsional shear stress to be resisted

$$= 282\cdot8 - \frac{90 \times 282\cdot8}{(282\cdot8 + 111)}$$

$$= 218\cdot2 \text{ lb/sq. in.}$$

Shear stress (due to shearing force) to be resisted

$$= 111 - \frac{90 \times 111}{(282\cdot8 + 111)} = 85\cdot6 \text{ lb/sq. in.}$$

Not more than this latter amount is to be resisted by bent-up bars. If $\frac{3}{8}$ in. diameter vertical stirrups at 3 in. centres are to be used, $P = 4,420$, $S = 3$ in., then from equation (5,35),

$$4,420 = \frac{3F}{a}$$

$$\therefore \quad \frac{F}{a} = 1,473$$

$$\therefore \quad \frac{F}{ab} = \frac{1,473}{6} = 245\cdot5 \text{ lb/sq. in.}$$

This is greater than 218·2; hence at least all the torsion is taken by stirrups, which is to be recommended. The shear stress to be resisted by bent-up bars is

$$303\cdot8 - 245\cdot5 = 58\cdot3 \text{ lb/sq. in. } \left(= \frac{F}{ab} \right)$$

Therefore shear force to be resisted by the bent-up bars

$$= 58\cdot3 \times 15\cdot13 \times 6 = 5,290 \text{ lb}$$

Referring to Example (2.2.1) there are only two 1 in. diameter bars as tension reinforcement. Suppose these are replaced by four $\frac{3}{4}$ in. diameter bars, say in two layers, the centroid of area of these bars having the same effective depth as the 1 in. diameter bars, the overall depth of the beam will then be slightly greater. If the $\frac{3}{4}$ in. diameter bars are bent-up at 45°, single system, then the shear strength of this system is given by equation (5,43) as

$$\frac{\pi}{4} \times \left(\frac{3}{4} \right)^2 \times 20,000 \sin 45° = 6,240 \text{ lb}$$

which is satisfactory as it is greater than 5,290 lb.

CHAPTER 6

PRESTRESSED REINFORCED CONCRETE

6.1 Prestressing

Prestressing consists of initially applying loads to a member to counteract the effects of the working loads to which it will eventually be subjected. Concrete is relatively weak in tension compared with compression, so the prestressing forces are used to compress zones which will subsequently be required to carry tension. Prestressing forces are usually applied in one of the following ways:

(a) Stretching wires, cables or bars on a bed, concreting the member around such wires, and then releasing the wires when the concrete is sufficiently hard. When the wires are released, they shorten, and compress the concrete member, the line of action of such compression being the profile of the wire in the beam. This procedure is known as *pretensioning*.

(b) A member is concreted and a duct is formed in the member either with an inflatable tube (e.g. Ductube) or with a metal sheath (e.g. Kopex tubing). A *tendon*, consisting of either a bar (e.g. Lee McCall bar), cable (Strand) or groups of wires (Freyssinet and Gifford-Udall systems), is threaded through the duct and tensioned, when the concrete is sufficiently hard, and anchored to the concrete member, so that the concrete member is compressed by this tendon. This procedure is known as *post-tensioning*, and it is usual to subsequently fill the duct surrounding the cable with grout. A neat cement grout with or without a plasticizer is a reliable material for this purpose.

(c) A variation on method (b) is to place the tendon in the sheath before concreting. It is usually easier to thread the tendon in the sheath before concreting than in the duct after concreting. This does not, of course, allow inflatable tubes to be used for forming the duct. The latter method appears to be cheaper from the point of view of forming the duct but on the whole, in Britain, when the extra cost of positioning the inflatable tubes and threading the ducts they form is considered, it is usually more economical to place the tendon in the expendable tubing before casting.

(d) Another variation on (b) is to make the concrete member in precast portions which are placed together on the site, the joints between such members being dry packed with cement: sand mortar usually after the tendons have been threaded through the blocks. This is a very useful and economical method in certain instances.

(e) Prestressing forces can be exerted on structures in suitable places by jacks. Hydraulic jacks are often used (e.g. Fressi jacks) and maintenance personnel need to check the pressures in the jacks regularly. Such methods are not normally applied to normal sized building members, but are applied to very large structures, chiefly dams.

6.2   Advantages and disadvantages of prestressing

The chief advantages of prestressed concrete are in reducing the quantities of steel and concrete required and in eliminating cracks. The disadvantages are the extra labour costs connected with the stressing of the tendons, and with other items.

Prestressing strengthens a beam in shear and this shows a great saving in shear reinforcement especially in view of the heavy shear reinforcement required by the British Code of Practice. Wilby has on occasions prestressed jointed precast structures solely because of the weakness of the joints in shear.

It would seem that the greater the cost of labour relative to steel and concrete materials, the less economical is prestressed concrete. For example, prestressed concrete is more economical on the Continent than in Britain and the U.S.A. In Britain, if a member can be equally well constructed in prestressed or ordinary reinforced concrete, then the latter is usually more economical. When however large spans are required with shallow depths, e.g. for bridges, precast floors and so on, and the ordinary reinforced concrete is structurally unacceptable, then prestressed concrete is the only answer in concrete, and, if there is a reasonable repetition in the making of members (to reduce shuttering costs), it is, in Britain, sometimes more economical than structural steelwork. When the spans for bridges are sufficiently short to make prestressing cheaper than steelwork, the prestressed concrete has the great advantages over steelwork in relative freedom from maintenance, and in fire resistance.

Prestressed concrete construction is often more expensive to design than ordinary concrete. In post-tensioned *in-situ* structures, prestressing procedures have to be carefully planned so that tensioning one cable does not make previously tensioned cables deficient in stress and also does not cause undesirable stresses to develop due to the eccentricity of the prestressing force; this eccentricity will be eliminated when the prestressing is satisfactorily completed. Sometimes this involves larger amounts of structures to be shuttered or alternatively supported before prestressing, than would be necessary if the structure were of ordinary reinforced concrete. In such circumstances prestressing sometimes slows down the speed of construction and increases the shuttering required for a contract. Members designed with prestressed concrete can be very flexible and the designer must be careful that deflections, cambers and flexibilities are satisfactory, as some of these factors can be the criterion as regards design.

It is conceivable even to pay more for prestressed concrete structures than for ordinary reinforced concrete structures when resistance to corrosion is important; the life of the prestressed structure will be greater because of the absence of cracks. Such structures as docks, wharfs and jettys which are exposed to sea water, exposed structures at gas works, bridges over railways, dairies, are common examples of concrete structures exposed to very corrosive elements.

6.3 Losses of prestress

The stress initially effected in the tendons is reduced by the following *losses*:

(a) *Strain in Concrete:* When pretensioned wires are released they compress the concrete; the concrete strains, thus reducing the strain and hence the stress in the wires. This is known as the *loss of prestress due to strain.* A post-tensioned member with only one tendon does not experience a strain loss, as the jack compresses the concrete as it strains the tendon. When more than one tendon is used, then as each tendon is strained the jack increases the strain in the concrete; this reduces the strain in the tendons already anchored; i.e. strain losses occur in all but the last tendon to be stressed. All these losses are less than those experienced with pretensioned concrete. The British Code of Practice[33] recommends that for calculating strain losses Young's Modulus for steel should be assumed to be 28×10^6 lb/sq. in., and for the concrete the value given in Table 4 of the Code should be assumed. For pretensioning, the loss of stress in a tendon should be taken as the product of the modular ratio and the stress in the concrete adjacent to the tendon. For post-tensioning, with several tendons, the resulting loss of stress can be taken as half this amount.

(b) *Creep in Concrete: Creep* has already been explained and formulae given for estimating its effect, in §1.10. As the concrete creeps it reduces the strain and hence the stress in the prestressing tendons. With prestressed concrete, creep is not under a constant stress, as considered in §1.10, because the stress in the concrete is reducing as the concrete creeps. The creep loss may be estimated by reference to the Code of Practice.[33] The loss is greater for pretensioned than for post-tensioned members. Pretensioned tendons rely upon their bond to the concrete for anchorage and in time this releases slightly; this is not counted as a separate loss,[33] so it is accounted for as an increase in creep loss.

(c) *Shrinkage of Concrete:* Shrinkage is discussed in §1.10. As concrete shrinks after the tendons have been anchored to the concrete, the concrete member shortens and hence so does the tendon, thus releasing some stress in the tendon. In the case of pretensioned concrete, the shrinkage effect begins as soon as the concrete is cast, but with post-tensioned concrete the concrete is able to shrink prior to the tendon being stressed. If there were no longitudinal reinforcement the shrinkage would be restricted only by friction with moulds, etc. and the majority of the shrinkage would occur before stressing. Longitudinal reinforcement interferes with this process to some extent. Humidity and temperature also affect shrinkage. For practical design the Code[33] gives suitable recommendations for calculating the loss of prestress due to shrinkage of the concrete.

(d) *Creep of Steel:* The high stresses used in the tendons mean that the steel is often stressed slightly beyond its limit of proportionality. Hence, after anchorage to the concrete, the strain in the steel can increase slightly due to creep thus reducing the stress in the prestressed concrete. With pretensioned members, this loss can be greatly reduced by tensioning say in the afternoon and then suitably increasing the strain of the tendons the next morning before casting. This is an operation which interferes with progress and increases labour costs, and judging the overall economy, it is usually better not to try to eliminate creep but to consider it as a loss in prestress. This can be estimated from reference.[33]

(e) *Slip of Anchorage:* This refers to the tendons losing stress after anchorage due to the anchorage device slipping; e.g. wedges are pulled forward in their jaws as the stress is taken up by the anchorage. This should be assessed for the particular system used. For prestressing over short distances it is preferable that this allowance should be as small as possible, as the greater the allowance the greater the probable error in the reliability of this quantity. For this reason Wilby[34] has found Lee-McCall bars useful for prestressing over short lengths; the relative movement between the nuts and threads of this system causes only very little loss of stress.

6.4. Design of members

Members are designed elastically to have no cracks at working loads. They are also designed to have a reasonable load factor against failure. An alternative not often employed is to design with a suitable load factor against failure and to allow limited cracking at working loads. This is a most economical method for structures which rarely experience their full design load, or structures where corrosion is not important. Although this latter method is not often professed to be used by engineers, it is often used in effect when the concrete is theoretically allowed to withstand very high flexural tensile stresses at working loads, i.e. stresses of a magnitude that could not possibly be carried reliably by the concrete without cracking.

6.5 Assumption for elastic design

Of the following assumptions, (a) to (d) are the same as those described in §1.13:

(a) Plane sections subjected to bending remain plane after bending.
(b) Stress is proportional to strain for both the steel and the concrete.
(c) Perfect bond is assumed between the steel and the concrete. In the case of post-tensioning this theoretically applies after the tendon has been grouted (see later).
(d) Depth of reinforcements relative to the depth of the concrete member is considered to be negligible.
(e) Allowances must be made for shrinkage and creep losses, see §5.4.
(f) Young's Modulus for concrete is the same in tension as compression; this is reasonably true.

6.6 Elastic design of a doubly prestressed beam

The beam considered is shown in Fig. 34 and is symmetrical about its vertical axis. Prior to the member straining it can be considered as being loaded by prestressing forces $(P_T - p_T)$ and $(P_B - p_B)$. When considering the stresses caused by $(P_T - p_T)$, this tendon (consisting of five wires in the particular case shown in Fig. 34) is acting as a force, and its cross-sectional area is not included in the equivalent concrete section considered. The top fibre concrete stress due to this longitudinal eccentric load is thus,

$$\frac{(P_T - p_T)}{A_T} + \frac{(P_T - p_T) e_T}{I_{TR}} \cdot n_{TR} \qquad \ldots (6,1)$$

When considering the stresses caused by $(P_B - p_B)$, the tendon is acting as a force, and its cross-sectional area is not included in the equivalent concrete section considered. The top fibre concrete stress due to this longitudinal eccentric load is thus,

$$\frac{(P_B - p_B)}{A_B} - \frac{(P_B - p_B) e_B}{I_{BR}} \cdot n_{BR} \qquad \ldots (6,2)$$

Hence from equations (6,1) and (6,2),

$$f_T = \frac{(P_T - p_T)}{A_T} + \frac{(P_T - p_T)e_T}{I_{TR}} \cdot n_{TR} + \frac{(P_B - p_B)}{A_B}$$
$$- \frac{(P_B - p_B)e_B}{I_{BR}} \cdot n_{BR} \qquad \ldots(6,3)$$

similarly,

$$f_B = \frac{(P_B - p_B)}{A_B} + \frac{(P_B - p_B)e_B}{I_{BR}} \cdot (D - n_{BR}) + \frac{(P_T - p_T)}{A_T}$$
$$- \frac{(P_T - p_T)e_T}{I_{TR}} \cdot (D - n_{TR}) \qquad \ldots(6,4)$$

The stresses adjacent to the tendons are required so as to estimate the strain loss, see §6.3(a), according to the Code of Practice.[33] Some designers also use these stress values for the estimation of losses due to creep, see §6.3(b). The stress in the concrete at the level of the top steel (by simple proportions) is equal to,

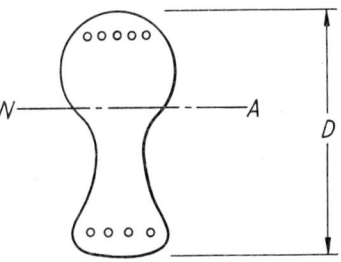

Fig. 34.

$$f_T \cdot \frac{(n_{TR} - z_1)}{n_{TR}} \qquad \ldots(6,5)$$

With the British Code of Practice, where this is related to the strain loss, the loss of strain in the top steel can be equated to the gain of strain in the adjacent concrete; thus,

$$\frac{p_T'}{E_s \cdot A_T'} = f_T \cdot \frac{(n_{TR} - z_1)}{E_c \cdot n_{TR}}$$
$$\therefore \quad p_T' = mf_T A_T' \cdot \frac{e_T}{n_{TR}} \qquad \ldots(6,6)$$

Similarly for the bottom reinforcement,

$$p_B' = mf_B A_B' \cdot \frac{e_B}{(D - n_{BR})} \qquad \ldots(6,7)$$

Now p_T and p_B in equations (6,3) and (6,4) are dependent on p_B' and p_T'; and p_T' and p_B' in equations (6,6) and (6,7) are dependent on f_T and f_B from equations (6,3) and (6,4). To obtain p_T' eliminate f_T between equations (6,3) and (6,6):

$$\frac{p_T' n_{TR}}{m A_T' e_T} = (P_T - p_T)Z_T + K_B \qquad \ldots(6,8)$$

where
$$Z_T = \frac{1}{A_T} + \frac{e_T n_{TR}}{I_{TR}} \qquad \dots (6,9)$$

and
$$K_B = \frac{(P_B - p_B)}{A_B} - \frac{(P_B - p_B) e_B n_{BR}}{I_{BR}} \qquad \dots (6,10)$$

now,
$$(P_T - p_T) = P_T - (p_T' + p_T'' + p_T''') = (P_T - p_T'' - p_T''') - p_T'$$
$$= P_T' - p_T' \qquad \dots (6,11)$$

$\therefore$ from equations (6,8) and (6,11),
$$\frac{p_T' n_{TR}}{m A_T' e_T} = (P_T' - p_T')Z_T + K_B$$

$$\therefore \quad p_T' = \frac{P_T' Z_T + K_B}{(n_{TR}/m A_T' e_T + Z_T)} \qquad \dots (6,12)$$

Similarly,
$$p_B' = \frac{p_B' Z_B + K_T}{[(D - n_{BR})/(m A_B' e_B)] + Z_B} \qquad \dots (6,13)$$

where,
$$Z_B = \frac{1}{A_B} + \frac{e_B(D - n_{BR})}{I_{BR}} \qquad \dots (6,14)$$

and
$$K_T = \frac{(P_T - p_T)}{A_T} - \frac{(P_T - p_T) e_T(D - n_{TR})}{I_{TR}} \qquad \dots (6,15)$$

Now let,
$$K_B = (P_B - p_B)Z_B' \qquad \dots (6,16)$$

and,
$$K_T = (P_T - p_T)Z_T' \qquad \dots (6,17)$$

$\therefore$ from equation (6,11),
$$K_T = (P_T' - p_T')Z_T' \qquad \dots (6,18)$$

and similarly,
$$K_B = (P_B' - p_B')Z_B' \qquad \dots (6,19)$$

Substituting for K_B from equation (6,18) in equation (6,12),
$$p_T'\left[\frac{n_{TR}}{m A_T' e_T} + Z_T\right] + p_B' Z_B' = P_T' Z_T + P_B' Z_B' \qquad \dots (6,20)$$

Substituting for K_T from equation (6,19) in equation (6,13),
$$p_B'\left[\frac{D - n_{BR}}{m A_B' e_B} + Z_B\right] + p_T' Z_T' = P_B' Z_B + P_T' Z_T' \qquad \dots (6,21)$$

equations (6,20) and (6,21) are two simultaneous equations which can be solved for p_T' and p_B'. For a given section the procedure is to determine all the losses and then to determine the stresses f_T and f_B from equations (6,3) and (6,4) which can be expressed as,

$$f_T = (P_T - p_T)Z_T + K_B \qquad \dots (6,22)$$

and
$$f_B = (P_B - p_B)Z_B + K_T \qquad \dots (6,23)$$

Then the stresses due to the self weight and the external loading can be determined by dividing the bending moment by the respective section moduli for the top and bottom fibres of the beam; these stresses are

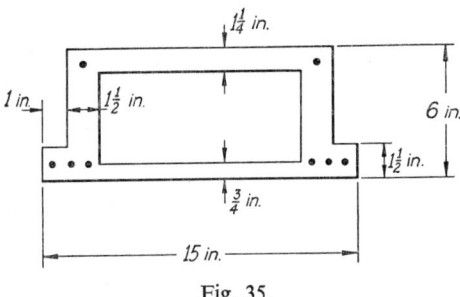

Fig. 35.

then superimposed on the prestresses f_T and f_B. The section moduli are computed for an effective area which includes the equivalent areas of the top and bottom tendons.

EXAMPLE 6.6.1

A precast concrete floor unit is essentially of the cross-section shown in Fig. 35. It is pretensioned with 0·2 in. dia. wires, two in the top and six in the bottom. Determine the top and bottom extreme fibre stresses and suggest a suitable uniformly distributed loading for it to carry over a simply supported span of 18 ft, given the following data:

70 % of tensile strength of wires = 70 ton/sq. in.

$z_1 = 0·625$ in., $z_2 = 0·75$ in.

Minimum concrete cube strength at transfer = 4,000 lb/sq. in.

Works cube strength = 6,000 lb/sq. in. at 28 days.

Young's Modulus for the wires = 28×10^6 lb/sq. in.

At transfer, i.e. release of the wires, according to reference,[33] the permissible compressive stress (in bending) $= \dfrac{4,000}{2} = 2,000$ lb/sq. in. and Young's Modulus for the concrete $= 4 \times 10^6$ lb/sq. in., i.e. $m = \dfrac{28 \times 10^6}{4 \times 10^6} = 7$. The calculations for A_T, n_{TR}, e_T and I_{TR} are made in Table 12, and then, $A_T = 42·07$ sq. in.

$$n_{TR} = \frac{125·63}{42·07} = 2·98 \text{ in.}$$

$$e_T = 2·98 - 0·63 = 2·35 \text{ in.}$$

$$I_{TR} = 574·4 - 42·07 \times 2·98^2 = 574·4 - 374 = 200 \text{ in.}^4$$

TABLE 12

Portion	Area	A	x	Ax	Ax^2	I_G
Gross concrete	78	78	3	234	702·0	$\dfrac{78 \times 6^2}{12} = 234$
Hollow	−40	−40	3·25	−130	−422·5	$-\dfrac{40 \times 4^2}{12} = -53·33$
Nibs	3	3	5·25	15·75	82·6	$\dfrac{3 \times 1·5^2}{12} = 0·5625$
Holes (top steel)	−0·0628	−0·0628	0·625	−0·0392	−0·0245	—
Bottom steel	0·188	1·128	5·25	5·92	31·1	—
		42·07		125·63	393·2	181·23 → 393·2
						574·4

The calculations for A_B, n_{BR}, e_B and I_{BR} are made in Table 13, and then

$$A_B = 41 \cdot 19 \text{ sq. in.}$$

$$n_{BR} = \frac{119 \cdot 0}{41 \cdot 19} = 2 \cdot 886 \text{ in.}$$

$$e_B = 6 - 2 \cdot 886 - 0 \cdot 75 = 2 \cdot 364 \text{ in.}$$

$$I_{BR} = 538 \cdot 2 - 41 \cdot 19 \times 2 \cdot 886^2 = 538 \cdot 2 - 343 = 195 \cdot 2 \text{ in.}^4$$

From equation (6,9),

$$Z_T = \frac{1}{42 \cdot 07} + \frac{2 \cdot 35 \times 2 \cdot 98}{200} = 0 \cdot 05873 \text{ in.}^{-2}$$

From equation (6,14),

$$Z_B = \frac{1}{41 \cdot 19} + \frac{2 \cdot 364 \times (6 - 2 \cdot 886)}{195 \cdot 2} = 0 \cdot 06205 \text{ in.}^{-2}$$

From equations (6,10) and (6,16),

$$Z_B' = \frac{1}{41 \cdot 19} - \frac{2 \cdot 364 \times 2 \cdot 886}{195 \cdot 2} = 0 \cdot 0108 \text{ in.}^{-2}$$

From equations (6,15) and (6,17),

$$Z_T' = \frac{1}{42 \cdot 07} - \frac{2 \cdot 35 \times (6 - 2 \cdot 98)}{200} = 0 \cdot 01175 \text{ in.}^{-2}$$

Now, $P_T' = P_T - p_T'' - p_T'''$, and referring to the Code,[33]

$$P_T = 0 \cdot 0628 \times 70 \times 2,240 = 9,860 \text{ lb}$$
$$p_T'' = 300 \times 10^{-6} \times (28 \times 10^6) \times 0 \cdot 0628 = 527 \cdot 8 \text{ lb}$$
$$p_T''' = 0, \text{ immediately after transfer}$$
$$\therefore \quad P_T' = 9,860 - 527 \cdot 8 - 0 = 9,332 \text{ lb}$$
$$P_B = 0 \cdot 188 \times 70 \times 2,240 = 29,500 \text{ lb}$$
$$p_B'' = 300 \times 10^{-6} \times (28 \times 10^6) \times 0 \cdot 188 = 1,579 \cdot 2 \text{ lb}$$
$$p_B''' = 0, \text{ immediately after transfer}$$
$$\therefore \quad P_B' = 29,500 - 1,579 \cdot 2 - 0 = 27,920 \text{ lb}$$

Substituting the above in equations (6,20) and (6,21),

$$p_T'\left[\frac{2 \cdot 98}{7 \times 0 \cdot 0628 \times 2 \cdot 35} + 0 \cdot 05873\right] + p_B'(-0 \cdot 0108)$$
$$= 9,332 \times 0 \cdot 05873 + 27,920 \times (-0 \cdot 0108)$$
$$\therefore \quad 2 \cdot 939 p_T' - 0 \cdot 0108 p_B' = 246 \qquad \dots(6,24)$$

$$p_B'\left[\frac{6 - 2 \cdot 886}{7 \times 0 \cdot 188 \times 2 \cdot 364} + 0 \cdot 06205\right] + p_T'(-0 \cdot 01175)$$
$$= 27,920 \times 0 \cdot 06205 + 9,332 \times (-0 \cdot 01175)$$
$$\therefore \quad 1 \cdot 061 p_B' - 0 \cdot 01175 p_T' = 1,620 \qquad \dots(6,25)$$

Solving equations (6,24) and (6,25),

$$p_T{}' = 89 \cdot 3 \text{ lb and } p_B{}' = 1,525 \text{ lb}$$

From equation (6,11),

$$P_T - p_T = 9,332 - 89 \cdot 3 = 9,243 \text{ lb}$$

Similarly,

$$P_B - p_B = 27,920 - 1,525 = 26,395 \text{ lb}$$

From equations (6,22) and (6,16),

$$f_T = 9,243 \times 0 \cdot 05873 + 26,395 \times (-0 \cdot 0108) = 258 \text{ lb/sq. in.}$$

From equations (6,23) and (6,17),

$$f_B = 26,395 \times 0 \cdot 06205 + 9,243 \times (-0 \cdot 01175) = 1,531 \text{ lb/sq. in.}$$

These stresses, shown in Fig. 36(i), are imposed immediately after release of the wires, i.e. before any creep has taken place. Upon release

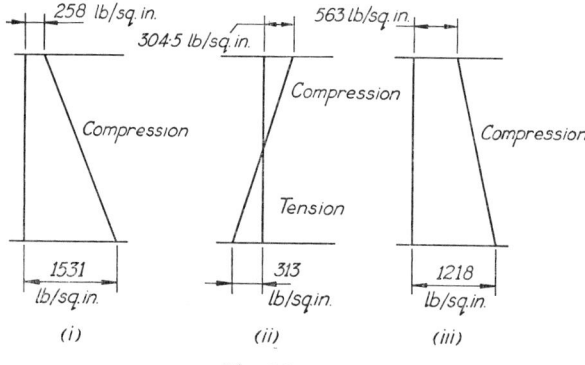

Fig. 36.

of the wires however the hollow beam will bow upwards due to the pre-stressing forces, hence the self weight of the beam will resist this upward movement. Also, the bending stresses due to the self weight should be superimposed upon the above prestresses to determine the resultant stresses immediately after prestressing. As no creep has taken place the calculation for determining the bending stresses due to the self weight should use a modular ratio of 7, as above. After creep has taken place this latter calculation should use a modular ratio of say 15, and the above calculations for f_T and f_B should be modified to allow for the values of $p_T{}'''$ and $p_B{}'''$. When the superimposed load is applied, initially a value of $m = 7$ should be used in the calculation of stresses, and then a value of $m = 15$ would apply when all the creep had taken place. All this makes the calculations unduly long, and sometimes this is necessary.

TABLE 13

Portion	Area	A	x	Ax	Ax^2	I_G
Gross concrete	78	78	3	234	702	234
Hollow	−40	−40	3·25	−130	−422·5	−53·33
Nibs	3	3	5·25	15·75	82·6	0·5625
Top steel	0·0628	0·377	0·625	0·236	0·1477	—
Holes (bottom steel)	−0·188	−0·188	5·25	−0·987	−5·19	—
		41·19		119·0	357·0	181·23 → 357·0
						538·2

TABLE 14

Portion	Area	A	x	Ax	Ax^2	I_G
Gross concrete	78	78	3	234	702	234
Hollow	−40	−40	3·25	−130	−422·5	−53·33
Nibs	3	3	5·25	15·75	82·6	0·56
Top steel	0·0628	0·377	0·625	0·236	0·147	—
Bottom steel	0·188	1·129	5·25	5·93	31·2	—
		42·51		125·9	393·4	181·23 → 393·4
						574·6

However, the work can often be shortened by calculating only the following:

(a) the resultant stresses due to prestressing and the self weight of the beam before creep occurs. This can usually be relied upon to give the maximum stresses experienced after release of the wires and before subsequent loading and creep take place.
(b) the resultant stresses due to prestressing, the self weight, and the superimposed loading, after creep has taken place.

In the present example, considering the self weight of the beam, Table 14 shows the calculations using $m = 7$,

$$n = \frac{125 \cdot 9}{42 \cdot 51} = 2 \cdot 96 \text{ in.}$$

$$I = 574 \cdot 6 - 42 \cdot 51 \times 2 \cdot 96^2 = 201 \cdot 6 \text{ in.}^4$$

Now the bending moment due to the self weight of the beam is,

$$(78 - 40 + 3) \times \frac{150}{144} \times \frac{18^2}{8} \text{ lb ft} = 20{,}760 \text{ lb in.}$$

Top fibre stress due to this bending moment,

$$= 20{,}760 \times \frac{2 \cdot 96}{201 \cdot 6} = 304 \cdot 5 \text{ lb/sq. in.}$$

and the corresponding bottom fibre stress,

$$= 20{,}760 \times \frac{(6 - 2 \cdot 96)}{201 \cdot 6} = 313 \text{ lb/sq. in.}$$

These stresses are shown in Fig. 36(ii). Upon release these occur simultaneously with the stresses of Fig. 36(i). Adding the stresses of Figs. 36(i) and (ii) algebraically gives the stresses shown in Fig. 36(iii). These are the stresses as described in (a) above, and are satisfactory[33] because 1,218 is less than $0 \cdot 5 \times 4{,}000$ and there is no tension developed in the top of the beam; i.e. the permissible tensile stress is not exceeded.

When the full creep is realized the precise method of determining p_T''' and p_B''' is to relate these losses to the accurate stresses due to prestressing at the locations of the respective reinforcements. Strictly speaking these will modify very slightly the above values of p_T' and p_B'. Using equation (6,5), and in accordance with the Code,

$$p_T''' = \left\{ 0 \cdot 33 \times 10^{-6} \times \frac{6{,}000}{4{,}000} \right\} \times \left\{ f_T \frac{(n_{TR} - z_1)}{n_{TR}} \right\} \times E_s \times A_T' \quad (6,26)$$

Similarly,

$$p_B''' = \left\{ 0 \cdot 33 \times 10^{-6} \times \frac{6{,}000}{4{,}000} \right\} \times \left\{ \frac{f_B e_B}{(D - n_{BR})} \right\} \times E_s \times A_B' \quad \ldots (6,27)$$

11

Now between the six basic equations (6,3), (6,4), (6,6), (6,7), (6,26) and (6,27) there are six unknowns, namely, $f_T, f_B, p_T', p_B', p_T'''$ and p_B'''. These quantities can therefore be determined. The process is long and not usually necessary. For the purpose of this present example, for simplicity, the creep loss will be based on the stresses obtained [see Fig. 36(i)] ignoring creep. The stress, from Fig. 36(i), at the level of the top steel

$$= 258 + (1{,}531 - 258) \times \frac{0{\cdot}625}{6} = 390{\cdot}6 \text{ lb/sq. in.}$$

$$\therefore \quad p_T''' = \left\{0{\cdot}33 \times 10^{-6} \times \frac{6{,}000}{4{,}000}\right\} \times 390{\cdot}6 \times (28 \times 10^6) \times 0{\cdot}0628$$

$$= 344 \text{ lb}$$

Similarly the stress, from Fig. 33(i), at the level of the bottom steel

$$= 258 + (1{,}531 - 258) \times \frac{(6 - 0{\cdot}75)}{6} = 1{,}371 \text{ lb/sq. in., and}$$

$$\therefore \quad p_B''' = \left\{0{\cdot}33 \times 10^{-6} \times \frac{6{,}000}{4{,}000}\right\} \times 1{,}371 \times (28 \times 10^6) \times 0{\cdot}188$$

$$= 3{,}617 \text{ lb.}$$

These creep losses can be used in lieu of the previous values of zero, to determine, similarly as before, slightly different values of the strain losses; f_T and f_B are then determined from equation (6,22) and (6,23). It is simpler and sacrifices little accuracy to assume that the strain losses are as previously calculated.

$$\therefore \quad p_T = 89{\cdot}3 + 527{\cdot}8 + 344 = 961{\cdot}1 \text{ lb}$$

and $\qquad p_B = 1{,}525 + 1{,}579{\cdot}2 + 3{,}617 = 6{,}721 \text{ lb}$

$$\therefore \quad P_T - p_T = 9{,}860 - 961 = 8{,}899 \text{ lb}$$

and $\qquad P_B - p_B = 29{,}500 - 6{,}721 = 22{,}779 \text{ lb}$

Substituting these values in equations (6,22) and (6,23),

$$f_T = 8{,}899 \times 0{\cdot}05873 + 22{,}779 \times (-0{\cdot}0108) = 277 \text{ lb/sq. in.}$$

$$f_B = 22{,}779 \times 0{\cdot}06205 + 8{,}899 \times (-0{\cdot}01175) = 1{,}308 \text{ lb/sq. in.}$$

These are represented in Fig. 37(i). The stresses due to the self weight and superimposed loading (i.e. the total loading) after creep has taken place can be calculated assuming $m = 15$; in Table 15 are tabulated the calculations for A, n and I, hence

$$n = \frac{134{\cdot}13}{44{\cdot}51} = 3{\cdot}02 \text{ in.}$$

$$I = 616{\cdot}2 - 44{\cdot}51 \times 3{\cdot}02^2 = 210 \text{ in.}^4$$

TABLE 15

Portion	Area	A	x	Ax	Ax^2	I_G
Gross concrete	78	78	3	234	702	234
Hollow	−40	−40	3·25	−130	−422·5	−53·33
Nibs	3	3	5·25	15·75	82·6	0·56
Top steel	0·0628	0·879	0·625	0·55	0·344	—
Bottom steel	0·188	2·63	5·25	13·83	72·6	—
		44·51		134·13	435·	181·23 → 435
						616·2

Now the total load must be such that at the top fibre the resultant compressive stress[33] does not exceed $0.33 \times 6,000 = 2,000$ lb/sq. in.; and the resultant tensile stress[33] does not exceed 300 lb/sq. in. Hence, due solely to the total load, the top fibre compressive stress must not exceed $2,000 - 277 = 1,723$ lb/sq. in. and the bottom fibre tensile stress must not exceed $300 + 1,308 = 1,608$ lb/sq. in. Using the top fibre as

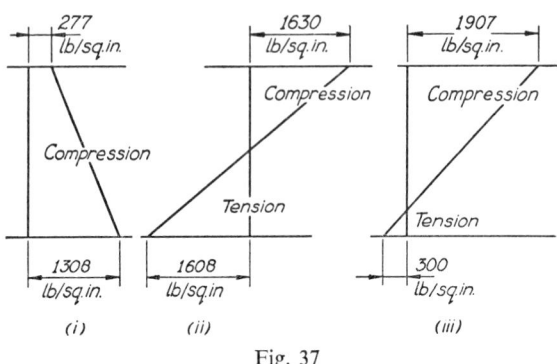

Fig. 37

the criterion, the bending moment due to the total load $= 1,723 \times \dfrac{210}{3 \cdot 02}$

$= 119,800$ lb in., and the corresponding bending moment based on the bottom fibre stress $= 1,608 \times \dfrac{210}{(6 - 3 \cdot 02)} = 113,300$ lb in. Therefore the bending moment due to the total load must not exceed the lesser of these amounts, namely 113,300 lb in. This bending moment causes a bottom fibre tensile stress of 1,608 lb/sq. in. and a top fibre compressive stress of $113,300 \times \dfrac{3 \cdot 02}{210} = 1,630$ lb/sq. in.; these are shown in Fig. 37(ii). The resultant stresses due to the total load and prestressing, i.e. the condition described in (b) above, are shown in Fig. 37(iii); the stresses of Figs. 34(i) and (ii) being algebraically added.

∴ a suitable total uniformly distributed load

$$= \frac{113,300}{12} \times \frac{8}{18^2} = 232 \cdot 6 \text{ lb/ft.}$$

6.7   Simplified elastic design of a doubly prestressed beam

Many designs are of a preliminary nature for estimate purposes, and the schemes are often revised. The method of design now discussed is suitable for such purposes and also for deciding sections for subsequent analysis as in §6.6. For many purposes, the present method can even be used in lieu of the method in §6.6.

The steel reinforcements are ignored in all the calculations for A, n, and I. The losses are firstly taken as percentages of the initial prestressing forces; this enables the concrete stresses due to prestressing to be obtained. The losses are then assessed more accurately from these stresses. The method is illustrated in the following example:

EXAMPLE 6.7.1

Repeat Example (6.6.1) using the simplified method in §6.7.

The calculations for A, n and I are shown in Table 16,

TABLE 16

Portion	A	x	Ax	Ax^2	I_G
Gross concrete	78	3	234	702	234
Hollow	−40	3·25	−130	−422·5	−53·33
Nibs	3	5·25	15·75	82·6	0·563
	41		119·8	362·1	181·2
					→ 362·1
					543·3

$$\therefore \quad n = \frac{119\cdot8}{41} = 2\cdot92 \text{ in.}$$

$$I = 543\cdot3 - 41 \times 2\cdot92^2 = 194 \text{ in.}^4$$

$$P_T = 0\cdot0628 \times 70 \times 2,240 = 9,860 \text{ lb}$$

$$P_B = 0\cdot188 \times 70 \times 2,240 = 29,500 \text{ lb}$$

Assume total loss of prestress (due to strain, creep and shrinkage) to be 13 % (it is usually between 10 and 15 %),

$$\therefore \quad P_T - p_T = 8,580 \text{ lb}$$

and $$P_B - p_B = 25,700 \text{ lb}$$

Considering these as eccentric loads on a plain concrete section,

$$f_T = \frac{8,580 + 25,700}{41} + \frac{8,580(2\cdot92 - 0\cdot625)}{194} \times 2\cdot92$$

$$- \frac{25,700(6 - 2\cdot92 - 0\cdot75)}{194} \times 2\cdot92$$

$$= 837 + 297 - 902 = 232 \text{ lb/sq. in. compression.}$$

and $\quad f_B = 837 - \dfrac{8{,}580(2 \cdot 92 - 0 \cdot 625)}{194} \times (6 - 2 \cdot 92)$

$$+ \frac{25{,}700(6 - 2 \cdot 92 - 0 \cdot 75)}{194} \times (6 - 2 \cdot 92)$$

$$= 837 - 313 + 951 = 1{,}475 \text{ lb/sq. in. compression.}$$

$\therefore$ The stress at the level of the top steel

$$= 232 + (1{,}475 - 232) \times \frac{0 \cdot 625}{6} = 361 \cdot 4 \text{ lb/sq. in.}$$

and the stress at the level of the bottom steel

$$= 232 + (1{,}475 - 232) \times \frac{(6 - 0 \cdot 75)}{6} = 1{,}319 \text{ lb/sq. in.}$$

$\therefore \quad p_T' = 361 \cdot 4 \times m \times A_T' = 361 \cdot 4 \times 7 \times 0 \cdot 0628 = 159 \text{ lb}$

$p_B' = 1{,}319 \times 7 \times 0 \cdot 188 = 1{,}736 \text{ lb}$

then referring to the Code,

$$p_T''' = \left(0 \cdot 33 \times 10^{-6} \times \frac{6{,}000}{4{,}000}\right) \times 361 \cdot 4 \times 28 \times 10^6 \times 0 \cdot 0628 = 318 \text{ lb}$$

$$p_B''' = \left(0 \cdot 33 \times 10^{-6} \times \frac{6{,}000}{4{,}000}\right) \times 1{,}319 \times 28 \times 10^6 \times 0 \cdot 188 = 3{,}473 \text{ lb}$$

Referring to the Code (or to Example (6.6.1)):

$$p_T'' = 300 \times 10^{-6} \times (28 \times 10^6) \times 0 \cdot 0628 = 527 \cdot 8 \text{ lb}$$

$$p_B'' = 300 \times 10^{-6} \times (28 \times 10^6) \times 0 \cdot 188 = 1{,}579 \cdot 2 \text{ lb}$$

$$P_T - p_T' - p_T'' = 9{,}860 - 159 - 528 = 9{,}173 \text{ lb}$$

$$P_B - p_B' - p_B'' = 29{,}500 - 1{,}736 - 1{,}579 = 26{,}185 \text{ lb}$$

Hence the top fibre stress due to prestressing, after the strain and shrinkage losses have occurred but before the creep loss has been realized,

$$= \frac{9{,}173 + 26{,}185}{41} + \frac{9{,}173 \times (2 \cdot 92 - 0 \cdot 625)}{194} \times 2 \cdot 92$$

$$- \frac{26{,}185 \times (6 - 2 \cdot 92 - 0 \cdot 75)}{194} \times 2 \cdot 92$$

$$= 862 + 318 - 920 = 260 \text{ lb/sq. in. (compression)}$$

Similarly the corresponding bottom fibre stress

$$= 862 - \frac{9{,}173 \times (2 \cdot 92 - 0 \cdot 625)}{194} \times (6 - 2 \cdot 92)$$

$$+ \frac{26{,}185 \times (6 - 2 \cdot 92 - 0 \cdot 75)}{194} \times (6 - 2 \cdot 92)$$

$$= 862 - 335 + 970 = 1{,}497 \text{ lb/sq. in. (compression)}.$$

These stresses are shown in Fig. 38(i), [corresponding to those of Fig. 36(i)]. The bending moment due to the self weight of the beam

$$= 41 \times \frac{150}{144} \times \frac{18^2}{8} \text{ lb ft.} = 20{,}760 \text{ lb in.}$$

The top fibre stress due to this bending moment

$$= \frac{20{,}760}{194} \times 2 \cdot 92 = 312 \cdot 4 \text{ lb/sq. in.}$$

and the corresponding bottom fibre stress,

$$= \frac{20{,}760}{194} \times (6 - 2 \cdot 92) = 329 \cdot 5 \text{ lb/sq. in.}$$

These stresses are shown in Fig. 38(ii) [and correspond to those of Fig. 36(ii)]. Upon release, before creep has taken place, the stresses of

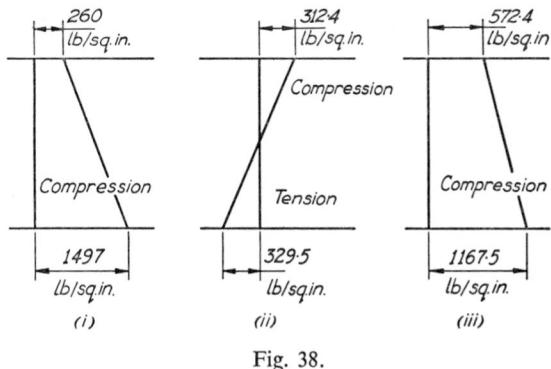

Fig. 38.

Figs. 38(i) and (ii) are algebraically added together, and shown in Fig. 38(iii) [these correspond to the stresses of Fig. 36(iii)]. These are satisfactory[33] because 1,167·5 is less than 0·5 × 4,000 and there is no tension developed in the top of the beam,

$$P_T - p_T = (P_T - p_T' - p_T'') - p_T''' = 9{,}173 - 318 = 8{,}855 \text{ lb}$$
$$P_B - p_B = 26{,}185 - 3{,}473 = 22{,}712 \text{ lb}$$

Hence the top fibre stress due to prestressing, when all losses have been realized,

$$= \frac{8{,}855 + 22{,}712}{41} + 318 \times \frac{8{,}855}{9{,}173} - 920 \times \frac{22{,}712}{26{,}185}$$
$$= 770 + 307 - 798 = 279 \text{ lb/sq. in.}$$

Similarly the corresponding bottom fibre stress,

$$= 770 - 335 \times \frac{8{,}855}{9{,}173} + 970 \times \frac{22{,}712}{26{,}185} = 1{,}287 \text{ lb/sq. in.}$$

These stresses are shown in Fig. 39(i) and correspond to the stresses shown in Fig. 37(i).

Now the total loading must be designed so that at the top fibre the resultant compressive stress[33] does not exceed $0.33 \times 6,000 = 2,000$ lb/sq. in.; i.e. the top fibre compressive stress due to the total loading can be $2,000 - 279 = 1,721$ lb/sq. in., and hence the bending moment due to this load can be $1,721 \times \dfrac{194}{2.92} = 114,300$ lb in. The total loading must also be designed so that at the bottom fibre the resultant tensile

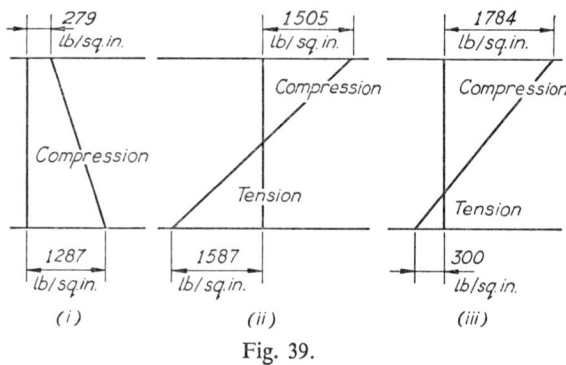

Fig. 39.

stress[33] does not exceed 300 lb/sq. in.; i.e. the bottom fibre stress due to the total loading can be $1,287 + 300 = 1,587$ lb/sq. in., and hence the bending moment due to this loading can be

$$1,587 \times \frac{194}{(6 - 2.92)} = 100,000 \text{ lb in.}$$

Therefore the bending moment due to the total load must not exceed the lesser of the above quantities, namely, 100,000 lb in. This bending moment causes a bottom fibre stress of 1,587 lb/sq. in. and a top fibre stress of $\dfrac{100,000 \times 2.92}{194} = 1,505$ lb/sq. in. These stresses are shown in Fig. 39(ii); this corresponds to Fig. 37(ii). Hence when these stresses are superimposed upon the stresses of Fig. 39(i), the resultant stresses are as shown in Fig. 39(iii); this corresponds to Fig. 37(iii).

$$\therefore \quad \text{the uniformly distributed total load} = \frac{100,000}{12} \times \frac{8}{18^2}$$

$$= 205.5 \text{ lb/ft. run}$$

This answer is more conservative than the 232·6 lb/ft run obtained in Example (6.6.1).

N.B. In practice, handling stresses would also have to be considered as superimposed upon the prestressing; i.e. prior to the unit experiencing its full design load when in its final position. The deflections are also of important practical importance, as is also the load factor against failure.

6.8 Elastic design of a singly prestressed beam

This is exactly the same procedure as in §6.6 and §6.7 except that $A_T{'} = 0, P_T = p_T{'} = p_T{''} = p_T{'''} = 0$, etc. There is a simplified design method similar to the method in §6.7.

6.9 Elastic design of a singly prestressed beam (cracked due to prestressing)

Maximum economy is obtained in the quantities of steel and concrete used in a prestressed beam, when the top of the beam takes as much tension as possible after prestressing, and the bottom of the beam takes as much tension as possible at working loads. The tension taken by the top of the beam after prestressing can be increased by allowing the concrete to crack, and providing reinforcement to take higher tensile forces than could be taken by the concrete in tension. Such reinforcement is also useful for resisting handling stresses if the member is precast. It must of course be remembered when designing minimum sized structural sections, that the deflections and resistances to vibrations and fire are sometimes of crucial importance.

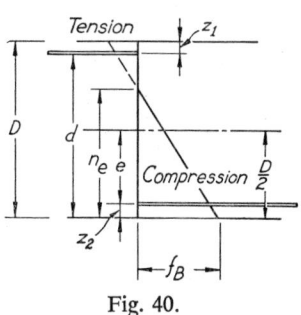

Fig. 40.

Fig. 40 shows the distribution of stresses in a rectangular beam when the tension is taken entirely by the top reinforcement. Resolving longitudinally,

$$(P_B - p_B) = \frac{bf_Bn_e}{2} - A_B'f_B\frac{(n_e - z_2)}{n_e} - mA_T'f_B\frac{(d - n_e)}{n_e} \quad ....(6,28)$$

Taking moments about the centre line,

$$(P_B - p_B)e = \frac{bf_Bn_e}{2}\left(\frac{D}{2} - \frac{n_e}{3}\right) - A_B'f_B\left(\frac{n_e - z_2}{n_e}\right)\left(\frac{D}{2} - z_2\right)$$
$$+ mA_T'f_B\frac{(d - n_e)}{n_e}\left(\frac{D}{2} - z_1\right) \quad ....(6,29)$$

If equation (6,29) is divided by equation (6,28), $(P_B - p_B)$ and f_B are eliminated and an equation is obtained for determining n_e, provided the section is fully defined. Equating the loss of strain in the prestressing steel to the gain of strain in the surrounding concrete,

$$\frac{p_B{}'}{A_B{}'E_s} = \frac{f_B\,(n_e - z_2)}{E_c\ n_e} \qquad \dots(6,30)$$

$$p_B{}' = mf_B A_B{}' \frac{(n_e - z_2)}{n_e} \qquad \dots(6,31)$$

Substituting $p_B{}'$ from equation (6,31) in equation (6,28),

$$P_B{}' - mf_B A_B{}' \frac{(n_e - z_2)}{n_e} = \frac{bf_B n_e}{2} - A_B{}'f_B \frac{(n_e - z_2)}{n_e}$$

$$- mA_T{}'f_B \frac{(d - n_e)}{n_e} \qquad \dots(6,32)$$

$$\therefore\ f_B \left\{ \frac{bn_e}{2} - A_B{}' \frac{(n_e - z_2)}{n_e} - mA_T{}' \frac{(d - n_e)}{n_e} + mA_B{}' \frac{(n_e - z_2)}{n_e} \right\}$$

$$= P_B{}' \qquad \dots(6,33)$$

This enables f_B to be calculated. Now,

$$f_{TS} = f_B \frac{(d - n_e)}{n_e} m \qquad \dots(6,34)$$

and $$f_{BS} = \frac{P_B - p_B}{A_B{}'} \qquad \dots(6,35)$$

EXAMPLE 6.9.1

A rectangular beam 10 in. wide by 18 in. deep by 32 ft long is loaded vertically; it has two $\frac{1}{2}$ in. dia. bars in the top and is post-tensioned by two 1 in. dia. Lee-McCall bars (acting in $1\frac{1}{8}$ in. dia. ducts) in the bottom. The concrete cover to the top of the mild steel bars is 1 in. and the centre of each post-tensioning bar is 3 in. above the soffit of the beam. If the Lee-McCall bars are stressed simultaneously to a tensile stress of 42 ton/sq. in., determine a suitable moment of resistance for the central section. It is assumed that these bars are bent up at the supports, where there are no stresses due to the self weight of the beam, to reduce the prestresses. Design in accordance with the British Code of Practice[33] and assume the following data: Young's Modulus for Lee-McCall bars = 25×10^6 lb/sq. in., and for mild steel = 30×10^6 lb/sq. in.; permissible tensile stress in mild steel = 20,000 lb/sq. in.; permissible compressive stress in mild steel = 20,000 lb/sq. in.; the permissible compressive concrete stress at transfer = 2,500 lb/sq. in. (i.e. the minimum works cube strength = $\dfrac{2,500}{0\cdot5}$ = 5,000 lb/sq. in.); and the permissible compressive concrete stress when subjected to the working load = 2,000 lb/sq. in. (i.e. the minimum works cube strength at this stage $= \dfrac{2,000}{0\cdot33} = 6{,}000$ lb/sq. in.). In this particular instance, say for reasons of durability, there must be no tensile stresses in the soffit of the beam.

From the Code,[33] $E_c = 4\cdot5 \times 10^6$ lb/sq. in. (at transfer)

$$\therefore \quad \text{for mild steel, } m = \frac{30 \times 10^6}{4\cdot5 \times 10^6} = 6\cdot67 \text{ (at transfer)}$$

and for Lee-McCall bars, $\quad m = \dfrac{25 \times 10^6}{4\cdot5 \times 10^6} = 5\cdot56$ (at transfer)

Now, $\qquad\qquad e = 6$ in

$$z_2 = 3 \text{ in}$$

$$A_T' = 2 \times \frac{\pi}{4} \times (\tfrac{1}{2})^2 = 0\cdot393 \text{ sq. in.}$$

$$z_1 = 1\cdot31$$
$$d = 16\cdot69$$

The A_B' in equations (6,28) and (6,29) refers to the area displaced by the bottom tendon, but in post-tensioning, this is the area of the ducts,

i.e. $A_B' = 2 \times \dfrac{\pi}{4} \times (1\tfrac{1}{8})^2 = 1\cdot99$ sq. in.

Hence substituting in equation (6,28)

$$(P_B - p_B) = \frac{10 f_B n_e}{2} - 1\cdot99 f_B \frac{(n_e - 3)}{n_e} - 6\cdot67 \times 0\cdot393 f_B \left(\frac{16\cdot75 - n_e}{n_e} \right)$$
$$\dots\text{(6,36)}$$

Superimposed upon the couple due to prestressing, and acting oppositely to it, is the bending moment due to the self weight of the beam. This is $\dfrac{10 \times 18}{144} \times 150 \times \dfrac{32^2}{8}$ lb ft $= 288{,}600$ lb in. Hence applying equation (6,29),

$$(P_B - p_B)6 - 288{,}600 = \frac{10 f_B n_e}{2} \left(9 - \frac{n_e}{3} \right) - 1\cdot99 f_B \frac{(n_e - 3)}{n_e} (9 - 3)$$
$$+ 6\cdot67 \times 0\cdot393 f_B \frac{(16\cdot75 - n_e)}{n_e} (9 - 1\cdot25)$$
$$\dots\text{(6,37)}$$

For obtaining P_B, the $A_B' = 2 \times \dfrac{\pi}{4} \times 1^2 = 1\cdot571$

$$\therefore \quad P_B = 42 \times 2{,}240 \times 1\cdot571 = 148{,}000 \text{ lb}$$

At transfer, the bars are stressed simultaneously, hence $p_B' = 0$; shrinkage and creep are only just commencing to reduce the stress in the bars hence $p'' = p''' = 0$

$$\therefore \quad P_B - p_B = 148{,}000 \text{ lb}$$

Substituting this in equations (6,36) and (6,37) and dividing equation (6,37) by equation (6,36),

$$\frac{148{,}000 \times 6 - 288{,}600}{148{,}000}$$

$$= \frac{5n_e\left(9 - \dfrac{n_e}{3}\right) - 11{\cdot}95\dfrac{(n_e - 3)}{n_e} + 20{\cdot}3\dfrac{(16{\cdot}75 - n_e)}{n_e}}{5n_e - 1{\cdot}99\dfrac{(n_e - 3)}{n_e} - 2{\cdot}62\dfrac{(16{\cdot}75 - n_e)}{n_e}}$$

This is a cubic equation for n_e and gives:

$$n_e = 14{\cdot}86 \text{ in.}$$

Substituting these values of P_B, p_B and n_e in equation (6,36),

$$148{,}000 = f_B\left\{5 \times 14{\cdot}86 - 1{\cdot}99\frac{(14{\cdot}86 - 3)}{14{\cdot}86} - 2{\cdot}62\frac{(16{\cdot}75 - 14{\cdot}86)}{14{\cdot}86}\right\}$$

$$f_B = 2{,}042 \text{ lb/sq. in.}$$

From equation (6,34),

$$f_{TS} = 2{,}042 \times \frac{(16{\cdot}75 - 14{\cdot}86)}{14{\cdot}86} \times 6{\cdot}67 = 1{,}734 \text{ lb/sq. in.}$$

These stresses, immediately after stressing, are shown in Fig. 41(i); and represent the condition (a) described in Example (6.6.1). The concrete and steel stresses are less than their respective permissible values at this stage.

When the superimposed load is applied, the top fibres of the beam will become in compression and the compression in the bottom fibres will be

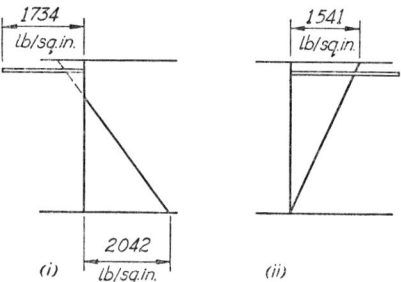

Fig. 41.

reduced and even made tensile within the limits allowed by the Code.[33] In this particular problem however no such tensile stress is allowed. Hence for the condition when all the losses have fully occurred, the cracks are closed, and the analysis is the same as in §6.6 and §6.7.

The concrete stress at the level of the tendon in Fig. 41(i),

$$= 2,042 \times \frac{(14 \cdot 86 - 3)}{14 \cdot 86} = 1,630 \text{ lb/sq. in.}$$

Referring to the Code,[33]

$$p_B''' = 1,630 \times 0 \cdot 25 \times 10^{-6} \times \frac{6,000}{5,000} \times (25 \times 10^6) \times 1 \cdot 571 = 19,240 \text{ lb}$$

and $p_B'' = 200 \times 10^{-6} \times (25 \times 10^6) \times 1 \cdot 571 = 7,855 \text{ lb}$

$$\therefore \quad P_B' = 148,000 - 19,240 - 7,855 = 127,095 \text{ lb}$$

At the stage being considered, the cube strength is 6,000 lb/sq. in., hence the corresponding Young's Modulus[33] is 5×10^6 lb/sq. in. On this basis the modular ratio for the mild steel is $\dfrac{30 \times 10^6}{5 \times 10^6} = 6$. The calculations for A_B, n_{BR}, e_B, and I_{BR} are made in Table 17 and then,

$$A_B = 180 \cdot 0 \text{ sq. in.}$$

$$n_{BR} = \frac{1,592 \cdot 6}{180} = 8 \cdot 85 \text{ in.}$$

$$e_B = 18 - 8 \cdot 85 - 3 = 6 \cdot 15 \text{ in.}$$

$$I_{BR} = 18,995 - 180 \times 8 \cdot 85^2 = 4,895 \text{ in.}^4$$

From equation (6,14),

$$Z_B = \frac{1}{180} + \frac{6 \cdot 15(18 - 8 \cdot 85)}{4,895} = 0 \cdot 01705$$

From equations (6,10) and (6,16),

$$Z_B' = \frac{1}{180} - \frac{6 \cdot 15 \times 8 \cdot 85}{4,895} = -0 \cdot 00557$$

Now the modular ratio for the tendon is $\dfrac{25 \times 10^6}{5 \times 10^6} = 5$. Substituting the above in equation (6,21),

$$p_B' \left[\frac{18 - 8 \cdot 85}{5 \times 1 \cdot 571 \times 6 \cdot 15} + 0 \cdot 01705 \right] = 127,095 \times 0 \cdot 01705$$

$$\therefore \quad p_B' = 10,490 \text{ lb}$$

Similarly, as for equation (6,11),

$$P_B - p_B = 127,095 - 10,490 = 116,605 \text{ lb}$$

TABLE 17

Portion	Area	A	x	Ax	Ax^2	I_G
Gross concrete	180	180·	9	1,620	14,580	$\frac{10 \times 18^3}{12} = 4,860$
Top steel	0·393	1·965	1·25	2·456	3·07	—
Duct	−1·99	−1·99	15·	−29·85	−448·	—
		180·0		1,592·6	14,135	4,860 → 14,135
						18,995

From equations (6,23) and (6,17),

$$f_B = 116,605 \times 0.01705 = 1,987 \text{ lb/sq. in. (comp.)}$$

From equations (6,22) and (6,16),

$$f_T = -116,605 \times 0.00557 = 649 \text{ lb/sq. in. (tens.)}$$

If greater accuracy is desired, p_B''' can be revised in accordance with these stresses and the calculation for f_B and f_T repeated. This can be done several times until the designer is satisfied with the solution; it will soon be realized however that such trouble is not usually justified for the accuracy required in practice. In the present example a fine adjustment of this type is not considered to be necessary. Now, to obtain the required condition, the total loading considered to be acting at the same time as the above stresses is associated with full creep, and hence a modular ratio of 15 must be used[3] for determining the properties of the section. The calculations are shown in Table 18, and give,

$$n = \frac{1,957}{207.5} = 9.44 \text{ in.}$$

$$I = 24,399 - 207.5 \times 9.44^2 = 5,899 \text{ in.}^4$$

If it is decided not to allow any tensile stress in the bottom fibres, then the tensile stress at the extreme bottom fibre due to the externally applied bending moment must not exceed the above compressive stress of 1,987 lb/sq. in. On this basis therefore the externally applied bending moment must be limited to,

$$\frac{1,987 \times 5,899}{(18 - 9.44)} = 1,370,000 \text{ lb in.}$$

Now the permissible compressive stress in the concrete is 2,000 lb/sq. in., hence the compressive stress at the extreme top fibre due to the externally applied bending moment can be $2,000 + 649 = 2,649$ lb/sq. in. On this basis therefore the externally applied bending moment must be limited to

$$\frac{2,649 \times 5,899}{9.44} = 1,655,000 \text{ lb in.}$$

Hence the externally applied bending moment (due to the self weight and superimposed loading) must be restricted to the lower of the above two values, namely 1,370,000 lb in. In this event there is no resultant stress in the bottom fibre, and the resultant stress in the top fibre will be equal to

$$\frac{1,370,000}{5,899} \times 9.44 - 649 = 1,541 \text{ lb/sq. in.}$$

TABLE 18

Portion	Area	A	x	Ax	Ax^2	I_G
Gross concrete	180	180	9	1,620	14,580	4,860
Top steel	0·393	5·5	1·25	6·87	8·6	—
Bottom steel	1·571	22·	15·	330·	4,950	—
		207·5		1,957·	19,539	4,860 → 19,539
						24,399

Fig. 41(ii) shows the final stress distribution. The maximum concrete stress of 1,541 lb/sq. in. is less than 2,000 lb/sq. in. and therefore satisfactory. The compressive stress in the mild steel reinforcement can be calculated from Fig. 41(ii) to be

$$\frac{(18 - 1{\cdot}25)}{18} \times 1{,}541 \times 15 = 21{,}500 \text{ lb/sq. in.}$$

This exceeds the permissible value of 20,000 lb/sq. in., hence in this problem the moment of resistance must be reduced accordingly. (Alternatively the practical designer might change from this steel to high-tensile steel, or increase its amount.)

Of the above stress of 21,500, the amount contributed by the bending moment

$$= 1{,}987 \times \frac{(9{\cdot}44 - 1{\cdot}25)}{9{\cdot}44} \times 15 = 25{,}900 \text{ lb/sq. in.}$$

Now this needs to be reduced by $(21{,}500 - 20{,}000) = 1{,}500$ to obtain a suitable moment of resistance of,

$$\frac{(25{,}900 - 1{,}500)}{25{,}900} \times 1{,}370{,}000 = 1{,}290{,}000 \text{ lb. in.}$$

6.10 Simplified design of a singly prestressed beam (cracked due to prestressing)

The method is similar to the one described in §6.7 and is illustrated by the following example:

EXAMPLE 6.10.1

Repeat Example (6.9.1) using the simplified method below.

$$P_B = 42 \times 2{,}240 \times 1{\cdot}571 = 148{,}000 \text{ lb}$$
$$A = 10 \times 18 = 180 \text{ sq. in.}$$
$$I = \frac{10 \times 18^3}{12} = 4{,}860 \text{ in.}^4$$

At transfer, the bars are stressed simultaneously hence $p_B' = 0$; shrinkage and creep are only just commencing to reduce the stress in the bars hence $p'' = p''' = 0$

$$\therefore \quad P_B - p_B = 148{,}000 \text{ lb}$$

This force acts at an eccentricity of $\dfrac{18}{2} - 3 = 6$ in., so that it is equivalent to an axial force of 148,000 lb together with a couple of $148{,}000 \times 6 = 888{,}000$ lb in. Superimposed upon this and acting oppositely is the bending moment due to the self weight of the beam. This bending

$$\text{moment} = \frac{10 \times 18}{144} \times 150 \times \frac{32^2}{8} \text{ lb ft} = 288,600 \text{ lb in.}$$

Hence at transfer the section needs to resist an axial force of 148,000 lb and a bending moment of $888,000 - 288,600 = 599,400$ lb in. Assuming an uncracked section,

$$\text{top fibre stress} = \frac{148,000}{180} - \frac{599,400}{4,860} \times 9 = 823 - 1,110$$

$$= -287 \text{ lb/sq. in. (tensile)}$$

$$\text{bottom fibre stress} = 823 + 1,110 = 1,933 \text{ lb/sq. in. (compressive)}$$

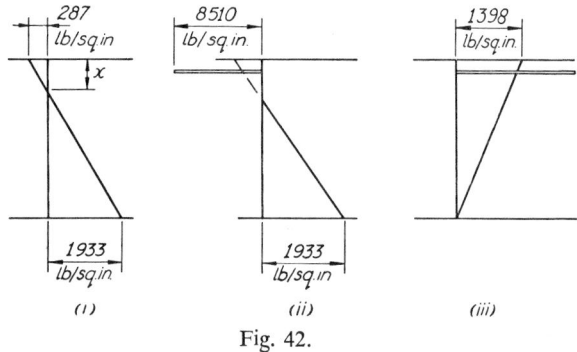

Fig. 42.

This latter stress is satisfactory as it is less than 2,500 lb/sq. in. The stresses are shown in Fig. 42(i); then by similar triangles,

$$\frac{x}{18} = \frac{287}{287 + 1,933}$$

$$x = 2 \cdot 33 \text{ in.}$$

The total tensile force in the top of the section

$$= \frac{287}{2} \times 2 \cdot 33 \times 10 = 3,346 \text{ lb}$$

Assuming this is resisted by the two $\frac{1}{2}$ in. dia. bars only, the stress in the bars is $\dfrac{3,346}{0 \cdot 393} = 8,510$ lb/sq. in. Hence Fig. 42(ii) is an approximation to Fig. 41(i). The concrete stresses compare favourably; the simplified design however overestimates the steel stress. Even so it is not stressed to anything like its permissible stress of 20,000 lb/sq. in., and this is usual for this type of problem.

N.B. A more accurate analysis can of course be made by using the normal methods of designing an eccentrically loaded column, helped by the use of design tables and graphs.

The manufacturers of Lee-McCall bars say that after all losses have occurred and the beam has been loaded with its working load, the total losses do not exceed 15%; hence

$$p_B = \frac{15}{100} \times 148,000 = 22,200 \text{ lb}$$

$$\therefore P_B - p_B = 148,000 - 22,200 = 125,800 \text{ lb}$$

Therefore due to this prestressing force,

$$\text{top fibre stress} = \frac{125,800}{180} - \frac{125,800 \times 6}{4,860} \times 9 = 699 - 1,400$$

$$= -701 \text{ lb/sq. in. (tensile)}$$

bottom fibre stress $= 699 + 1,400 = 2,099$ lb/sq. in. (comp.)

If it is decided not to allow any tensile stress in the bottom fibres, then the tensile stress at the extreme bottom fibre due to the externally applied bending moment must not exceed the above compressive stress of 2,099 lb/sq. in. On this basis therefore the externally applied bending moment must be limited to,

$$2,099 \times \frac{4,860}{9} = 1,134,000 \text{ lb in.}$$

Now the permissible compressive stress in the concrete is 2,000 lb/sq. in., hence the compressive stress at the extreme top fibre due to the externally applied bending moment can be $2,000 + 701 = 2,701$ lb/sq. in. On this basis the externally applied bending moment will obviously be higher than the above value of 1,134,000 lb in. The externally applied moment must therefore be restricted to this latter value. In this event there is no resultant stress in the bottom fibre, and the resultant stress in the top fibre will be equal to $2,099 - 701 = 1,398$ lb/sq. in.

Fig. 42(iii) therefore shows the final stress distribution. The maximum concrete stress of 1,398 lb/sq. in. is less than 2,000 lb/sq. in. and is therefore satisfactory. The compressive stress in the mild steel reinforcement can be calculated from Fig. 42(iii) to be

$$\left(\frac{18 - 1 \cdot 25}{18}\right) \times 1,398 \times 15 = 19,500 \text{ lb/sq. in.}$$

which is satisfactory as it is less than 20,000 lb/sq. in.

By comparing this method with the more accurate method of Example (6.9.1) it can be seen that this simplified method is generally conservative. As this usually applies the designer is reasonably safe in using these approximate methods; he must however finally use the more accurate methods for important structures, structures which are sure to experience the full design load frequently and which on rare occasions are liable to be over-loaded.

6.11   Prestressed columns

If a satisfactory traditional reinforced concrete column can be designed so that all of its fibres are in compression, then to prestress such a member only reduces its efficiency. If however the bending moment in a column is high relative to the axial load, it might not be possible to design a traditional reinforced concrete column to within the architectural limits of girth. In such an instance, prestressing is useful and either a post-tensioning cable can be introduced to reduce the combined eccentricity of the combined loading and prestressing force, or a column can be pretensioned and precast, the prestresses being opposite to those subsequently to be introduced by the loading.

It is rarely economical or necessary in Britain to prestress columns. One example of prestressing columns is in the case of large span pitched-roofed portal frames; in this instance however the columns experience very small direct stresses relative to the bending stresses.

6.12   Prestressed ties

Prestressed ties are often extremely useful in modern constructions. Extensions of ties are often desired to be as small as possible; this means a low strain is desirable in a tie, hence a steel tie or a prestressed concrete tie is designed using a low stress. If the steel tie needs to be clad to resist fire or corrosion then the prestressed tie is often a more economical solution. Pretensioning is preferable to post-tensioning* when the ties are not adequately supported transversely against buckling. Such ties are sometimes used for space frames, arches, hyperbolic paraboloids, gable ties to barrel vault and folded plate roofs, suspenders to tied arch bridges, and ties beneath prestressing beds. One objection to steel ties to concrete structures is that their life and fire resistance is far less than that of the concrete members.

EXAMPLE 6.12.1

Design a pretensioned reinforced concrete tie to carry a tension of 100,000 lb. The tie is 30 ft long and its extension must not exceed $\frac{1}{4}$ in. Assume a Young's Modulus of 2,000,000 lb/sq. in. for the concrete; also 70% of the tensile strength of the wires is 70 ton/sq. in.

$$\text{maximum strain} = \frac{0\cdot25}{30 \times 12} = 0\cdot694 \times 10^{-3}$$

*Recent research shows that lateral instability is not as prohibitive to the design of post-tensional ties as past information has indicated.

Corresponding concrete stress $= 0.694 \times 10^{-3} \times 2{,}000{,}000$
$$= 1{,}388 \text{ lb/sq. in.}$$

Cross-sectional area of tie required $= \dfrac{100{,}000}{1{,}388} = 72$ sq. in.

hence the tie can be say 9 in. $\times$ 8 in. in cross-section (the area of the wires has been ignored for simplicity).

Essentially it is only necessary to prestress the tie to 1,388 lb/sq. in.; then the resultant stress at the working load is zero. In these circumstances cracks might be experienced due to shrinkage and temperature changes, hence it is better practice to have a residual compressive stress (say 330 lb/sq. in. in this instance). Hence the prestress needs to be $1{,}388 + 330 = 1{,}718$ lb/sq. in., and the corresponding prestressing force $= 1{,}718 \times 9 \times 8 = 123{,}700$ lb.

From Table 1 of reference (33) it can be seen that the specified works cube strength at 28 days must be $1{,}718 \times 4 = 6{,}872$ lb/sq. in. From Table 4 of reference (33) Young's Modulus for the concrete $= 5{,}436{,}000$ lb/sq. in.; hence, using a Young's Modulus of 28,000,000 lb/sq. in. for the wires, the modular ratio is 5·15. Using reference (33),

$$\therefore \quad p' \simeq 1{,}718 \times 5{\cdot}15 \times A' = 8{,}850\, A' \text{ lb}$$

$$p'' = 300 \times 10^{-6} \times 28{,}000{,}000 \times A' = 8{,}400\, A' \text{ lb}$$

$$p''' \simeq 0{\cdot}33 \times 10^{-6} \times 28{,}000{,}000 \times 0{\cdot}4 \times 6{,}000 \times A' = 22{,}200\, A' \text{ lb}$$

$$\therefore \quad p = 39{,}450\, A' \text{ lb}$$

$$P = 70 \times 2{,}240\, A' = 157{,}000\, A' \text{ lb}$$

$$\therefore \quad 157{,}000\, A' - 39{,}450\, A' = 123{,}700$$

$$\therefore \quad A' = \dfrac{123{\cdot}7}{117{\cdot}6} = 1{\cdot}052 \text{ sq. in.}$$

say thirty-four 0·2 in. diameter wires.

EXAMPLE 6.12.2

Design a steel tie for comparison with the prestressed tie of Example (6.12.1). Use $1\frac{1}{8}$ in. dia. bars; cross-sectional area at bottom of threads $= 0{\cdot}6969$ sq. in. Permissible tensile stresses are 9 ton/sq. in. for tie and 8 ton/sq. in. on area at bottom of threads. Young's Modulus $= 13{,}000$ ton/sq. in.

As before, maximum strain $= 0{\cdot}694 \times 10^{-3}$
corresponding steel stress

$$= 0{\cdot}694 \times 10^{-3} \times 13{,}000 = 9{\cdot}02 \text{ ton/sq. in.}$$

Hence use permissible stress of 9 ton/sq. in.

Tension in tie $= 100,000$ lb $= 44.6$ ton

$\therefore$ cross-sectional area of tie $= \dfrac{44.6}{9} = 4.95$ sq. in.

No. of $1\frac{1}{8}$ in. diameter bars required $= \dfrac{4.95}{0.994} = 4.98$

cross-sectional area at bottom of threads $= \dfrac{44.6}{8} = 5.57$ sq. in.

No. of $1\frac{1}{8}$ in. diameter bars required $= \dfrac{5.57}{0.6969} = 8$

Hence eight $1\frac{1}{8}$ in. bars would be required.

N.B. If this tie were to be subsequently encased with concrete for protection against fire and corrosion it would require nearly the same amount of concrete as the prestressed tie of Example (6.12.1), and also steel binders.

6.13 Simple assessment of size of prestressed members

It is quite common practice to prestress members so that they can subsequently develop extreme fibre stresses of 2,000 lb/sq. in. at working loads. On this basis an engineer can decide upon a structural section quite simply and rapidly as illustrated in the following example:

EXAMPLE 6.13.1

Decide upon a suitable I-shaped cross-section for a prestressed concrete beam which has to resist a total bending moment at working loads of 5,750,000 lb in.

Using an extreme fibre stress (see above) of 2,000 lb/sq. in., the section modulus of the section needs to be

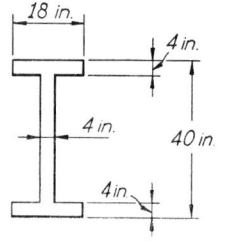

Fig. 43.

$$\dfrac{5,750,000}{2,000} = 2,875 \text{ in.}^3$$

Try the section shown in Fig. 43. Its moment of inertia equals

$$\dfrac{18 \times 40^3}{12} - \dfrac{14 \times 32^3}{12} = 57,700 \text{ in.}^4$$

and its section modulus is therefore

$$= \dfrac{57,700}{20} = 2,885 \text{ in.}^3$$

This will therefore be a suitable section for prestressing.

6.14   Shear resistance of prestressed concrete beams

At working loads, and of course prestressed concrete is principally designed to resist working loads, beams are uncracked and hence principal stresses can be calculated in the usual manner by combining stresses due to prestressing, bending and shear. The concrete is usually well able to resist the principal compressive stresses, and can usually resist the principal tensile stresses; if it cannot, then the section or the amount of prestressing has to be altered, or shear reinforcement in the form of inclined tendons, or vertical or inclined stirrups, or vertical prestressing, has to be introduced. The principal stresses can be calculated from the well-known expression

$$f = \tfrac{1}{2}\{f_1 + f_2 \pm \sqrt{(f_1 - f_2)^2 + 4f_s^2}\} \qquad \ldots.(6,38)$$

Permissible tensile stresses at working loads are recommended in Table 5 of reference (33). It is also necessary to ensure that a beam does not fail in shear prior to its failure in bending. The British Code does this by limiting the principal diagonal tensile stresses to the values in Table 6 of reference (33). The calculation of such principal stresses is based on the elastic theory; this is of course illogical but as yet research seems to have produced no better method. If diagonal tensile stresses at working and ultimate loads are in accordance with the above, the beam does not need shear reinforcement, and generally no web steel would be provided in the U.K., except in the case of thin webs to deep I beams, box sections, etc. In these latter cases nominal reinforcement in a web could comprise $\tfrac{1}{4}$in. diameter two-armed stirrups spaced at 0·8 times the overall depth of the beam, each side of the web would also contain longitudinal $\tfrac{1}{4}$in. diameter bars at the same centres. For beams exceeding 5 ft in depth $\tfrac{3}{8}$in. stirrups and longitudinal bars could be used in lieu of $\tfrac{1}{4}$in. diameter stirrups and bars.

If the diagonal tensile stresses exceed either of the above recommendations and it is decided not to alter the web thickness or the prestressing forces, then web reinforcement needs to be used. This should be designed for working and ultimate loads. The following formula can be used for designing vertical stirrups at working loads

$$\frac{P}{Sb} = 2\frac{f_t}{p_t}(f_t - p_t) \qquad \ldots.(6,39)$$

for values of f_t between p_t and $1\cdot 5\,p_t$. For values of f_t in excess of $1\cdot 5\,p_t$ the following formula can be used

$$\frac{P}{Sb} = f_t \qquad \ldots.(6,40)$$

With regard to the design of vertical stirrups for ultimate load conditions, the following formula can be used

$$\frac{P_u}{Sb} = f_{tu} \qquad \qquad \dots (6,41)$$

If inclined tendons are present then this formula becomes

$$\frac{P_u}{Sb} = f_t - \frac{A_w f_{y1} \sin \theta}{ab} \qquad \qquad \dots (6,42)$$

EXAMPLE 6.14.1

Design the floor unit of Example (6.6.1) to resist shear, and assume that the ratio of live to dead loading is 2·5 to 1.

Maximum shear force $= 232 \cdot 6 \times 9 = 2093 \cdot 4$ lb.

For simplicity consider the diagonal tensile stress at the neutral axis; this is not necessarily the maximum but is usually a good enough approximation for design purposes. The shear stress at the neutral axis is, applying Equation (5,11)

$$\frac{2,093}{210 \times 3} \left(\frac{13 \times 3 \cdot 02^2}{2} - \frac{10 \times 1 \cdot 77^2}{2} \right) = 145 \text{ lb/sq. in.}$$

The longitudinal compressive stress due to prestressing at the neutral axis is $277 + \dfrac{3 \cdot 02}{6} (1,308 - 277) = 796$ lb/sq. in.

Hence, from Equation (6,38), the principal diagonal tensile stress at the neutral axis is

$$\tfrac{1}{2}\{-796 + \sqrt{796^2 + 4 \times 145^2}\} = 25 \cdot 5 \text{ lb/sq. in.}$$

This is less than the permissible principal tensile stress from Table 5 of reference (33).

With regard to the ultimate load conditions, referring to clause 309 (ii) of reference (33); the shear force due to dead load $= \dfrac{2,093}{3 \cdot 5} = 597$ lb, hence the ultimate shear force due to dead load $= 597 \times 1 \cdot 5 = 897$ lb; the shear force due to live load $= 2,093 \times \dfrac{2 \cdot 5}{3 \cdot 5} = 1,493$ lb, hence the ultimate shear force due to live load $= 1,493 \times 2 \cdot 5 = 3,730$ lb. Hence the total ultimate shear force $= 897 + 3,730 = 4,627$ lb. The corresponding shear stress at the neutral axis is $145 \times \dfrac{4,627}{2,093} = 321 \cdot 5$ lb/sq. in.

The longitudinal compressive stress due to prestressing at the neutral axis is approximately 796 lb/sq. in. Hence the principal diagonal tensile stress at the neutral axis is

$$\tfrac{1}{2}\{-796 + \sqrt{796^2 + 4 \times 321 \cdot 5^2}\} = 113 \cdot 5$$

This is less than the permissible principal tensile stress from Table 6 of reference (33).

Hence no shear reinforcement is required.

EXAMPLE 6.14.2

Suppose a beam of the cross-section shown in Fig. 43 withstands a maximum shear stress of 400 lb/sq. in. Design a suitable shear reinforcement system assuming the following data:

   ratio of dead to live loading = 1:2

   longitudinal stress at neutral axis = 700 lb/sq. in.

   no inclined tendons available for resisting shear.

   limiting principal tensile stress at working loads = 150 lb/sq. in.

   limiting principal tensile stress at ultimate loads = 350 lb/sq. in.

   permissible stress in stirrups at working loads = 20,000 lb/sq. in.

From Equation (6,38)

$$f = \tfrac{1}{2}\{-700 \pm \sqrt{700^2 + 4 \times 400^2}\}$$
$$= \tfrac{1}{2}\{-700 \pm 1,063\}$$
$$= +181\cdot5 \text{ or } -881\cdot5 \text{ lb/sq. in.}$$

The principal tensile stress of 181·5 lb/sq. in. is greater than 150, hence shear reinforcement is required.

From Equation (6,39)

$$\frac{P}{S \times 4} = 2 \times \frac{181\cdot5}{150}(181\cdot5 - 150)$$
$$P = 305.S$$

Using 5/16 in. diameter (two-armed) stirrups

$$2 \times \frac{\pi}{4}\left(\frac{5}{16}\right)^2 \times 20,000 = 305.S$$
$$S = 10\cdot05 \text{ in.}$$

With regard to ultimate load conditions, referring to clause 309 (ii) of reference (33); the shear stress due to dead load = 400/3 = 133·3, hence the ultimate shear stress due to dead load = 133·3 × 1·5 = 200 lb/sq. in.; the shear stress due to live load = 400 × $\frac{2}{3}$ = 266·7, hence the ultimate shear stress due to live load = 266·7 × 2·5 = 666·7 lb/sq. in. Hence the total ultimate shear stress = 200 + 666·7 = 866·7 lb/sq. in. The corresponding principal tensile stress is

$$\tfrac{1}{2}\{-700 + \sqrt{700^2 + 4 \times 866\cdot7^2}\}$$
$$= 583\cdot5 \text{ lb/sq. in.}$$

This is greater than 350 lb/sq. in. so that shear reinforcement is required. The stirrups are to be of mild steel and the yield stress would not be less than 40,000 lb/sq. in.[3]   Using 80%[33] of this yield stress, using say 5/16 in. diameter (two-armed) stirrups, and applying Equation (6,41),

$$\frac{2 \times (\pi/4)(5/16)^2 \times 0 \cdot 8 \times 40,000}{4.S} = 583 \cdot 5$$

$$S = 2 \cdot 1$$

These are rather too close together, so using $\frac{3}{8}$ in. diameter (two-arm stirrups) in lieu of the 5/16 in. diameter stirrups,

$$S = 2 \cdot 1 \times \left(\frac{\frac{3}{8}}{\frac{5}{16}}\right)^2 = 3 \cdot 03$$

Hence use these stirrups at say 3 in. centres.

6.15   End splitting forces

Referring to Fig. 8, the prestressing wire upon release increases its diameter at A, and thus splitting forces are created between, and normal to a line between, A and B. Sometimes designers have been unaware of this problem and have experienced splitting cracks in pretensioned members along the line between A and B. Other end splitting forces are caused by the prestressing tendons being, in effect, a system of irregularly distributed point loads on the end of a member. Each point load causes splitting forces normal to its line of action.

Reinforcement should be provided to resist these splitting forces. This often takes the form of stirrups close together and as close to the end of the member as possible, and longitudinal bars are provided for anchoring the corners of these stirrups. Another system consists of helical reinforcement wrapped around and near to, say, the portion A to B, and another system uses welded mats of reinforcement wires which are placed perpendicularly to the prestressing tendons. These helices and mats of reinforcement are often sold by manufacturers of proprietary systems of prestressing equipment (e.g. Gifford-Udall-CCL System).

Magnel, Guyon and others have proposed theories* for designing the reinforcement. These theories have generally been satisfactory and the failures which have been experienced have been when guesswork has been used rather than theorization. Tests by the Cement and Concrete Association, however, show that the theories are not as accurate as desirable and this particular research work increases design knowledge on this subject.

---

* An account of these theories is given in *Pre-stressed Concrete* by R. H. Evans and E. W. Bennett (Chapman & Hall, London).

CHAPTER 7

SHELL ROOFS

7.1 Historical outline

Basic theoretical work was published by G. Lamé and E. Clapeyron in 1828 and A. E. H. Love in 1892. Neither reinforced concrete, timber, nor any other type of construction was sufficiently developed at that time for the conception of a large homogeneous shell to be visualized, (i.e. a shell large enough to act as the roof to a building), and it is reasonable to suppose that the writers mentioned above never imagined that their work would be of use for designing shell roofs. Before the era of reinforced concrete construction, arches and vaults were constructed of materials incapable of developing tensile stresses; hence such structures were relatively massive and limited in application compared with modern shell structures, which date from approximately 1924.

In France, prior to 1910, shells were designed as arches spanning between beams, giving heavy constructions compared with modern shells. Between about 1910 and 1924, short shells were constructed in France designed in the same way, but counting more and more of the arched slab in the depth of the beam, initially by intuition and later, additionally, by experience of former contracts.

In 1924, Carl Zeiss applied Love's theories to the design of a small shell roof which was constructed by Dyckerhoff and Widmann in the Zeiss Works at Jena. This shell was of semi-elliptical cross-section, no doubt to simplify the design, and was approximately 18 ft long by 12 ft wide. The system of design was patented and named *Zeiss-Dywidag*. It was used for the first major shell scheme, namely the Düsseldorf Planetarium, in 1926; and subsequently for schemes throughout the world, being called the *Shell-D* system in Britain and the *Z-D* system in the U.S.A.

Semi-elliptical and semi-circular shells are statically determinate and can be designed relatively simply by what is called a *Membrane theory*, providing edge and valley beams are not used. Such shells however have steep slopes near the springings which make concreting difficult; they are also deeper and therefore require more material than otherwise necessary. A shell which has a cross-section which is a segment of a circle can eliminate these difficulties, and also the shuttering is much simpler than that for a shell with an elliptical cross-section. There was therefore a demand for a method of designing shells consisting of segments of circles. Dischinger and Finsterwalder were studying shells from approximately 1924 onwards, and Finsterwalder, in 1933, was the first to publish a design method for shells comprising segments of circles. He presented the problem in two parts, namely a membrane condition and an *edge load* condition, and this basic idea has become a classic, being adopted by most subsequent theorizers. Dischinger modified Finsterwalder's theory in 1935, but gave greater complexity, and Aas Jakobsen expanded Finsterwalder's theories to deal with shells of shapes other than cylindrical.

In 1935, Schorer,[35] in the U.S.A., made several approximations and derived a method for cylindrical shells which was simpler to use than the previously mentioned methods, and hence a better commercial proposition for the designer. This method was probably first used in Britain by C. V. Blumfield. Schorer's method has been used successfully for a large number of shells (or *barrel vault roofs*) in Britain, and it has been illustrated that the approximations made do not affect the actual quantities of reinforcement used for the majority of shells encountered in practice (in Britain).

In 1947, Jenkins[36] expounded probably the most satisfactory mathematical analysis; the design method is however most laborious, this latter aspect not increasing its popularity with commercial designers.

Lundgren,[37] in 1949, published a further analysis. In 1954, Tottenham[38] simplified the use of Schorer's method by making a further assumption; this enabled design tables to be prepared and used for part of the analysis and the remainder to be effected with a slide rule in lieu of a calculating machine. This was a great step forward from the commercial designer's point of view; the designs were quicker and the office did not need to possess a calculating machine. Such views are of course now becoming greatly modified as the popularity of electronic computers increases. Tottenham considers that his method gives adequate accuracy for the quantities of reinforcement required, and many satisfactory shells have been designed in Britain with this method.

A further recently published method (1958) is by Yitzhaki. Beam analogy methods are limited in validity but can be most useful for preliminary schemes; one such method is described by Lundgren.[37] Elastic methods of design will no doubt always be of use for predicting deflections, stresses and therefore crack widths at working loads, but it is also to be hoped that ultimately there will also be reliable plastic methods of design. A. L. L. Baker was early to suggest a plastic method of design[39] and it is hoped that extensive research will eventually ratify such a method.

L. Nervi (Italy), F. Candella (Mexico), and others are currently pioneering unconventional shell structures. If these structures prove their reliability, with time no doubt they will be copied universally wherever it suits the economy, and there are sure to be clients willing to pay more for such structures because of their fine aesthetics. In Britain, the shuttering is almost certain to prove prohibitive in cost if attempted in a conventional manner, but with modifications of the competitive proprietary systems invented for cylindrical shells, this difficulty should be resolved as it has been with cylindrical shells, where the price of the curved shuttering is now sometimes no greater than for flat shuttering. Another point is that such structures become cheaper with popularity because contractor's personnel become more familiar and therefore more skilled with the operations involved.

7.2 Proportioning of shells

Multitudes of cylindrical shells have now been designed and constructed in Britain. This experience enables reasonably accurate assessments to be made of the dimensions of many such shells. Prior to this experience, dimensions had to be initially guessed then modified as felt necessary as a result of the shell analysis. This is a lengthy process

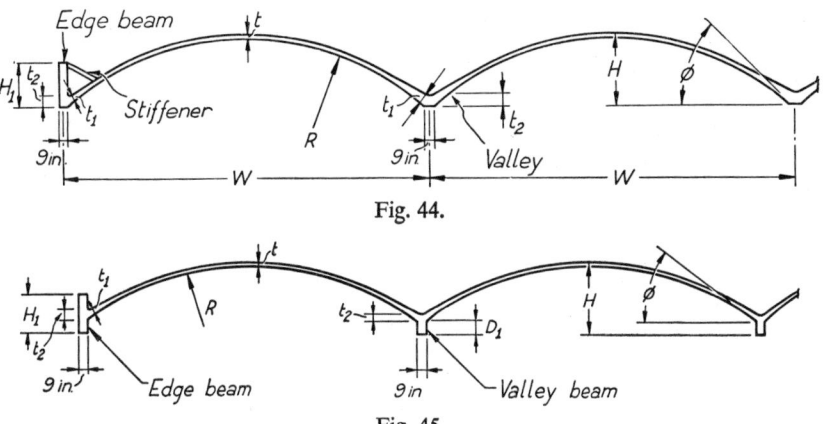

Fig. 44.

Fig. 45.

which might need repeating several times. The proportions at present suggested will suit many practical cases and will usually be found to be satisfactory upon analysis.

Figs. 44 and 45 illustrate typical cross-sections of *normal* barrel vault roofs (symmetrical shells apart from the end spans), and Fig. 46 shows a typical cross-section of a system of *North Light* barrel vault roofs. Using the notation shown in these illustrations, if W is large compared with L (the span between end stiffening beams, see Fig. 48), then the structure chiefly comprises stiffening beams, little use being made of the shell action of the slab. Sometimes in these instances R is taken as equal to W.

In the extreme case, the shell slab can be designed ignoring its curvature, without a great loss in economy. Short shells spanning between large arches (in lieu of stiffening beams) are extremely useful for spanning very large distances, for example, several aircraft hangars have been constructed in this manner in the U.S.A., one such scheme having a clear span of 370 ft (= W in this instance). If W is small compared with L, then a relatively large proportion of the area covered comprises valleys, together with the necessary thickenings and usually valley beams in these instances. Otherwise the shell at the springings in a system such as Fig. 44 becomes very steep, and this increases the construction costs; hence full advantage is not being taken of the economy of materials associated with the thin shell portion of the construction. Such constructions are sometimes necessary for large spans especially if loads are hung from the shells or the valley beams. In this connection the maximum practical span, L, for *normal* barrel vault roofs is approximately 120 ft, if the shell is not prestressed or arched longitudinally; in these latter cases the maximum practical span is approximately 200 ft. In Britain, certain specialists consider that the most suitable ratio of L to W for economy is approximately 2:1, using the system shown in Fig. 44. If H is low comparably with L then insufficient shell action is obtained for economy, and if H is high compared with L then too much material may be used and the springings of the shell can become too steep for economy. The optimum ratio of H to L for economy consistent with strength and deflection is considered to be approximately 1 to 10; sometimes 1 to 12 is used for spans less than about 60 ft. If the edge beams are supported by intermediate columns, then H_1 may be a nominal amount and 2 ft 6 in. has been found to be satisfactory from experience; in this instance *stiffeners* are not required. For unsupported edge beams a ratio of H_1 to L of 1 to 15 is usually satisfactory, and *stiffeners* are usually required; these are sometimes of the order of 6 in. square in cross-section at third points of the spans, but have to be decided from the accurate design to prevent lateral instability of the compression zone of the edge beam. The angle ϕ should not exceed 45° if double shuttering and other extra expenses associated with steep springings to shells are to be avoided. If the above suggested proportions of H, L, and W are used, ϕ will automatically be less than 45°. Shrinkage and temperature movement are not normally considered in the analysis of barrel vault roofs, and early experience showed that shells needed thickening near their springings to avoid cracking due to these effects. Hence t_2 should be not less than 1 ft 6 in. and t_1 can be taken as $L/120$ with upper and lower limits of 9 in. and 5 in. The thickness of the shell t is usually not less than $2\frac{1}{2}$ in. in Britain, and when W exceeds 45 ft t is often increased to 3 in., when W exceeds 60 ft t is often increased to $3\frac{1}{2}$ in. This is not consistent with the work of Candella and Nervi; for example, both advocate that shells should be just thick enough to allow the reinforcement to be covered with concrete. Candella often uses shell thicknesses of $1\frac{1}{4}$ in., and Nervi with his philosophy of *ferro-cemento* sometimes uses shell thicknesses as thin as $\frac{1}{2}$ in. Some British engineers feel that these very thin shells might not prove to have the durability normally expected of reinforced concrete work, especially when exposed to severe industrial atmospheres. Time will tell, but it is of course true that many shells are protected with roofing felt and often decorated regularly underneath.

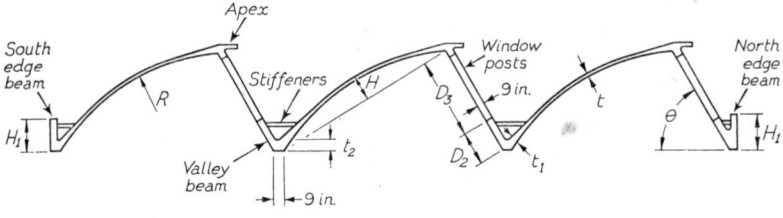

Fig. 46.

Too great a thickness of shell is uneconomical because the self weight of the shell is the largest proportion of the load to be carried, e.g. a $2\frac{1}{2}$ in. shell weighs 31 lb/sq. ft, out of a total design load of say 50 lb/sq. ft. It is usual in Britain to increase the thickness t by 1 in. for a distance $L/10$ from each end. This is necessary, together with extra reinforcement, to resist moments ignored in many principal analyses (e.g. those due to Schorer and Finsterwalder) but yet which are not negligible near to the supports. If barrel vault roofs need to be narrower than suggested above, i.e. $W < L/2$, then the system shown in Fig. 44 results in the shell being too steep near the springings. Consequently the system shown in Fig. 45 is preferable in such instances, and D_1 is made so that ϕ is less than 45°. Sometimes valley beams are necessary for supporting cranes or suspended loads.

The above remarks refer to normal shells; we now consider a *North-Light* system as shown in Fig. 46. Again $W = L/2$ gives an economical solution. The curvature of the shell is often reduced as much as possible so that it is not too steep at the valley, and also for architectural appearance; H can be taken as $L/18$ but should not normally be reduced much below this amount. The value of H_1 is as above or sometimes deeper to suit the requirements of the gutter. In Britain, θ is often taken as 60° and in this instance 0·075 L is usually a satisfactory value for D_2, and 0·22 L for D_3.

Stiffening (or gable) beams, arches and trusses are frequently made 9 in. wide, except when they are upstand when they then need to be 15 in. to 18 in. wide according to the design. Columns can quickly be assessed for estimate purposes by considering only vertical load—unless cranes or other loads are supported in addition—and are not usually made less than 12 in. square because of the difficulty of detailing reinforcement at junctions with stiffening and valley beams.

7.3   Estimating reinforcement for symmetrical shells

The methods in §7.2 enable the dimensions of a preliminary scheme to be determined, and the amount of reinforcement required for such a scheme can be estimated as illustrated in the following example. This method is often used for tendering purposes in Britain.

EXAMPLE 7.3.1

Estimate the quantity of reinforcement required for a barrel vault roof scheme as represented in Fig. 44, when $L = 60$ ft (simply supported), $W = 30$ ft, $H = 6$ ft, $t = 2\frac{1}{2}$ in., $t_1 = 6$ in., and $t_2 = 1$ ft 6 in.

From Fig. 47, by Pythagoras,

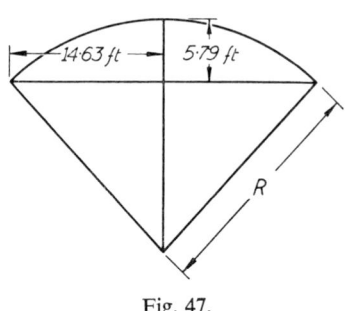

Fig. 47.

$$R^2 = 14\cdot63^2 + (R - 5\cdot79)^2$$
$$R^2 = 14\cdot63^2 + R^2$$
$$\qquad - 2R \times 5\cdot79 + 5\cdot79^2$$
$$R = \frac{14\cdot63^2}{2 \times 5\cdot79} + \frac{5\cdot79}{2} = 21\cdot395 \text{ ft.}$$
$$\sin \phi = \frac{14\cdot63}{21\cdot4} = 0\cdot684$$
$$\phi = 43\cdot2° = 0\cdot754 \text{ radians}$$

Half length of arc = $0\cdot754 \times 21\cdot4 = 16\cdot14$ ft.

Load on shell: superimposed (snow) = 15 lb/sq. ft
self weight ($2\frac{1}{2}$ in. shell) = 31 lb/sq. ft
insulation and felting = 4 lb/sq. ft
total = 50 lb/sq. ft

Load on half width of internal shell:

from shell = $50 \times 16\cdot14$ = 807 lb/ft

shell thickening near springing = $\dfrac{(6 - 2\cdot5)}{2} \times 40$ (say) = 70 lb/ft

valley thickening = $18 \times 4\cdot5$ = 81 lb/ft

total   = 958 lb/ft

Considering the shell as a simply supported beam of span L, the maximum bending moment $= \dfrac{958 \times 60^2}{8} = 431,500$ lb ft. For estimate purposes, the lever arm (or moment arm) can be taken as $0 \cdot 73H$ (when there is a valley beam use $0 \cdot 75H$), hence the lever arm $= 0 \cdot 73 \times 6 = 4 \cdot 38$ ft.

The area of longitudinal steel required at mid-span for half width of the internal shell $= \dfrac{431,500}{4 \cdot 38 \times 20,000} = 4 \cdot 925$ sq. in., using mild steel reinforcement (permissible tensile stress $= 20,000$ lb/sq. in.).

In a complete valley there will be twice this quantity of steel, and in computing the equivalent (or average) weight per foot of steel in a

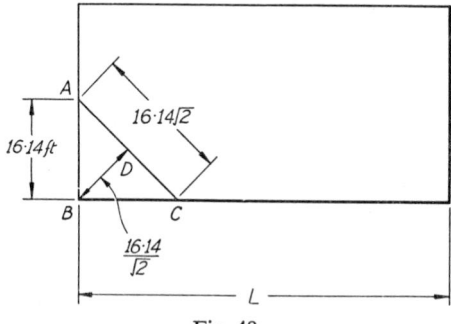

Fig. 48.

complete valley, the area of the steel is converted into weight per foot by multiplying by $3 \cdot 4$; also some of the steel will be curtailed before the supports, so $0 \cdot 9$ of the maximum amount is found to give an average figure for the complete valley. Hence the equivalent weight per foot in a complete internal valley $= 2 \times 4 \cdot 925 \times 3 \cdot 4 \times 0 \cdot 9 = 30 \cdot 17$ lb/ft.

The equivalent weight of steel per foot in the edge beam can be taken as $\frac{5}{8}$ of the equivalent weight of steel per foot for the complete internal valley, and is therefore $= \frac{5}{8} \times 30 \cdot 17 = 18 \cdot 84$ lb/ft.

Continuing this analogy of the half internal shell to a beam of span L, the maximum shear force $= 958 \times \dfrac{60}{2} = 28,740$ lb, and an approximate assessment of the maximum shear stress is given by $\dfrac{28,740}{(12 \times 4 \cdot 38) \times 3 \cdot 5} =$ 156 lb/sq. in., (*N.B.* the shell is $3 \cdot 5$ in. in lieu of $2 \cdot 5$ in. thick near the supports), and this is also the maximum diagonal tensile stress. Hence the maximum diagonal force per foot $= 156 \times 3 \cdot 5 \times 12 = 6,560$ lb/ft, and the maximum area of the diagonal tensile steel required per foot $= \dfrac{6,560}{20,000} = 0 \cdot 328$ sq. in./ft. Now Fig. 48 represents a curved shell laid

13

flat, so that AB = half the arc length = 16·14 ft; by geometry AC = 16·14$\sqrt{2}$ and BD = 16·14/$\sqrt{2}$. The shear reinforcement can take the form of diagonal bars normal to BD, and comprises a maximum amount of 0·328 sq. in./ft along BD. It is found that the average amount of steel can be taken as 0·7 of this value. The diagonal bars will lap with *ell-bars* near to both the valley and the stiffening beam. These ell-bars turn vertically downwards into stiffening beams and traverse valleys to give continuity with the diagonal tension steels of adjacent valleys. The average length of the diagonal bars plus the laps and corresponding ell-bars can be taken as $\dfrac{AC}{2} + 7\,\text{ft} = \dfrac{16·14}{2} + 7 = 18·42\,\text{ft}$. Hence the total weight of steel required for one support of an internal half shell = 0·7 × 0·328 × 3·4 × BD × 18·42 = 164·5 lb, and therefore the total diagonal tension steel for one complete shell (span L by width W) = 4 × 164·5 = 658 lb.

Reinforcement for resisting moments, M_2, usually consists of two layers of fabric, in the top and bottom respectively. The choice of fabrics can be estimated by assuming one to weigh 2·17 lb/sq. yd, and the other to be the same for radii up to 25 ft but for greater radii to weigh $\dfrac{R^2 \times 2·17}{625}$ lb/sq. yd, this figure being increased to suit the nearest of the following fabrics (specially designed for shells):

main wires	6 g at 6 in. centres	4 g at 6 in. centres	2g at 6 in. centres
cross wires	10 g at 12 in. centres	9 g at 12 in. centres	8 g at 12 in. centres
weight (lb/sq. yd)	2·17	3·09	4·28

In this example the radius <25 ft, hence assume, for estimate purposes only, two layers of fabric (top and bottom respectively) weighing 2·17 lb/sq. yd. These will be curtailed at say 2 ft from each springing point; in this example they will therefore be used for a curved distance of 2(16·14 − 2) = 28·28 ft per shell. Hence the area of fabric per shell = 2 × 28·28 × 60 = 3,400 sq. ft = 377 sq. yd, and this must be increased by 10%, to allow for laps, to give a total of 415 sq. yd of fabric per shell.

The reinforcement at the junction of the shell and stiffening beam varies from 3 to 12 lb/ft run. In this example, from experience, it can be assumed that this reinforcement will comprise $\frac{5}{16}$ in. diameter bars at 12 in. centres in both the top and the bottom of the shell. The length of each bar is $\dfrac{L}{10}$ + hook length + thickness of stiffening beam = 6 ft 0 in. + 3 in. + 9 in. = 7 ft 0 in. Hence the weight of this reinforcement = 2 × 7 ft × 0·261 lb/ft = 3·66 lb/ft.

The reinforcement at the junction of the shell and valley beam usually consists of $\frac{5}{16}$ in. dia. bars at 12 in. centres in both the top and the bottom of the shell. This reinforcement laps with the fabrics which are curtailed before the springing points, and therefore needs to cover a distance of about 4 ft from the centre line of the valley. Hence per foot run of one complete valley, this steel will be 2 × (4 ft 0 in. × 2) × 0·261 = 4·18 lb. Longitudinal lacing bars will be required for positioning this reinforcement and will consist of say eight $\frac{5}{16}$ in. dia. bars; 10% must be allowed for laps, so the weight of this steel per foot run of one complete valley = 8 × 0·261 × 1·1 = 2·3 lb. Hence the total steel required between the junctions of shells and valleys in this instance is 4·18 + 2·3 = 6·48 lb/ft run of valley.

The reinforcement required at the junction between the shell and the edge beam is similar to that above except that the bars have to be anchored in the edge beam and they will be approximately 5 ft long. Hence the steel required here will be $4{\cdot}18 \times \dfrac{5}{8} + \dfrac{2{\cdot}3}{2} = 3.76$ lb/ft.

Between the fabrics it is usual to place bars which are sometimes called 'spacer' bars. These bars can be packed up with small concrete blocks to keep the top fabric in position. They are also desirable to take care of longitudinal stresses due to temperature and shrinkage movement; the thin shell is of course very sensitive to such effects. This enables the fabric to have only a 3 in. side lap. The spacer bars are also useful in resisting the flow of wet concrete from the shell surfaces into the valleys. A useful guide, based upon experience, for utilizing these bars is as follows: for shells up to a span of 60 ft use $\frac{5}{16}$ in. square twisted (or $\frac{3}{8}$ in. diameter) bars at 15 in. centres; for shells of longer spans use $\frac{3}{8}$ in. square twisted (or $\frac{1}{2}$ in. dia.) bars at 15 in. centres. The square twisted bars are preferable for their greater bulk and better bond for controlling cracks.

We have now dealt with all the steel required for the shells and their edge and valley beams.

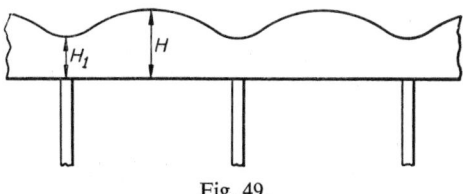

Fig. 49.

A common type of end stiffening beam is shown in Fig. 49. Suppose the edge beams are unsupported then $H_1 = 60/15 = 4$ ft. For estimate purposes an approximate design is as follows:

Loading:

$$\text{shell,} \quad \frac{958 \times 30}{15} = 1{,}916 \text{ lb/ft}$$

$$\text{self weight,} \left(\frac{4 + 6}{2}\right) \times 0.75 \times 150 = \underline{563} \text{ lb/ft}$$
$$2{,}479$$

$$\text{Max. bending moment} = \frac{2{,}479 \times 30^2}{8} = 279{,}000 \text{ lb/ft}$$

$$\text{lever arm} = H - 4 \text{ in.} = 5.67 \text{ ft}$$

$$\text{Flexural tension (or compression)} = \frac{279{,}000}{5.67} = 49{,}200 \text{ lb}$$

T_2 per foot run at the crown of the shell
$\backsimeq Q_1$ (weight/sq. ft) (radius) $= 1.4 \times 50 \times 21.395 = 1{,}500 \text{ lb/ft}$.

Hence the tension at the crown of the stiffening beam due to these forces T_2 is approximately

$$1{,}500 \times \frac{60}{2} = 45{,}000 \text{ lb.}$$

$$\therefore \quad \text{Max. steel required in the bottom of the beam} = \frac{49{,}200}{20{,}000} = 2.46 \text{ sq. in.}$$

Max. tensile steel required in the top of the beam

$$= \frac{45{,}000 - 49{,}200}{20{,}000} \text{ sq. in.}$$

In this instance there is no resultant tension in the top of the beam at mid-span, hence the latter figure is negative, and no tensile steel is required. Generally the concrete can easily withstand any small compression force at this position, as in this example. A nominal amount of reinforcement, two $\frac{1}{2}$ in. dia. bars ($= 0.393$ sq. in.), will be allowed for however, because the preceding calculation is only an approximate estimate of the forces involved; also temperature and shrinkage stresses should not be forgotten.

Experience shows the desirability of using intermediate longitudinal steel between the top and bottom reinforcement; say $\frac{1}{2}$ in. dia. bars at 15 in. centres at both sides of the beam. As the beam is 6 ft deep this will necessitate four intermediate pairs of bars. The equivalent area of these bars per foot run of beam can be taken as $4 \times 0.393 \times 0.7 = 1.1$

sq. in.; the factor 0·7 allows for the fact that many of the bars stop at the curved boundary of the beam.

Hence the equivalent weight of longitudinal steel in the stiffening beams per foot = (2·46 + 0·393 + 1·1) × 3·4 = 13·43 lb/ft.

The shear reinforcement and nominal stirruping in the stiffening beams now needs to be estimated. The maximum shear force is not more than approximately 2,479 × 30 = 74,370 lb. The lever arm of the beam near the supports can be assumed to be 0·67 × 48 = 32 in. Hence the maximum shear stress = $\dfrac{74,370}{32 \times 9}$ = 264·6 lb/sq. in., so that shear reinforcement will be required. If the stirrups are calculated to resist this shearing force they are far too numerous to fit into the section, so that some of the shear must be resisted by inclined bars. Now regarding the 2·46 sq. in. of bottom steel, supposing this consists of two 1 in. dia. bars and two $\frac{7}{8}$ in. dia. bars, then the two $\frac{7}{8}$ in. dia. bars can be bent-up together at 45° as part of a 'single shear' system; these give a shear resistance

$$= 1·203 \times 20,000 \times \frac{1}{\sqrt{2}} = 17,000 \text{ lb}.$$

Hence the stirrups need to carry a shear force of 74,370 − 17,000 = 57,370 lb, using $\frac{3}{8}$ in. dia., two-arm, mild steel stirrups. From equation (5,35) the spacing required

$$= \frac{0·221 \times 20,000 \times 32}{57,370} = 2·463 \text{ in.,}$$

say 2 in. centres. Referring to Chapter 5 it can be calculated that the single bent-up bar system will be effective for an approximate distance of 5 ft from a support. Hence at a section 5 ft from the support, the shear force $\simeq \frac{10}{15} \times$ 74,370 = 49,600 lb. From a sketch of the stiffening beam, the depth at this section is approximately 54 in., hence the spacing of the $\frac{3}{8}$ in. dia. (two-arm) stirrups now required

$$= \frac{0·221 \times 20,000 \times 0·67 \times 54}{49,600} = 3·23 \text{ in., say 3 in. centres.}$$

A 1:2:4 concrete is usually adequate for a stiffening beam of this type, hence the permissible[3] concrete shear stress = 100 lb/sq. in. For simplicity, if the variation in depth is ignored, the length of the beam from mid-span which requires no shear reinforcement = $\dfrac{100}{264·6} \times 15 = 5·66$ ft.

The $\frac{3}{8}$ in. (two-arm) stirrups in a stiffening beam for estimate purposes can therefore be as follows: at 2 in. centres for a distance of 5 ft from a support, at 3 in. centres for a distance from 5 ft to 10 ft from a support, and at 9 in. centres (nominal) for the remainder of the span. Hence the

total weight of the stirrups per 30 ft long stiffening beam can be calculated as follows:

  total length of ⅜ in. dia. bar:
    60 stirrups (at 2 in. centres) × approx. average length
    of a stirrup (4 ft 3 in. + 4 ft 3 in. + 7 in. + 7 in. + 6 in.) = 610 ft
    40 stirrups (at 3 in. centres) × approx. average length
    of a stirrup (4 ft 9 in. + 4 ft 9 in. + 7 in. + 7 in. + 6 in.) = 447 ft
    14 stirrups (at 9 in. centres) × approx. average length
    of a stirrup (5 ft 8 in. + 5 ft 8 in. + 7 in. + 7 in. + 6 in.) = 182 ft
  ∴ 610 + 447 + 182 = 1,239 ft.
  ∴ total weight of the ⅜ in. dia. stirrups per stiffening beam = 1,239
    × 0·375 = 466 lb.

The reinforcement in the columns is estimated by designing the
columns to resist the vertical loads, due allowance being made in the
assessment of these loads if the shells are spanning continuously. Bending moments can be assessed, and considered in the design, for the external (i.e. boundary) columns by considering the elastic distribution of
bending moments between the columns and shell, the relative moments
of inertia being calculated assuming the members to be uncracked (for
simplicity) and the shells to act as beams transmitting bending moments
to the columns. Some engineers ignore moments in all columns; there
are doubts whether these can be transmitted effectively from such shells
to infrequent columns, and in any case the moments in the columns
could plastically redistribute into the shells to some extent towards
failure. Wilby usually prefers to consider moments in the columns as
this controls the size of cracks at working loads and the extra reinforcement required is often negligible compared to the total reinforcement in
the scheme.

7.4 Estimating reinforcement for unsymmetrical shells

Similar procedures to those in §7.3 can be quite simply developed.
Probably the most common type of unsymmetrical shell is the N-light
barrel vault roof. For estimate purposes the component of the total
load in a direction parallel to the glazing can be regarded as supported
by the shell and valley beam independently; 45% of the load being
resisted by the shell and the rest by the valley beam. The steel in the
valley beam is simply estimated and the steel in the shell portion is
estimated as in §7.3. For shells of 40 ft span the total steel in a N-light
scheme of shells is approximately three times the amount of steel in a
symmetrical scheme of shells, for 60 ft span shells the N-lights require
approximately 1·7 times the steel required for the symmetrical shells, and

for 90 ft span shells the N-lights require approximately 1·3 times the
the steel required for the symmetrical shells.

7.5   Design of shells

The design consists of estimating the dimensions of the members and
then analysing elastically for the internal stresses. Reinforcement is designed to resist the tensile stresses and the permissible concrete compressive stresses must not be exceeded; deflections can also be calculated.
If the reinforcement is too heavy to fit into the sections, if the concrete
compressive stresses or the deflections are too great, then the dimensions
of the shell have to be increased and the analysis repeated until a satisfactory solution is found. Experience and approximate designs (such as
the beam analogy) can usually decide upon dimensions which will not
need to be altered as a result of the subsequent elastic analysis. The
information in §7.2 is based on experience and can be used in this respect.

7.6   Elastic analysis of cylindrical shells

The problem is usually split into two parts for convenience, namely
the membrane condition and the edge load problem. Imagine a vertical
stand pipe, of the cross-section, and with pressures acting, as shown in
Fig. 50. The section considered is not restricted by ends, these being

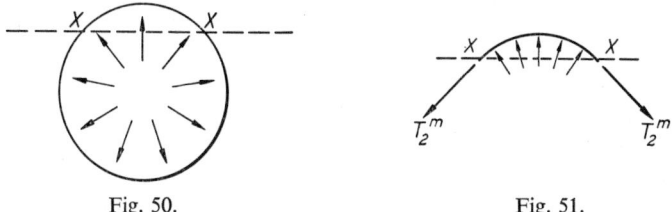

Fig. 50.   Fig. 51.

very remote. It is obvious that the pipe is subjected only to tensile
stresses around its periphery. In other words no bending moments occur
and the stresses are all within the plane of the pipe. Hence to satisfy
this theory, the pipe can be any thin membrane so thin and flexible that
it cannot resist bending moments but yet it must be able to resist tensile
stresses. This pipe could therefore be described as being in a *membrane
condition*. This means generally that it is incapable of taking bending
moments but able to withstand tensile or compressive stresses in two
dimensions, and shear stresses within its plane. The important point
about this membrane condition is that it is a statically determinate condition and hence relatively simple to analyse.

The pipe can be cut at a section, say XX in Fig. 50, and the segment
shown in Fig. 51 remains in the same membrane condition, providing
membrane reactions (T_2^m) at the edges replace the previous internal

stresses at the section *XX*. If instead of this being a segment of a pipe it were now considered to be the cross-section of the shell portion of a barrel vault roof, then the membrane reactions ($T_2{}^m$) would normally have to be provided by edge beams, see Fig. 52. The edge beams how-ever are not usually rigid enough to provide the necessary membrane reactions ($T_2{}^m$). The analytical approach is therefore as follows:

   (i) Assume the shell carries the loading in a statically determinate membrane condition.
  (ii) Calculate the elastic displacements of the edges of the shell in the membrane condition (i).
 (iii) Assume the edge beams provide the membrane reactions required by the shell in the membrane condition (i). Then calculate the

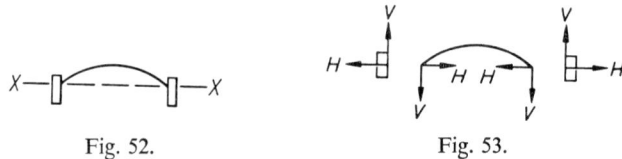

Fig. 52.   Fig. 53.

displacements of the point of the edge beam which is in contact with the shell due to it carrying these membrane reactions.

 (iv) The displacements of (ii) and (iii) do not normally agree, but yet the two members are fastened together and always remain together. Equal and opposite forces have therefore to be introduced between the edge of the shell and the edge beam at both sides to make the displacements (ii) and (iii) equal one another. These forces are equal and opposite internal forces and do not of course alter the external equilibrium. The calculation of these forces is a statically indeterminate problem. Such forces are edge loads on the shell e.g. see Fig. 53 (*V* and *H*). The membrane theory cannot apply to these loads because the shell must, fairly obviously, resist bending moments and radial shears, (cf. an arch), to support edge loads only.
  (v) The internal forces or stresses and moments at various points in the shell are calculated for the edge loads of (iv).
 (vi) The internal forces or stresses at various points in the shell are calculated for the membrane condition (i).
(vii) The stresses of (v) and (vi) are superimposed upon one another to obtain the final stresses in the barrel vault roof.
(viii) The edge beams are designed to resist the membrane reactions mentioned in (iii) and also the edge forces of (iv), superimposed upon one another.

The above is a simple explanation of the procedure usually adopted for designing barrel vault roofs. Hence it is only necessary to calculate the following:

(a) The forces in the shell for the membrane condition, and the corresponding edge displacements.

(b) The forces and moments in the shell for pairs of symmetrical and anti-symmetrical unit edge loads; also the corresponding edge displacements. These quantities for other than unit loads are obtained *pro rata* from the values for unit loads, see §7.9.

(c) The stresses and displacements of an edge beam for unit edge loads (i.e. loads at the position of the edge of the shell). These quantities for other than unit loads are obtained *pro rata* from the values for unit loads.

7.7 Load harmonics

To solve the various mathematical equations employed in the design of shells it is necessary to express the loading on the shell in terms of a Fourier's Series. In practice, shells are often designed to carry their self weight and a snow load of 15 lb/sq. ft of curved surface area. This is slightly more conservative than taking the snow as 15 lb/sq. ft of plan area, but simplifies the design, as all the loading can then be considered as a load per unit of curved surface area. Thus, assuming the origin of x to be at the centre of the span L, the loading can be expressed as:

$$g \cdot \frac{4}{\pi} \left[\cos \frac{\pi x}{L} - \frac{1}{3} \cos \frac{3\pi x}{L} + \frac{1}{5} \cos \frac{5\pi x}{L} \cdots \right]$$

Experience shows that generally it is satisfactory to consider only the first term of this series; hence the loading is considered as $\frac{4}{\pi} g \cdot \cos \frac{\pi x}{L}$ per unit area of the surface.

7.8 Membrane analysis

Considering an infinitesimally small element of a shell, see Fig. 54, and a loading of $\frac{4}{\pi} g \cdot \cos \frac{\pi x}{L}$ it can be proved[38] that:

$$T_1 = \frac{-4}{\pi} \cdot \frac{L^2}{\pi^2} \cdot \frac{2g}{R} \cos (\theta - \phi) \cos \frac{\pi x}{L} \qquad \ldots (7,1)$$

$$T_2 = \frac{-4}{\pi} \cdot gR \cos (\theta - \phi) \cos \frac{\pi x}{L} \qquad \ldots (7,2)$$

$$\frac{dS}{dx} = \frac{4}{\pi} \cdot 2g \sin (\theta - \phi) \cos \frac{\pi x}{L} \qquad \ldots (7,3)$$

$$v = \frac{4L^2g}{\pi\pi^2Ed}\left[\frac{2L^2}{\pi^2R^2}+4\right]\sin(\theta-\phi)\cos\frac{\pi x}{L} \qquad \ldots\ldots(7,4)$$

$$w = \frac{4L^2g}{\pi\pi^2Ed}\left[\frac{\pi^2R^2}{L^2}+4+\frac{2L^2}{\pi^2R^2}\right]\cos(\theta-\phi)\cos\frac{\pi x}{L} \qquad \ldots\ldots(7,5)$$

$$\sigma = \frac{-4}{\pi}\frac{L^2}{\pi^2}\frac{2g}{RdE}\cos(\theta-\phi)\cos\frac{\pi x}{L} \qquad \ldots\ldots(7,6)$$

These equations give the information required for §7.6(a).

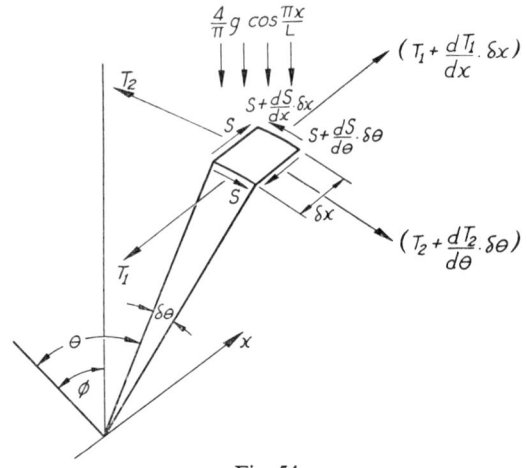

Fig. 54.

7.9 Edge load analysis

We now consider the calculations for §7.6(b). An eighth order partial differential equation results from an elastic analysis. This equation varies according to the approximations made in its derivation, that is according to the author of the theory. Popular theories in Britain are due to Schorer,[35] 'Shell-D', Jenkins,[36] Finsterwalder, and Tottenham's[38] modification of Schorer's theory. Tottenham[38] gives an indication of the range of shells for which Schorer's theory is adequate; see also Wilby[34] where a comparison is made between the Schorer and Jenkins equations for a N-light shell. For the purposes of this book Schorer's theory will be considered.

The solution of an eighth order differential equation contains eight arbitrary constants. These can be solved providing eight 'boundary' conditions are known. These conditions will be considered at the edges; at their mid-span points. If pairs of unit loads, see §7.9, are considered then the arbitrary constants can be reduced to four, and this can facilitate computation; it is assumed that electronic computers are not used but only ordinary calculating machines dealing with say 10 significant figures, or say 7 figure logarithms. The forces, moments and displacements for the shell subjected to pairs of unit loads are as follows:

$$M_2 = Q_{M2}(Aa_1 + Bb_1 + Cc_1 + Dd_1)\cos\frac{\pi x}{L} \quad \ldots(7,7)$$

$$N_2 = Q_{N2}(Aa_2 + Bb_2 + Cc_2 + Dd_2)\cos\frac{\pi x}{L} \quad \ldots(7,8)$$

$$T_2 = Q_{T2}(Aa_3 + Bb_3 + Cc_3 + Dd_3)\cos\frac{\pi x}{L} \quad \ldots(7,9)$$

$$\frac{dS}{ds} = Q_S(Aa_4 + Bb_4 + Cc_4 + Dd_4)\cos\frac{\pi x}{L} \quad \ldots(7,10)$$

$$T_1 = Q_{T1}(Aa_5 + Bb_5 + Cc_5 + Dd_5)\cos\frac{\pi x}{L} \quad \ldots(7,11)$$

$$v = Q_v(Aa_6 + Bb_6 + Cc_6 + Dd_6)\cos\frac{\pi x}{L} \quad \ldots(7,12)$$

$$w = Q_w(Aa_7 + Bb_7 + Cc_7 + Dd_7)\cos\frac{\pi x}{L} \quad \ldots(7,13)$$

$$\psi = Q_\psi(Aa_8 + Bb_8 + Cc_8 + Dd_8)\cos\frac{\pi x}{L} \quad \ldots(7,14)$$

where the coefficients are given in Table 19, and the infinitesimally small element of shell considered in deriving the above equations is shown in Fig. 55.

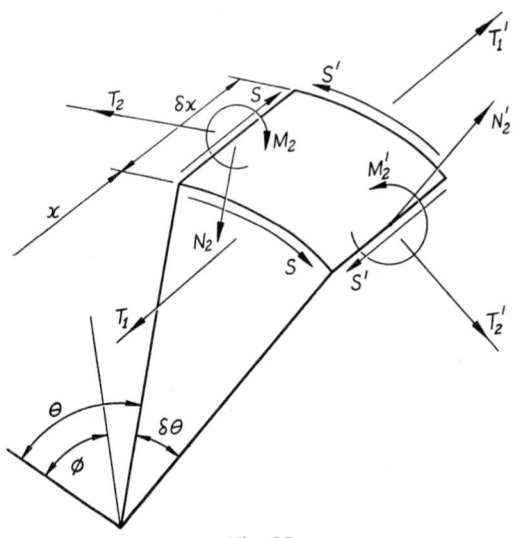

Fig. 55.

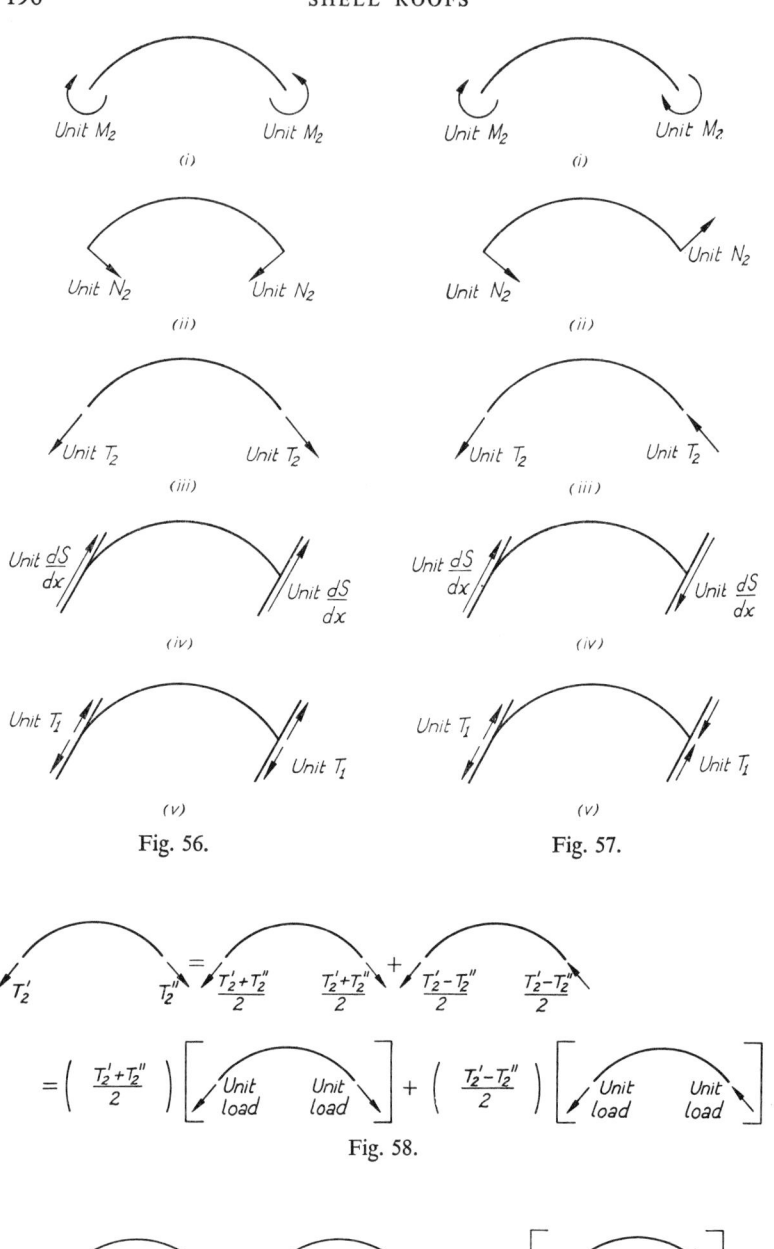

Fig. 56.

Fig. 57.

Fig. 58.

(i) Symmetrical loads   (ii) Anti-symmetrical loads   (iii)

Fig. 59.

7.10 Unit loads

Pairs of unit symmetrical and anti-symmetrical edge loads and moments are considered to simplify the design, see §7.9 and §7.6(b). Fig. 56 shows pairs of unit symmetrical edge loads and moments and Fig. 57 shows pairs of anti-symmetrical edge loads. Edge loads and

TABLE 19

Symmetrical Edge Loads
(lower sign gives values for anti-symmetrical edge loads)

a_1	$e^{-J_1\theta} \sin K_1\theta \pm e^{-J_1(\phi_K - \theta)} \sin K_1(\phi_K - \theta)$
b_1	$e^{-J_1\theta} \cos K_1\theta \pm e^{-J_1(\phi_K - \theta)} \cos K_1(\phi_K - \theta)$
c_1	$e^{-K_1\theta} \sin J_1\theta \pm e^{-K_1(\phi_K - \theta)} \sin J_1(\phi_K - \theta)$
d_1	$e^{-K_1\theta} \cos J_1\theta \pm e^{-K_1(\phi_K - \theta)} \cos J_1(\phi_K - \theta)$
a_2	$e^{-J_1\theta}(-\sin K_1\theta + k\cos K_1\theta) \mp e^{-J_1(\phi_K-\theta)}(-\sin K_1(\phi_K - \theta) + k\cos K_1(\phi_K - \theta))$
b_2	$e^{-J_1\theta}(-\cos K_1\theta - k\sin K_1\theta) \mp e^{-J_1(\phi_K-\theta)}(-\cos K_1(\phi_K - \theta) - k\sin K_1(\phi_K - \theta))$
c_2	$e^{-K_1\theta}(-k\sin J_1\theta + \cos J_1\theta) \mp e^{-K_1(\phi_K-\theta)}(-k\sin J_1(\phi_K - \theta) + \cos J_1(\phi_K - \theta))$
d_2	$e^{-K_1\theta}(-k\cos J_1\theta - \sin J_1\theta) \mp e^{-K_1(\phi_K-\theta)}(-k\cos J_1(\phi_K - \theta) - \sin J_1(\phi_K - \theta))$
a_3	$e^{-J_1\theta}(-\sin K_1\theta + \cos K_1\theta) \pm e^{-J_1(\phi_K-\theta)}(-\sin K_1(\phi_K - \theta) + \cos K_1(\phi_K - \theta))$
b_3	$e^{-J_1\theta}(-\cos K_1\theta - \sin K_1\theta) \pm e^{-J_1(\phi_K-\theta)}(-\cos K_1(\phi_K - \theta) - \sin K_1(\phi_K - \theta))$
c_3	$e^{-K_1\theta}(\sin J_1\theta + \cos J_1\theta) \pm e^{-K_1(\phi_K-\theta)}(\sin J_1(\phi_K - \theta) + \cos J_1(\phi_K - \theta))$
d_3	$e^{-K_1\theta}(\cos J_1\theta - \sin J_1\theta) \pm e^{-K_1(\phi_K-\theta)}(\cos J_1(\phi_K - \theta) - \sin J_1(\phi_K - \theta))$
a_4	$e^{-J_1\theta}(-k\sin K_1\theta + \cos K_1\theta) \mp e^{-J_1(\phi_K-\theta)}(-k\sin K_1(\phi_K - \theta) + \cos K_1(\phi_K - \theta))$
b_4	$e^{-J_1\theta}(-k\cos K_1\theta - \sin K_1\theta) \mp e^{-J_1(\phi_K-\theta)}(-k\cos K_1(\phi_K - \theta) - \sin K_1(\phi_K - \theta))$
c_4	$e^{-K_1\theta}(\sin J_1\theta - k\cos J_1\theta) \mp e^{-K_1(\phi_K-\theta)}(\sin J_1(\phi_K - \theta) - k\cos J_1(\phi_K - \theta))$
d_4	$e^{-K_1\theta}(\cos J_1\theta + k\sin J_1\theta) \mp e^{-K_1(\phi_K-\theta)}(\cos J_1(\phi_K - \theta) + k\sin J_1(\phi_K - \theta))$
a_5	$e^{-J_1\theta}(-\cos K_1\theta) \pm e^{-J_1(\phi_K-\theta)}(-\cos K_1(\phi_K - \theta))$
b_5	$e^{-J_1\theta} \sin K_1\theta \pm e^{-J_1(\phi_K - \theta)} \sin K_1(\phi_K - \theta)$
c_5	$e^{-K_1\theta} \cos J_1\theta \pm e^{-K_1(\phi_K - \theta)} \cos J_1(\phi_K - \theta)$
d_5	$e^{-K_1\theta}(-\sin J_1\theta) \pm e^{-K_1(\phi_K-\theta)}(-\sin J_1(\phi_K - \theta))$
a_6	$e^{-J_1\theta}(k\sin K_1\theta + \cos K_1\theta) \mp e^{-J_1(\phi_K-\theta)}(k\sin K_1(\phi_K - \theta) + \cos K_1(\phi_K - \theta))$
b_6	$e^{-J_1\theta}(k\cos K_1\theta + \cos K_1\theta) \mp e^{-J_1(\phi_K-\theta)}(k\cos K_1(\phi_K - \theta) - \cos K_1(\phi_K - \theta))$
c_6	$e^{-K_1\theta}(-\sin J_1\theta - k\cos J_1\theta) \mp e^{-K_1(\phi_K-\theta)}(-\sin J_1(\phi_K - \theta) - k\cos J_1(\phi_K - \theta))$
d_6	$e^{-K_1\theta}(-\cos J_1\theta + k\sin J_1\theta) \mp e^{-K_1(\phi_K-\theta)}(-\cos J_1(\phi_K - \theta) + k\sin J_1(\phi_K - \theta))$
a_7	$e^{-J_1\theta}(-\sin K_1\theta + \cos K_1\theta) \pm e^{-J_1(\phi_K-\theta)}(-\sin K_1(\phi_K - \theta) - \cos K_1(\phi_K - \theta))$
b_7	$e^{-J_1\theta}(-\cos K_1\theta + \sin K_1\theta) \pm e^{-J_1(\phi_K-\theta)}(-\cos K_1(\phi_K - \theta) + \sin K_1(\phi_K - \theta))$
c_7	$e^{-K_1\theta}(\sin J_1\theta - \cos J_1\theta) \pm e^{-K_1(\phi_K-\theta)}(\sin J_1(\phi_K - \theta) - \cos J_1(\phi_K - \theta))$
d_7	$e^{-K_1\theta}(\cos J_1\theta + \sin J_1\theta) \pm e^{-K_1(\phi_K-\theta)}(\cos J_1(\phi_K - \theta) + \sin J_1(\phi_K - \theta))$
a_8	$e^{-J_1\theta}(\sin K_1\theta + k\cos K_1\theta) \mp e^{-J_1(\phi_K-\theta)}(\sin K_1(\phi_K - \theta) + k\cos K_1(\phi_K - \theta))$
b_8	$e^{-J_1\theta}(\cos K_1\theta - k\sin K_1\theta) \mp e^{-J_1(\phi_K-\theta)}(\cos K_1(\phi_K - \theta) - k\sin K_1(\phi_K - \theta))$
c_8	$e^{-K_1\theta}(k\sin J_1\theta + \cos J_1\theta) \mp e^{-K_1(\phi_K-\theta)}(k\sin J_1(\phi_K - \theta) + \cos J_1(\phi_K - \theta))$
d_8	$e^{-K_1\theta}(k\cos J_1\theta - \sin J_1\theta) \mp e^{-K_1(\phi_K-\theta)}(k\cos J_1(\phi_K - \theta) - \sin J_1(\phi_K - \theta))$

hence unit edge loads need to be expressed in terms of Fourier's series, and experience shows that it is only usually necessary to consider the first terms of these series. Unit edge loads or moments are therefore $\dfrac{4}{\pi}\cos\dfrac{\pi x}{L}$, which is the first term of Fourier's series for unity, see §7.7.

Any edge loads can be expressed in terms of unit symmetrical and anti-symmetrical edge loads. This is illustrated for different edge loads T_2 in Fig. 58.

A unit load at one edge only can be considered by adding together the effect of pairs of unit symmetrical and anti-symmetrical loads and dividing the result by two; this is illustrated in the case of a unit force T_2 in Fig. 59.

7.11 Edge beam analysis

For simplicity, the edge beam can be considered to resist only the forces $\dfrac{dS}{dx}$, T_2 and N_2 at the edge of the shell; it also has to support its own weight. Experience shows that this gives satisfactory results in most practical cases.

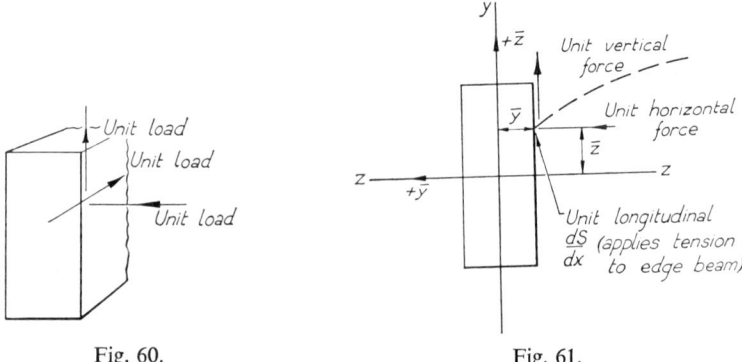

Fig. 60.   Fig. 61.

It can be shown that[38] a unit vertical load of $\dfrac{4}{\pi}\cos\dfrac{\pi x}{L}$, applied as shown in Figs. 60 and 61, produces the following displacements:

$$\text{Vertical upward deflection} = \frac{4}{\pi}\frac{L^4}{\pi^4}\frac{1}{EI_z}\cos\frac{\pi x}{L} \qquad \dots(7,15)$$

$$\text{Horizontal deflection} = \text{zero} \qquad \dots(7,16)$$

$$\sigma = \frac{4}{\pi}\frac{L^2}{\pi^2}\frac{\bar{z}}{EI_z}\cos\frac{\pi x}{L} \qquad \dots(7,17)$$

A unit horizontal load of $\dfrac{4}{\pi}\cos\dfrac{\pi x}{L}$, applied as shown in Figs. 60 and 61, produces the following displacements:

$$\text{Horizontal deflection to the left} = \frac{4}{\pi}\frac{L^4}{\pi^4}\frac{1}{EI_y}\cos\frac{\pi x}{L} \qquad \dots(7,18)$$

$$\text{Vertical deflection} = \text{zero} \qquad \dots(7,19)$$

$$\sigma = \frac{4}{\pi}\frac{L^2}{\pi^2}\frac{\bar{y}}{EI_y}\cos\frac{\pi x}{L} \qquad \dots(7,20)$$

A unit load $\dfrac{dS}{dx}$ of $\dfrac{4}{\pi}\cos\dfrac{\pi x}{L}$, applied as shown in Figs. 60 and 61, produces the following displacements:

$$\text{Vertical upward deflection} = \frac{4}{\pi} \frac{L^4}{\pi^4} \frac{\bar{z}}{EI_z} \cos \frac{\pi x}{L} \qquad \ldots(7,21)$$

$$\text{Horizontal deflection to the left} = \frac{4}{\pi} \frac{L^4}{\pi^4} \frac{\bar{y}}{EI_y} \cos \frac{\pi x}{L} \qquad \ldots(7,22)$$

$$\sigma = \frac{4}{\pi} \frac{L^2}{\pi^2} \frac{1}{E} \left[\frac{1}{A} + \frac{\bar{z}^2}{I_z} + \frac{\bar{y}^2}{I_y} \right] \cos \frac{\pi x}{L} \qquad \ldots(7,23)$$

7.12 Design procedure for an internal symmetrical shell

We now consider internal shells as indicated in Fig. 44, and it is assumed that such internal shells continue *ad infinitum* in both directions. As the shell is symmetrical and symmetrically loaded only four boundary conditions are required. These must not be conditions of symmetry, such as may be quoted at the crown, but must in fact be conditions at the junctions of adjacent shells. The boundary conditions at this junction are as follows:

(i) Horizontal deflection = zero, i.e. $v = -w \tan \phi$ $\qquad \ldots(7,24)$

(ii) The vertical components of T_2 and N_2 at the edge and the self weight of the valley thickening must summate to zero. This is a requirement of symmetry. Thus, $T_2 \sin \phi = N_2 \cos \phi + q$ $\qquad \ldots(7,25)$

(iii) Another requirement of symmetry at the edge is that,

$$\psi = 0 \qquad \ldots(7,26)$$

(iv) Also, from symmetry, $\dfrac{dS}{dx} = 0$ at the edge. $\qquad \ldots(7,27)$

The analysis, as described before, can be considered as a membrane analysis added to an edge load analysis. If the edge loads are T_{2E}, N_{2E} and $\dfrac{dS}{dx_E}$, then equations (7,24), (7,25), and (7,27) can be expressed as:

$$v^m + v_T T_{2E} + v_N N_{2E} + v_s \frac{dS}{dx_E}$$

$$= -\tan \phi \left(w^m + w_T T_{2E} + w_N N_{2E} + w_s \frac{dS}{dx_E} \right) \qquad \ldots(7,28)$$

$$(T_2{}^m + T_{2E}) \sin \phi = N_{2E} \cos \phi + q \qquad \ldots(7,29)$$

$$\frac{dS^m}{dx} + \frac{dS}{dx_E} = 0 \qquad \ldots(7,30)$$

where v_T is the displacement v of the shell edge for a pair of unit symmetrical edge loads T_2. It is calculated by substituting $T_2 = \dfrac{4}{\pi}$, $N_2 = \dfrac{dS}{dx}$ $= \psi = 0$, $x = \theta = 0$, in equations (7,8), (7,9), (7,10), and (7,14), determining the values this gives for A, B, C, and D. Then these values are used in equation (7,12) to determine v_T.

N.B. the coefficients used from Table 19 should refer to symmetrical edge loads.

Similarly v_N is calculated by substituting $N_2 = \dfrac{4}{\pi}$, $T_2 = \dfrac{dS}{dx} = \psi = 0$, $x = \theta = 0$, in equations (7,8), (7,9), (7,10), and (7,14), determining the values of A, B, C, and D, and then determining v_N from equation (7,12).

Similarly w_T is calculated substituting $T_2 = \dfrac{4}{\pi}$, $N_2 = \dfrac{dS}{dx} = \psi = 0$, $x = \theta = 0$, in equations (7,8), (7,9), (7,10), and (7,14), determining the values of A, B, C, and D, and then determining w_T from equation (7,13).

w_N, v_s, w_s, are obtained similarly. v^m, w^m, $T_2{}^m$ are calculated from equations (7,4), (7,5), and (7,2) for $x = \theta = 0$.

Hence equations (7,28), (7,29), and (7,30) can be solved for T_{2E}, N_{2E}, and $\dfrac{dS}{dx_E}$. Using these values and $\psi = 0$ in equations (7,8), (7,9), (7,10), and (7,14), values can be obtained for A, B, C, and D. With these values for A, B, C, and D substituted in equations (7,7) to (7,14), M_2, N_2, T_2, $\dfrac{dS}{dx}$, T_1, v, w, and ψ can be obtained for any values of θ and x, i.e. for any point in the shell. These values are due to the edge loads and must be added to the membrane values of T_2, $\dfrac{dS}{dx}$, T_1, v, w, and ψ at each point in the shell; the membrane forces are obtained from equations (7,1), (7,2), and (7,3) for any values of θ and x.

The only correction which needs to be made to these resultant values is to multiply the values of T_1 by $\dfrac{\pi^2}{8}$ [38].

7.13   Design procedure for an external symmetrical shell

This design procedure concerns a symmetrical shell with identical edge beams at both sides. In continuous systems such as those shown in Figs. 44 and 45, it is often satisfactory[38] to consider the end half shell and edge beam as half of a symmetrical system with edge beams.

For convenience, it is better with the edge beam to consider vertical and horizontal forces and displacements (V, H, δ_A and δ_B) at the junction of the shell and an edge beam in lieu of forces T_2 and N_2 and displacements v and w. Hence forces T_2 and N_2 and displacements v and w

need to be resolved horizontally and vertically. Thence from §7.11, the boundary conditions at the junction can be stated[40] as follows:

$$T_1 = \frac{L^2 d}{\pi^2} \left[T_2 \left(\frac{\bar{z} \sin \phi}{I_z} + \frac{\bar{y} \cos \phi}{I_y} \right) + N_2 \left(\frac{\bar{y} \sin \phi}{I_y} - \frac{\bar{z} \cos \phi}{I_z} \right) \right.$$
$$\left. + \frac{dS}{dx} \left(\frac{1}{A} + \frac{\bar{z}^2}{I_z} + \frac{\bar{y}^2}{I_y} \right) - \frac{q_2 \bar{z}}{I_z} \right] \qquad \dots (7,31)$$

$$T_2 = \frac{\pi^4 E}{L^4} \left[v(I_z \sin^2 \phi + I_y \cos^2 \phi) + w \sin \phi \cos \phi (I_y - I_z) \right]$$
$$- \frac{dS}{dx} (\bar{z} \sin \phi + \bar{y} \cos \phi) + q_2 \sin \phi \qquad \dots (7,32)$$

$$N_2 = \frac{\pi^4 E}{L^4} \left[v \sin \phi \cos \phi (I_y - I_z) + w(I_y \sin^2 \phi + I_z \cos^2 \phi) \right]$$
$$+ \frac{dS}{dx} (\bar{z} \cos \phi - \bar{y} \sin \phi) - q_2 \cos \phi \qquad \dots (7,33)$$

$$\psi = 0 \qquad \dots (7,34)$$

If the edge loads are T_{2E}, N_{2E}, and $\dfrac{dS}{dx_E}$ then,

$$v = v^m + v_T T_{2E} + v_N N_{2E} + v_S \frac{dS}{dx_E}$$

$$w = w^m + w_T T_{2E} + w_N N_{2E} + w_S \frac{dS}{dx_E}$$

$$T_2 = T_2{}^m + T_{2E}$$

$$T_1 = T_1{}^m + T_{1T} T_{2E} + T_{1N} N_{2E} + T_{1S} \frac{dS}{dx_E}$$

$$N_2 = N_{2E}$$

$$\frac{dS}{dx} = \frac{dS^m}{dx} + \frac{dS}{dx_E}$$

Where v_T is the deflection v for $T_2 = \dfrac{4}{\pi}$, $N_2 = \dfrac{dS}{dx} = \psi = \theta = x = 0$, using equations (7,8), (7,9), (7,10), (7,14), and (7,12) and Table 19.

w_T is the deflection w for $T_2 = \dfrac{4}{\pi}$, $N_2 = \dfrac{dS}{dx} = \psi = \theta = x = 0$, using equations (7,8), (7,9), (7,10), (7,14), and (7,13) and Table 19.

v_N is the deflection v for $N_2 = \dfrac{4}{\pi}$, $T_2 = \dfrac{dS}{dx} = \psi = \theta = x = 0$,

14

using equations (7,8), (7,9), (7,10), (7,14), and (7,12) and Table 19.

w_N is the deflection w for $N_2 = \dfrac{4}{\pi}$, $T_2 = \dfrac{dS}{dx} = \psi = \theta = x = 0$,

using equations (7,8), (7,9), (7,10), (7,14), and (7,13) and Table 19.

v_S is the deflection v for $\dfrac{dS}{dx} = \dfrac{4}{\pi}$, $T_2 = N_2 = \psi = \theta = x = 0$

using equations (7,8), (7,9), (7,10), (7,14), and (7,12) and Table 19.

w_S is the deflection w for $\dfrac{dS}{dx} = \dfrac{4}{\pi}$, $T_2 = N_2 = \psi = \theta = x = 0$,

using equations (7,8), (7,9), (7,10), (7,14), and (7,13) and Table 19.

T_{1T} is the force T_1 for $T_2 = \dfrac{4}{\pi}$, $N_2 = \dfrac{dS}{dx} = \psi = \theta = x = 0$,

using equations (7,8), (7,9), (7,10), (7,14), and (7,11) and Table 19.

T_{1N} is the force T_1 for $N_2 = \dfrac{4}{\pi}$, $T_2 = \dfrac{dS}{dx} = \psi = \theta = x = 0$,

using equations (7,8), (7,9), (7,10), (7,14), and (7,11) and Table 19.

T_{1S} is the force T_1 for $\dfrac{dS}{dx} = \dfrac{4}{\pi}$, $N_2 = T_2 = \psi = \theta = x = 0$,

using equations (7,8), (7,9), (7,10), (7,14), and (7,11) and Table 19.

$T_2{}^m$, $\dfrac{dS^m}{dx}$, $T_1{}^m$, v^m, w^m, are obtained from equations (7,1) to (7,5), for $x = \theta = 0$.

Hence from equations (7,31), (7,32), and (7,33), T_{2E}, N_{2E} and $\dfrac{dS}{dx_E}$ can be determined. Using these values and $\psi = 0$, in equations (7,8), (7,9), (7,10), and (7,14) values can be obtained for A, B, C, and D. With these values for A, B, C, and D substituted in equations (7,7) to (7,14), M_2, N_2, T_2, $\dfrac{dS}{dx}$, T_1, v, w, and ψ can be obtained for any values of θ and x, i.e. for any point in the shell. These values are due to the edge loads and must be added to the membrane values of T_2, $\dfrac{dS}{dx}$, T_1, v, w, and ψ at each point in the shell; the membrane forces are obtained from equations (7,1), (7,2), and (7,3) for any values of θ and x. The only correction is to multiply the values of T_1 by $\dfrac{\pi^2}{8}$.

The edge beam has to resist the resultant reaction between the shell and the edge beam and the self weight of the edge beam. Usually the main consideration is the bending moment about ZZ (see Fig. 61). This is caused by the vertical loading, i.e. the self weight algebraically added to the vertical components of $T_2{}^m$, $N_2{}^m$, T_{2E}, and N_{2E}, and the resultant longitudinal tension or compression caused by the algebraic sum of $\dfrac{dS^m}{dx}$ and $\dfrac{dS}{dx_E}$; the longitudinal stresses due to these latter forces must also be considered. The beam is often designed as though it were a homogeneous material; the maximum compressive stress should not exceed that permitted for the concrete and steel should be provided to take the tensile force.

EXAMPLE 7.13.1 (illustrating reinforcement system)

To design an external symmetrical shell roof given $L = 52$ ft, $R = 17.5$ ft, $d = 0.208$ ft, $W = 26$ ft, $H_1 = 3.75$ ft, $\bar{z} = -1.875$ ft, $\bar{y} = -0.375$ ft, and breadth of edge beam $= 0.75$ ft.

The method described above gives the results shown in Fig. 62, for the forces and moments in the shell at $x = 0$, except for S which refers to $x = 26$ ft, the units being lb and ft. The maximum (compressive) stress due to $T_2 = \dfrac{1,186}{12 \times 2.5} = 39.5$ lb/sq. in., which is insignificant. Similarly the maximum value of N_2 is insignificant. The steel required to resist the moments M_2 can therefore be calculated ignoring the effect of T_2 in this instance. One system is to have top and bottom layers of fabric to resist moments M_2. Area of fabric per ft to resist maximum negative $M_2 = \dfrac{281 \times 12}{30,000 \times 0.872 \times 1.7} = 0.0758$ sq. in. Use the fabric weighing 3.09 lb/sq. yd of Example (7.3.1). Area of fabric per foot to resist maximum positive $M_2 = \dfrac{211}{281} \times 0.0758 = 0.0569$ sq. in. Use the fabric weighing 2.17 lb/sq. yd of Example (7.3.1).

The maximum force $S \simeq 4,200$ lb/ft, the corresponding shear stress

$$= \frac{4,200}{3.5 \times 12} = 100 \text{ lb/sq. in.}$$

N.B. the shell has a thickness of 3.5 in. near to the support, see §7.2. It is good practice to provide shear reinforcement to resist this stress whatever the permissible shear stress of the concrete, as follows:

$$100 = \frac{\text{force in inclined bar}}{\text{spacing of bars} \times 3.5}$$

$$\therefore \quad \frac{20,000 \times \text{area bar}}{\text{spacing of bars}} = 350$$

$$\frac{\text{area bar}}{\text{spacing of bars}} = 0.017 \text{ sq. in/in.} = 0.204 \text{ sq. in/ft.}$$

Use $\frac{3}{8}$ in. dia. bars at 6 in. centres inclined at 45° to the junction of the shell with the stiffening beam.

The shear reinforcement is calculated at other points on the graph for S, shown in Fig. 62, in a similar way to the above. This steel is lapped with 'ell'-bars near to the valley and the stiffening beam. These ell-bars then tie into the valleys and the stiffening beams.

The maximum negative force $T_1 = 8,040$ lb/ft, hence the maximum compressive stress $= \dfrac{8,040}{12 \times 2 \cdot 5} = 268$ lb/sq. in., which can easily be resisted by the concrete. The maximum positive, or tensile, force

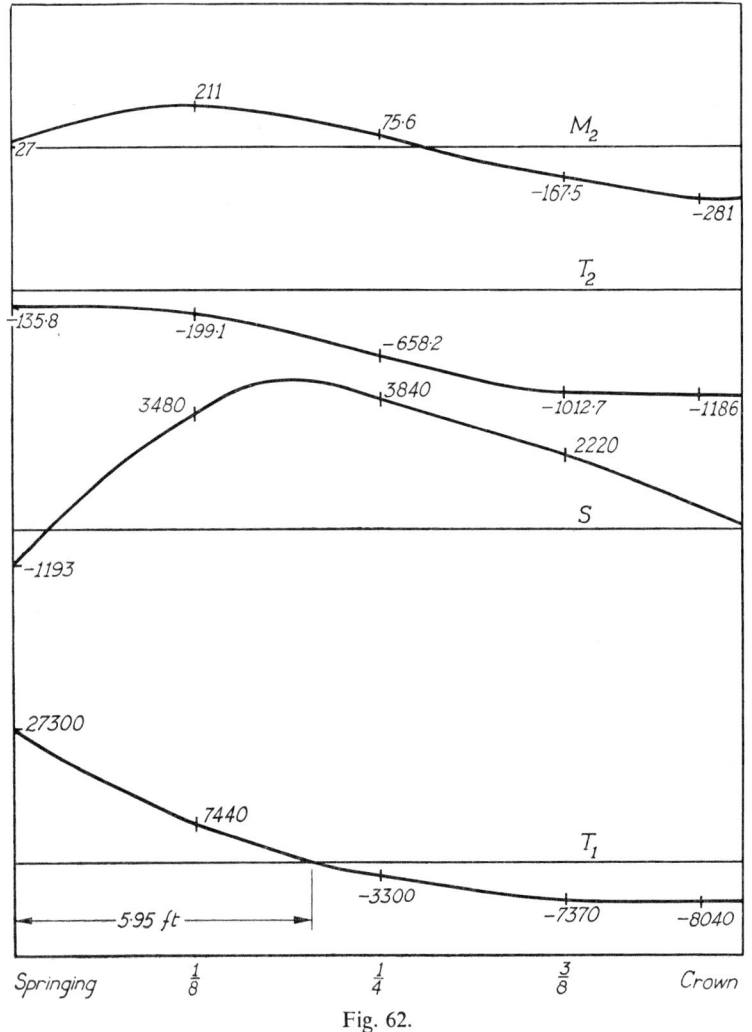

Fig. 62.

$T_1 = 27,300$ lb/ft. This has to be resisted by reinforcement and the area of such reinforcement at this particular locality $= \dfrac{27,300}{20,000} = 1\cdot365$ sq. in. per ft. Use, say, $\frac{7}{8}$ in. dia. bars at 5 in. centres. The spacing of these bars is increased according to the positive values of T_1. Referring to Fig. 62, this reinforcement is not required for points further away from the springing point than 5·95 ft.

With regard to the design of the edge beam. The vertically downwards load on the edge beam is 590 lb/ft due to its own weight plus 435·1 lb/ft due to the vertical components of $T_2{}^m$ and $N_2{}^m$ minus 282 lb/ft due to the vertical components of T_{2E} and N_{2E}, and this gives 743·1 lb/ft. The maximum bending moment (at mid-span) due to this load $= \dfrac{743\cdot1 \times 52^2}{8} = 252,000$ lb ft sagging. The longitudinal force imposed on the edge beam (at mid-span) due to the longitudinal shear force between the shell and the edge beam is $\dfrac{1,193 \times 52}{4} = 15,500$ lb (compression). The hogging bending moment due to this force $= 15,500 \times 1\cdot875 = 29,100$ lb ft. The resultant bending moment is therefore $252,000 - 29,100 = 222,900$ lb ft. The extreme fibre stresses are therefore:

$$\frac{-15,500}{9 \times 45} \pm \frac{222,900 \times 12}{\left(\dfrac{9 \times 45^2}{6}\right)} = -921 \text{ or } + 845 \text{ lb/sq. in.}$$

The concrete can withstand the top fibre compressive stress of 921 lb/sq. in. (*N.B.* this upstand beam will need stiffeners, see Fig. 44). The height of the neutral axis $= \dfrac{845 \times 45}{921 + 845} = 21\cdot55$ in.; the tensile force is therefore $= \dfrac{845}{2} \times 21\cdot55 \times 9 = 82,000$ lb. The total area of the tensile reinforcement therefore $= \dfrac{82,000}{20,000} = 4\cdot1$ sq. in., say six 1 in. dia. bars. The maximum shear force on the edge beam $= \dfrac{743\cdot1 \times 52}{2} = 19,350$ lb, giving a maximum shear stress $= \dfrac{19,350}{\frac{2}{3} \times 45 \times 9} = 71\cdot6$ lb/sq. in. No shear reinforcement is thus required; use nominal stirruping of say $\frac{3}{8}$ in. dia. at 9 in. centres.

7.14 Design procedure for an unsymmetrical shell

This design procedure concerns shells with different boundary conditions; a common example is a *N*-light shell, see Fig. 46. To illustrate the method an internal *N*-light shell will be considered; external shells are also dealt with in references (40) and (42).

As explained in §7.9, a unit load at one edge only can be considered by adding the effects of pairs of unit symmetrical and antisymmetrical loads and halving the result, see Fig. 59. The boundary conditions[40,42] at the shell edge (denoted by suffix L), immediately adjacent to the valley beam, are

$$(a) \quad T_{1L} = \frac{L^2 \, d}{\pi^2} \left[T_{2L} \left(\frac{\bar{z} \sin \phi_2}{I_z} + \frac{\bar{y} \cos \phi_2}{I_y} \right) + N_{2L} \left(\frac{\bar{y} \sin \phi_2}{I_y} - \frac{\bar{z} \cos \phi_2}{I_z} \right) \right.$$

$$\left. + \frac{dS}{dx_L} \left(\frac{1}{A} + \frac{\bar{z}^2}{I_z} + \frac{\bar{y}^2}{I_y} \right) - q_3 \left(\frac{\bar{z}}{I_z} \cos \phi_1 + \frac{\bar{y}}{I_y} \sin \phi_1 \right) - \frac{\bar{z}}{I_z} P \right]$$

$$\dots (7,35)$$

$$(b) \quad T_{2L} = \frac{\pi^4 E}{L^4} v_L [(I_z \sin^2 \phi_2 + I_y \cos^2 \phi_2) + w_L \sin \phi_2 \cos \phi_2 (I_y - I_z)]$$

$$- \frac{dS}{dx_L} (\bar{z} \sin \phi_2 + \bar{y} \cos \phi_2) + 0{\cdot}5 \, q_3 \sin (\phi_1 + \phi_2) + P \sin \phi_2$$

$$\dots (7,36)$$

$$(c) \quad N_{2L} = \frac{\pi^4 E}{L^4} [v_L \sin \phi_2 \cos \phi_2 (I_y - I_z) + w_L (I_y \sin^2 \phi_2 + I_z \cos^2 \phi_2)]$$

$$+ \frac{dS}{dx_L} (\bar{z} \cos \phi_2 - \bar{y} \sin \phi_2) - q_3 \cos (\phi_1 + \phi_2) - P \cos \phi_2$$

$$\dots (7,37)$$

$$(d) \quad \psi_L = 0 \qquad \dots (7,38)$$

Also the boundary conditions at the apex (denoted by suffix R) are:

$$(i) \quad P + T_{2R} \sin (\phi_1 + \phi_3) + N_{2R} \cos (\phi_1 + \phi_3) - q_4 \cos \phi_1 = 0 \dots (7,39)$$

$$(ii) \quad T_{2R} \cos (\phi_1 + \phi_3) - N_{2R} \sin (\phi_1 + \phi_3) + q_4 \sin \phi_1 = 0 \quad \dots (7,40)$$

$$(iii) \quad v_L \sin \phi_2 - w_L \cos \phi_2 + v_R \sin (\phi_1 + \phi_3) + w_R \cos (\phi_1 + \phi_3) = 0$$

$$\dots (7,41)$$

$$(iv) \quad \psi_R = 0 \qquad \dots (7,42)$$

$$(v) \quad \frac{dS}{dx_R} = 0 \qquad \dots (7,43)$$

Similarly, as in §7.12, if the edge loads are T_{2LE}, N_{2LE}, $\dfrac{dS}{dx_{LE}}$, T_{2RE}, N_{2RE}, and $\dfrac{dS}{dx_{RE}}$ then,

$$T_{2L} = T_{2L}{}^m + T_{2LE}$$

$$N_{2L} = N_{2LE}$$

$$\frac{dS}{dx_L} = \frac{dS^m}{dx_L} + \frac{dS}{dx_{LE}}$$

$$v_L = v_L{}^m + v_{TL}T_{2LE} + v_{TRL}T_{2RE} + v_{NL}N_{2LE}$$
$$+ v_{NLR}N_{2RE} + v_{SL}\frac{dS}{dx_{LE}} + v_{SLR}\frac{dS}{dx_{RE}}$$

$$w_L = w_L{}^m + w_{TL}T_{2LE} + w_{TRL}T_{2RE} + w_{NL}N_{2LE}$$
$$+ w_{NLR}N_{2RE} + w_{SL}\frac{dS}{dx_{LE}} + w_{SLR}\frac{dS}{dx_{RE}}$$

$$T_1 = T_1{}^m + T_{1TL}T_{2LE} + T_{1TRL}T_{2RE} + T_{1NL}N_{2LE}$$
$$+ T_{1NLR}N_{2RE} + T_{1SL}\frac{dS}{dx_{LE}} + T_{1SLR}\frac{dS}{dx_{RE}}$$

Similarly for the apex,

$$T_{2R} = T_{2R} + T_{2RE}$$

$$N_{2R} = N_{2RE}$$

$$\frac{dS}{dx_R} = \frac{dS^m}{dx_R} + \frac{dS}{dx_{RE}} \text{, etc.}$$

where v_{TL} is the deflection v_L for $T_{2L} = \frac{4}{\pi}$, $N_{2L} = \frac{dS}{dx_L} = \psi_L = \theta = x = 0$. Using equations (7,8), (7,9), (7,10), (7,14), and (7,12) and Table 19, symmetrical and anti-symmetrical loads are considered, added together and halved as explained before; v_{TRL} is the deflection v_L for $T_{2R} = \frac{4}{\pi}$, $N_{2R} = \frac{dS}{dx_R} = \psi_R = x = \theta = 0$, in equations (7,8), (7,9), (7,10), (7,14),

and $\theta = \phi_k$ in equation (7,12). Using Table 19 for the necessary coefficients, symmetrical and anti-symmetrical loads are considered, added together and halved as explained before; v_{TR} is similar to v_{TL} except that $\theta = \phi_k$, etc.

$T_{2L}{}^m$, $\dfrac{dS^m}{dx_L}$, $T_{1L}{}^m$, $v_L{}^m$, and $w_L{}^m$, are obtained from equations (7,1) to (7,5) for $x = \theta = 0$. $T_{2R}{}^m$, $\dfrac{dS^m}{dx_R}$, $T_{1R}{}^m$, $v_R{}^m$, and $w_R{}^m$, are obtained from equations (7,1) to (7,5) for $x = 0$, $\theta = \phi_k$.

Using the above and equation (7,43), $\dfrac{dS}{dx_{RE}}$ can be obtained. Then equations (7,35), (7,36), (7,37), (7,39), (7,40), and (7,41) can be used to obtain $\dfrac{dS}{dx_{LE}}$, N_{2LE}, N_{2RE}, T_{2LE}, T_{2RE} and P. Splitting these into symmetrical and anti-symmetrical cases, see Fig. 63, the forces, moments and displacements at any point in the shell can be obtained for these two cases and superimposed upon the relevant membrane values. The only correction is to multiply the values of T_1 by $\dfrac{\pi^2}{8}$.

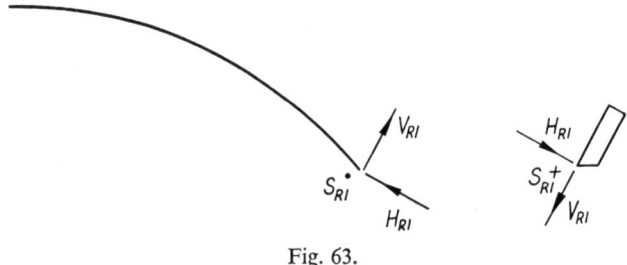

Fig. 63.

The valley beam is designed to resist the forces from the shell at its junction with the shell; its self weight and the force P in the window posts.

7.15 Electronic methods of designing shells

There are two possibilities; electronic digital[41] and analogue[40] computers. If the type of shell has already been programmed on an electronic digital computer, then this is an extremely rapid method; if this is not so the programming time can be prohibitive where only one certain type of shell is required to be designed. Wilby and Bellamy[40] have shown how an inexpensive electronic analogue computer may be used; the computing time compares favourably with the digital computer, but the programming time is relatively much more rapid. The analogue computer has a further advantage in that the problem can be observed in computation and it facilitates a partial design technique, as opposed to the usual trial and error method of estimating proportions and then modifying these in accordance with the results of the analysis. An electronic analogue computer may cost about £2,000 compared with about £35,000 for an electronic digital computer; it is thus more reasonable to acquire as part of the drawing office equipment.

The electronic digital computer is made to calculate the results in accordance with methods similar to the one outlined previously in this chapter; essentially it adds, subtracts, multiplies and divides. The electronic analogue computer can also integrate and hence it can deal directly with an eighth order differential equation representing the behaviour of the structure.

REFERENCES

1. Evans, R. H., 'Effect of Rate of Loading on Some Mechanical Properties of Concrete', *Proceedings* of the 1958 London Conference organized by the Mining Research Establishment of the N.C.B. in consultation with the Building Research Station, D.S.I.R., pp. 157–175.
2. Hajnal-Kónyi, K., Discussion to 'Recent Research on Deformed Reinforcing Bars", *Reinforced Concrete Review*, Vol. III, No. 7, 1955.
3. B.S. C.P. 114 (1957).
4. B.S. C.P. 2007 (1960).
5. 'Concrete versus Steel as a Building Frame', *The Times*, Oct. 3 1956.
6. Wilby, C. B., 'Overstrain in High-Tensile Reinforcing Bars and Resultant Design Recommendations concerning the Use of High-Tensile Steel at Bends and in Stirrups', *Indian Concrete Journal*, 1962.
7. Armstrong, W. E. I., 'Bond in Prestressed Concrete', *Jour. Inst. Civil Engineers*, 33, Nov. 1949.
8. Evans, R. H., and Robinson, G. W., "Bond Stresses in Prestressed Concrete from X-Ray Photographs', Paper No. 6025, *Proc. Inst. Civil Engineers*, Part 1, March 1953.
9. Bate, E. E. H., and Stewart, D. A., *Proc. Inst. Civil Engineers*, Part 3, Dec. 1955.
10. Evans, R. H., 'The Plastic Theories for the Ultimate Strength of Reinforced Concrete Beams', *Jour. Inst. Civil Engineers*, Dec. 1943.
11. B.S. 785 (1938).
12. Bennett, J. D., 'Design of Eccentrically-loaded Columns by the Load-Factor Method', *Concrete and Constructional Engineer*, Nov. 1957.
13. A.C.I. Building Code, 'Building Code Requirements for Reinforced Concrete', ACI 318–56, 1956.
14. Morgan, W., *Elementary Reinforced Concrete Design*, 2nd edition (Edward Arnold (Publishers) Ltd., London, 1958).
15. Reynolds, C. E., *Reinforced Concrete Designer's Handbook*, 6th edition (Concrete Publications Ltd., London, 1961).
16. Wilby, C. B., 'The Strength of Reinforced Concrete Beams in Shear', Ph.D. Thesis, University of Leeds, May 1949.
17. Wilby, C. B., 'The Strength of Reinforced Concrete Beams in Shear', *Magazine of Concrete Research*, Aug. 1951.
18. Wilby, C. B., 'Permissible Shear Stresses of the 1957 British Code of Practice', *J. Amer. Concrete Institute*, June 1958.
19. Talbot, A. N., University of Illinois Engineering Experimental Station, *Bull.* No. 14, 1907; *Bull.* No. 28, 1908; *Bull.* No. 29, 1909.
20. Mörsch, E., *Concrete-Steel Construction*, New York, 1910.
21. Hognestad, E., *University of Illinois Bulletin, Circular Series* No. 64, 1952.
22. Subbiah, K., and Smith, R. B. L., *Structural Engineer*, Nov. 1958.
23. Laupa, A., Siess, C. P., and Newmark, N. M., 'Strength in Shear of Reinforced Concrete Beams', *University of Illinois Bulletin* No. 428, 1955.
24. Jones, R., 'The Ultimate Strength of Reinforced Concrete Beams in Shear', *Magazine of Concrete Research*, No. 23, Aug. 1956.
25. Paduart, A., *Résistance du Béton Armé à l'Effort Tranchant* (Éditions Descer, Liège, 1947).
26. Hajnal-Kónyi, K., 'Recent Research on Deformed Reinforcing Bars', *Reinforced Concrete Review*, Vol. III, No. 7, 1955.

27. Andersen, P., *Proc. Amer. Soc. Civil Engineers*, Paper No. 2009, Oct. 1937.
28. Cowan, H. J., *Civil Engineering and Public Works Review*, Sept. 1953.
29. Andersen, P., *J. Amer. Concrete Institute*, Sept.–Oct. 1937.
30. Armstrong, S., *Proceedings* of a Symposium on the Strength of Concrete Structures, Cement and Concrete Association, London, May 1956.
31. Baker, A. L. L., *Reinforced Concrete* (Concrete Publications Ltd., London, 1949).
32. Turner, L., and David, V. C., *Inst. Civil Engineers Selected Engineering Papers*, No. 165, 1934.
33. B.S. C.P. 115 (1959).
34. Wilby, C. B., 'Precast Concrete Framed Roofs—Design of Joints and Use of Post-tensioning', *Indian Concrete Journal*, Feb. 1960.
35. Schorer, H., 'Line Load Action on Thin Cylindrical Shells', *Proc. Amer. Soc. Civil Engineers*, 1935.
36. Jenkins, R. S., '*Theory and Design of Cylindrical Shell Structures*', (The O.N. Arup Group of Consulting Engineers, London, 1947).
37. Lundgren, H., *Cylindrical Shells* (Danish Technical Press, Inst. Danish Civil Engineers, Copenhagen, 1951).
38. Tottenham, H., 'A Simplified Method of Design for Cylindrical Shell Roofs', *Structural Engineer*, June 1954.
39. Baker, A. L. L., 'A Plastic Design Theory for Reinforced and Prestressed Concrete Shell Roofs', *Magazine of Concrete Research*, July 1950.
40. Wilby, C. B., and Bellamy, N. W., *Elastic Analysis of Shells by Electronic Analogy* (Edward Arnold (Publishers) Ltd., London, 1962).
41. Gibson, J. E., *Computer Analysis of Cylindrical Shells* (E. & F. N. Spon Ltd., London, 1961).
42. Wilby, C. B. , 'A Method of Designing Northlight Shell Roofs', *Indian Concrete Journal*, Jan. 1961.

NOMENCLATURE

Chapter 1

$K, b, c, C, m \ldots$ constants
p = stress
t = time for §1.10; tensile stress for §1.14
n = 0·4
e = 2·7183
$P, P' \ldots$ forces (see Fig. 9)
l = bond length
T = tensile force in bar
A = cross-sectional area of bar
o = perimeter of bar
D = length of side of a square bar
d = diameter of bar
c_b = average bond stress between the steel and the concrete

Chapter 2

b = breadth of a rectangular beam
d = effective depth of the tension reinforcement
A_s = area of reinforcement in tension
C = longitudinal compressive force in concrete
T = longitudinal tensile force in reinforcement
m = modular ratio
c = extreme fibre stress in concrete
t = tensile stress in reinforcement
n = depth of neutral axis
E_c = Young's Modulus for concrete
E_s = Young's Modulus for steel
n_1 = n/d
p = percentage of tension reinforcement = $\dfrac{A_s}{bd} \times 100$
a = moment arm
a_1 = height above N.A. of line of action of C
a_2 = depth below N.A. of line of action of T
M = externally applied bending moment, or internal moment of resistance
r = t/c
a_1 = a/d
Q = $0·5cn_1a_1$

p_{st} = permissible stress in steel in tension (i.e. of t)
p_{cb} = permissible compressive stress in concrete in bending (i.e. of c)
W = point load required
δA_c = area of a small portion of concrete
δA_s = area of a small portion of steel
y = distance of δA_c from the neutral axis
y_1 = distance of δA_s from the neutral axis
s = strain at unit distance from the N.A.
I = Moment of Inertia, or Second Moment of Area, of whole of a section about the N.A.
A = equivalent area of a portion, or of the whole, of a cross-section
x = distance of centroid of the area of a portion of the cross-section from the axis XX
I_G = moment of inertia of a portion of a cross-section about its centroid
I_x = moment of inertia of whole of cross-section about axis XX
d_1 = effective depth of the compression reinforcement
t_c = stress in compression reinforcement
C' = force in compression reinforcement
A_{sc} = area of steel in compression
p' = percentage of compression reinforcement = $\dfrac{A_{sc}}{bd} \times 100$
d_s = depth of slab portion of a T-beam
B = breadth of slab portion of a T-beam
n_1 = n/d
w = uniformly distributed load
l = span of a beam

Chapter 3

d_s, B, C, T, d, b, A_s, p, p_{cb}, p_{st}, A_{sc}, p', d_1, n ... as in Chapter 2
c_1 = average compressive stress in compression zone
f_y = yield stress in tension reinforcement
n' = depth of compression zone
$k_2 n'$ = depth of line of action of C
M_u = ultimate moment of resistance
f_c' = compressive strength of 6 in. diameter by 12 in. long American standard concrete cylinder
u_w = compressive strength of 6 in. British standard concrete cube
M_r = moment of resistance at working loads
γ = a coefficient given in equation (3,25)
f_y' = yield stress in compression reinforcement
C_1 = gross compression force in concrete
C_1' = compression force in steel extra over the compression force in concrete it displaces

C' = compression force in steel

p_{sc} = permissible stress in steel in compression

Chapter 4

$E_s, E_c, m, I, I_G \ldots$ as in Chapter 2

$u_w, f_y', p_{sc}, f_y \ldots$ as in Chapter 3

P = working load on column

A_c' = net cross-sectional area of concrete

A_{sc} = area of steel in compression

P_u = ultimate load on column

P_0 = permissible axial load on column (i.e. permissible working load)

p_{cc} = permissible stress in concrete in direct compression

e = eccentricity of load on column

$g, b, d, D, d_1 \ldots$ dimensions shown in Fig. 25

$c, c' \ldots$ concrete stresses

$t_c, t_{c1} \ldots$ compressive steel stresses

$A_c, A_{c1} \ldots$ areas of compression reinforcement

$C_s, C_{s1} \ldots$ forces in compression steel

$C_3, C_4 \ldots$ gross compression forces in concrete

C_1 = gross compression force in concrete

A = gross cross-sectional area of column for §4.3; equivalent area of a portion, or of the whole of, a cross-section elsewhere than for §4.3

t = stress in steel in tension

A_t = area of tension reinforcement

n = depth of N.A.

T = force in steel in tension

x = distance of the centroid of the area of a portion of the cross-section from the axis XX for Table 11; dimension shown in Fig. 27 elsewhere than for Table 11

C = force resisted by concrete

c' = force in compression reinforcement

P_b = load on column for *balanced design* condition

$Xd = 0.85\,n$

E_s = Young's Modulus for steel

e_b = eccentricity of load on column for *balanced design* condition

A_b = equivalent area of the helical reinforcement

A_k = area of core of column bounded by helix reinforcement

Chapter 5

x = distance along a beam

δx = small portion of x (see Fig. 28)

M = bending moment at section distance x along beam (see Fig. 28)

δM = small portion of M

y, δy, b_1, y_1, y_2, b_2 ... dimensions shown in Fig. 28

c = extreme fibre concrete stress (see Fig. 28)

c' = concrete stress shown in Fig. 28

δc = small portion of c

$\delta c'$ = small portion of c'

n = depth of neutral axis

d = effective depth of tensile reinforcement

C = resultant compressive force in concrete

T = tensile force in reinforcement

F' = longitudinal force on elemental strip of breadth b and depth δy

F = shear force

q = shear stress

I, a, A_{sc}, d_1, p_{st} ... as in Chapter 2

b = breadth

B = breadth of slab portion of a T-beam

d_s = depth of slab portion of a T-beam

F_t = diagonal tensile force (see Fig. 29)

S = horizontal spacing of stirrups

r = percentage of web reinforcement

w = load per unit length

θ = angle of inclination of web reinforcement to horizontal

ψ, ϕ ... angles shown in Fig. 30

P = total force in all the arms of a stirrup, or in all the bent-up bars at one locality

C_w, T_1, T_2 ... forces shown in Fig. 30

αA_s = area of bars bent up at one locality

p_{ss} = permissible tensile stress in inclined bar when used as shear reinforcement

l = total length of a bar (see page 130)

σ = total perimeter of bars in tension

c_{lb} = local bond stress

m_s = modular ratio in shear = modulus of elasticity in shear for steel divided by the modulus of elasticity in shear for concrete

A_s = area of steel

R, R_s ... radii shown in Fig. 32

J = polar moment of inertia

M_T = torsional moment

D = dimension shown in Fig. 33

q_T, q_T' ... shear stresses shown in Fig. 33

p_{cs} = permissible stress in concrete in shear (i.e. diagonal tension)

u_w = compressive strength of 6 in. British standard concrete cubes

Chapter 6

A_T = equivalent area of beam section excluding area of top or compression reinforcement

A_B = equivalent area of beam section excluding area of bottom or tension reinforcement

A_T' = area of top or compression reinforcement

A_B' = area of bottom or tension reinforcement

m = modular ratio

e_T = eccentricity of P_T when top reinforcement is excluded (measured from N.A.)

e_B = eccentricity of P_B when bottom reinforcement is excluded (measured from N.A.)

f_T = stress of concrete at top (compression) fibre

f_B = stress of concrete at bottom fibre

f_t = tensile stress

f_{TS} = top steel stress

f_{BS} = bottom steel stress

I_{TR} = moment of inertia excluding top reinforcement

I_{BR} = moment of inertia excluding bottom reinforcement

I_{TC} = moment of inertia excluding top concrete (owing to tensile cracks in top concrete)

I_{BC} = moment of inertia excluding bottom concrete (owing to tensile cracks in bottom concrete)

n_{TR} = depth of N.A. excluding top reinforcement

n_{BR} = depth of N.A. excluding bottom reinforcement

n_{TC} = depth of N.A. excluding top concrete

n_{BC} = depth of N.A. excluding bottom concrete

P_T = Initial Prestressing Force in top reinforcement

P_B = Initial Prestressing Force in bottom reinforcement

p_T' = loss in P_T due to strain

p_B' = loss in P_B due to strain

p_T'' = loss in P_T due to shrinkage

p_B'' = loss in P_B due to shrinkage

p_T''' = loss in P_T due to creep

p_B''' = loss in P_B due to creep

p_T = total loss in $P_T = p_T' + p_T'' + p_T'''$

p_B = total loss in $P_B = p_B' + p_B'' + p_B'''$

z_1 = depth of top reinforcement from top

z_2 = depth of bottom reinforcement from bottom

$P_T' = P_T - p_T'' - p_T''' = P_T -$ shrinkage loss $-$ creep loss

$P_B' = P_B - p_B'' - p_B''' = P_B -$ shrinkage loss $-$ creep loss

D = the overall depth of the beam

I_G, I, n, a, E_s, E_c ... as in Chapter 2
b = breadth of rectangular beam
n_e, e, d ... dimensions shown in Fig. 40
A ... for Tables 12 to 18, as in Chapter 2; in text on pages 157 and
          169 = total cross-section of beam ignoring reinforcement
x ... on page 170, dimension shown in Fig. 42; elsewhere, as in
          Chapter 2
f = principal stress (tensile is positive)
f_1, f_2 ... direct stresses perpendicular in direction to one another
f_s = shear stress
P, S ... as in Chapter 5
f_t = principal tensile stress at working loads
p_t = limiting principal tensile stress at working loads
θ = angle of inclination of tendon to horizontal
f_{tu} = principal tensile stress calculated for ultimate loads
A_w = cross-sectional area of inclined tendons
Z_T, Z_B, $Z_T{}'$, $Z_B{}'$, K_B, K_T ... defined on page 146
f_{y1} = maximum stress in shear reinforcement at the ultimate shearing
          force, i.e. a stress not exceeding 80% of the yield stress (or
          0·2% proof stress where appropriate)
P_u = ultimate value of P, corresponding to a stress f_{y1}

Chapter 7

R = radius of shell
t = thickness of shell
t_1 = thickness of shell at springing
t_2 = dimension shown in Figs. 44, 45, 46
L = span of shell (see Fig. 48)
D_2, D_3 ... dimensions shown in Fig. 46
D_1 = depth of valley beam
W = width of shell
H_1 = depth of edge beam
$T_2{}^m$ ... membrane force shown in Fig. 51
V = vertical edge load on shell (see Fig. 53)
H ... in §7.2 and §7.3 = overall height of shell; elsewhere = hori-
          zontal edge load on shell (see Fig. 53)
g = total load on shell per unit of curved surface area
x = distance in direction of span of shell measured from centre of
          span
T_1 = longitudinal force per unit distance
T_2 = tangential force per unit distance
S = shear force per unit distance
v = tangential displacement in direction of T_2

w = radial displacement

σ = stress in direction of T_1

d = thickness of shell

E = Young's Modulus for concrete

ϕ ... in §7.2 and §7.3, angle shown in Figs. 44 and 45; elsewhere, angle shown in Figs. 54 and 55

θ ... in §7.2, angle shown in Fig. 46; elsewhere, angle shown in Figs. 54 and 55

M_2 = bending moment shown in Fig. 55

N_2 = radial shear force shown in Fig. 55

$$\psi = \frac{1}{R}\frac{dw}{d\theta} \qquad Q_{M2} = 1 \qquad Q_{N2} = \frac{1 \cdot 098\sqrt{r}}{R}$$

$$Q_{T2} = \frac{r}{R} \qquad Q_S = \frac{1 \cdot 554 r\sqrt{r}}{R^2} \qquad Q_{T1} = \frac{2\sqrt{3}}{d}$$

$$Q_v = \frac{2 \cdot 196 r^2 \sqrt{r}}{Eda^2} \qquad Q_w = \frac{2r^3}{Eda^2} \qquad Q_\psi = \frac{3 \cdot 108 r^3 \sqrt{r}}{Eda^2 R}$$

$a_1, b_1, c_1, d_1, a_2, b_2 \ldots c_8, d_8 \ldots$ defined in Table 19

$A, B, C,$ and $D \ldots$ arbitrary constants of integration

e = $2 \cdot 7183$

J_1 = $1 \cdot 098\sqrt{r}$

K_1 = $0 \cdot 455\sqrt{r}$

ϕ_K = angle subtended by whole segment of shell at centre of circle to which it belongs = 2ϕ

k = $0 \cdot 4142$

$y, \bar{y}, z, \bar{z} \ldots$ coordinates shown in Fig. 61

I_z = moment of inertia of edge beam about axis zz

I_y = moment of inertia of edge beam about axis yy

q = self weight of valley thickening, for a half-shell

E as a suffix denotes edge loads (see page 199)

m as a superscript denotes membrane condition at edge of shell where $x = \theta = 0$ (see page 200)

v_T = value of v at edge of shell for unit symmetrical edge loads T_2 (for more detail see pages 200 and 201)

v_N = value of v at edge of shell for unit symmetrical edge loads N_2 (for more detail see pages 200 and 201)

v_S = value of v at edge of shell for unit symmetrical edge loads $\dfrac{dS}{dx}$ (for more detail see pages 200 and 202)

w_T = value of w at edge of shell for unit symmetrical edge loads T_2 (for more detail see pages 200 and 201)

w_N = value of w at edge of shell for unit symmetrical edge loads N_2 (for more detail see pages 200 and 202)

w_S = value of w at edge of shell for unit symmetrical edge loads $\dfrac{\mathrm{d}S}{\mathrm{d}x}$ (for more detail see pages 200 and 202)

δ_A = deflection in direction of V in Fig. 53

δ_B = deflection in direction of H in Fig. 53

q_2 = weight of edge beam per unit length; the weight of the shell thickening near to the edge beam is usually included in this quantity

T_{1T} = value of T_1 at edge of shell for unit symmetrical edge loads T_2 (for more detail see page 202)

T_{1N} = value of T_1 at edge of shell for unit symmetrical edge loads N_2 (for more detail see page 202)

T_{1S} = value of T_1 at edge of shell for unit symmetrical edge loads $\dfrac{\mathrm{d}S}{\mathrm{d}x}$ (for more detail see page 202)

L, R as suffixes are described on page 206

ϕ_2 = angle between the bottom edge radius and glazing posts of a Northlight

q_3 = weight of raker beam per unit length of a Northlight shell

P = force per unit width transmitted by glazing posts in a Northlight

ϕ_3 = angle between the vertical and the top edge radius of a Northlight

ϕ_1 = angle of inclination to the vertical of Northlight glazing posts

Abbreviations

M.S. mild steel

N.A. neutral axis

kip. thousand pounds

MISCELLANEOUS EXAMINATION QUESTIONS

[B.S. CP114 was available for use by the candidate in Questions 11, 13, 16, 36, 37]

1. For singly reinforced concrete beams of rectangular section show that under economic conditions of design the neutral axis depth factor is given by $n_1 = 1/(1 + p_{st}/m \cdot p_{cb})$. Prepare a design chart for such beams by plotting M/bd^2 to r for values of r between 0·5% and 3·5% and using $p_{st} = 19,000$ lb/sq. in., $p_{cb} = 1,200$ lb/sq. in. and $m = 16$. A beam section has an effective depth of 20 in. and main steel consisting of four 1 in. diameter bars. Using the chart or otherwise, calculate the economic width of the section and find the ratios between the moment of resistance for this section and those of similar sections with:—
(a) half the width
(b) twice the width.
(Univ. of London, Part II, 1962, time allowed = 36 minutes)

2. A reinforced concrete beam is simply supported over an effective span of 16 ft. with a clear span of 15 ft. The section is constant, having an overall depth of 22 in. and a width of 9 in. The longitudinal tensile steel consists of two rows, each of four $\frac{3}{4}$ in. diameter bars. The beam carries a load that varies linearly in intensity from zero at one end of the clear span to 4,200 lb/ft at the other.
Design shear reinforcement for the full length of the beam. One or more bent up bars are to be used together with $\frac{3}{8}$ in. diameter stirrups.
$p_{st} = 20,000$ lb/sq. in., $p_{cb} = 800$ lb/sq. in., $a_1 = \frac{6}{7}$
density of concrete = 144 lb/cu. ft.
(Univ. of London, Part II, 1962, time allowed = 36 minutes)

3. Design a doubly reinforced concrete beam section of overall size 23 inch × 10 inch, having cover to bar centres of 2 inches, capable of carrying a bending moment of 90,000 lb ft. Steel must develop 20,000 lb/in.² in tension and concrete 1,000 lb/in.² in compression, being assumed to have no strength in tension. The modular ratio is 15. What is the stress in the compression steel?
(Univ. of London, Part II, 1962, time allowed = 36 minutes)

4. A reinforced concrete beam has a rectangular section, 15 in. wide by 16 in. deep overall. It is required to have an ultimate moment of 3·5 × 10⁶ lb-in. Determine suitable numbers of main reinforcing bars at the top and bottom of the section, ensuring that ample warning of

219

failure would be given should the beam be grossly overloaded. The only bar size available is 1 in. diameter and $1\frac{1}{2}$ in. cover to the steel is required; the bottom steel should be arranged in two equal rows. Calculate the resistance moment of the section you design.

$$f_y = 42,000 \text{ lb/sq. in., } \quad f_y' = 38,000 \text{ lb/sq. in., } \quad u_w = 4,500 \text{ lb/sq. in.}$$

(Univ. of London, Part III, 1962, time allowed = 36 minutes)

5. A symmetrical post-tensioned concrete beam of 30 ft span has the following characteristics:

Depth = 15 in.
$I = 2,000$ in.⁴
Initial tension = 120,000 lb/sq. in.
Weight of concrete = 144 lb/cu. ft
Cross sectional area = 100 sq. in.
Area of steel wires = 0·88 sq. in.
Eccentricity at mid-span = 4 in.

A series of such beams are placed at 3 ft centres and a $4\frac{1}{2}$ in. slab is cast on to the upper flanges making a composite floor construction, $19\frac{1}{2}$ in. deep. Shear connectors between beam and slab ensure combined structural action. Two construction procedures are possible:

(a) allow the beam to carry the dead load of the slab while it is cast,
or (b) prop the beam during casting of the slab and until it has hardened.

In both cases full composite action is achieved when the slab has matured and the floor is then required to carry a uniform live load. Neglecting changes in the tension of the steel calculate, in the two cases, those live loads which would cause zero stress at the bottom of the beam. Sketch diagrams showing the distribution of stresses at all stages. Disregard shrinkage and assume that the concretes in the beam and slab are similar.

(Univ. of London, Part III, 1962, time allowed = 36 minutes)

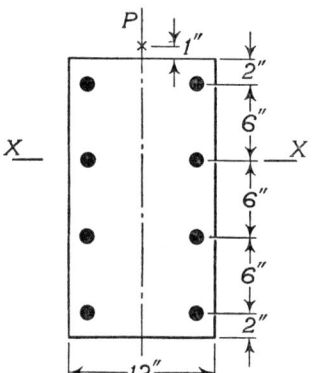

6. A short reinforced concrete column of the section shown is reinforced with 8 bars, each of 0·5 sq. in. area. A load, normal to the section, is applied at P, 1 in. from the compression face. The line XX shows the position of the neutral axis under ultimate conditions. Calculate the *working* load using the ultimate load method.

Determine the position of the neutral axis under elastic conditions. Why does this differ from the line XX? Assuming that elastic conditions exist at working load, find the maximum steel and concrete stresses when the column is subjected to the load previously calculated.

$$p_{cc} = 1,400 \text{ lb/sq. in.}, \qquad p_{st} = p_{sc} = 20,000 \text{ lb/sq. in.},$$

$$\text{maximum strain in concrete} = 0 \cdot 0033$$

$$E_s = 30 \times 10^6 \text{ lb/sq. in.}, \qquad m = 15.$$

(Univ. of London, Part III, 1962, time allowed = 36 minutes)

7. A reinforced concrete frame is shown, made up of columns AB and BC and beam BD. The ends A, C, and D are fixed and B is a rigid joint. The sections of the columns are 12 in. × 12 in. and the beam is 12 in. wide by 18 in. deep overall. Column BC is reinforced with a 1 in. diameter bar in each corner with $1\frac{1}{2}$ in. cover. Calculate the maximum steel and concrete stresses in column BC when:—

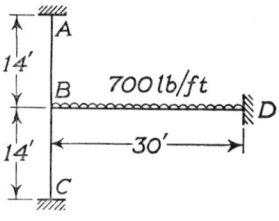

(a) beam BD is unloaded giving an axial load of 60 tons at B. Derive and use the modular ratio formula.
(b) the axial load is applied together with a bending moment due to the beam loading shown.

$$m = 15, \text{ and density of concrete} = 144 \text{ lb/cu. ft.}$$

(Univ. of London, Part II, 1962, time allowed = 36 minutes)

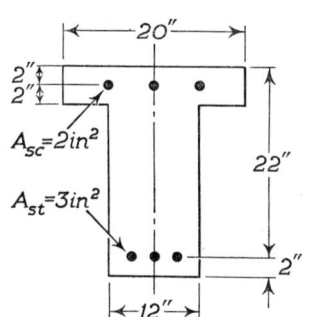

8. State the assumptions made in the analysis by the elastic theory of T-beam sections in reinforced concrete.

Calculate the moment of resistance of the doubly reinforced T-beam section shown.

$$p_{st} = 20,000 \text{ lb/sq. in.},$$

$$p_{cb} = 800 \text{ lb/sq. in.},$$

$$m = 15.$$

(Univ. of London, Part II, 1962, time allowed = 36 minutes)

9. A reinforced concrete T-beam is required to carry a uniformly distributed load of 2,900 lb per foot run (including its own weight) on a simply supported span of 20 ft. The slab is 5 in. thick, the rib is 10 in. wide, the overall depth is 24 in. and the centroid of the steel reinforcement may be assumed to be at $2\frac{1}{2}$ in. from the lower edge. The working stresses are 1,200 lb/sq. in. in the concrete and 20,000 lb/sq. in. in the steel, and the modular ratio is 15. Making reasonable assumptions as to the position of the neutral axis, find approximately:

(a) the area of steel reinforcement required;
(b) the minimum breadth of the compression flange of the T-beam.

Give a dimensional sketch of the cross-section of the T-beam showing the arrangement of the steel.

(Univ. of London, Part II, 1962, time allowed = 36 minutes)

10. Derive the modular ratio formula for calculating the safe axial load on a reinforced concrete column section and use it to design the section of a column which is 9 ft long; it is fixed at the bottom and unrestrained at the top. The load is 30 tons. Do not design the transverse steel.

If the column is later fixed at the top, find the maximum bending moment that can be safely applied, in addition to the axial load. Consider the moment acting about one of the principal axes of the section.

The reduction factor for long columns is given by

$$R = 1 \cdot 5 - L_E/30D_L$$

where L_E = effective length
and D_L = least lateral dimension.

The following can also be assumed:

p_{cb} = 1,200 lb/sq. in., m = 16,   density of concrete = 144 lb/cu. ft.
(Univ. of London, Part II, 1962, time allowed = 36 minutes)

11. A reinforced concrete beam of rectangular cross-section, 12 in. wide by 23 in. deep, carries a uniformly distributed load over a simply supported span. The maximum bending moment is 1,500,000 lb in. and the maximum shearing force is 30,000 lb. Design the beam with reasonable accuracy and illustrate a complete reinforcement system. Formulae need not be proved, use may be made of B.S. C.P. 114, and the following data are to be assumed:

Permissible compressive concrete stress in bending = 1,000 lb/sq. in.
Permissible compressive steel stress   = 18,000 lb/sq. in.
Permissible tensile steel stress   = 20,000 lb/sq. in.

(Univ. of Sheffield, Second Year Design, Sept. 1962,
time allowed = 1 hour)

12. The reinforced concrete frame shown is pin-jointed at A, B, and C. The roof sheeting, D, weighs 8 lb/sq. ft and spans between the frames

which are at 25-ft centres. The frames are of in-situ construction and have a constant rectangular cross-section. The dimensions of breadth and depth should be given in multiples of 4 inches to suit proprietory shutters.

Consider a snow load of 15 lb/sq. ft of plan area and design for bending only a suitable cross-section for the frame, specifying suitable

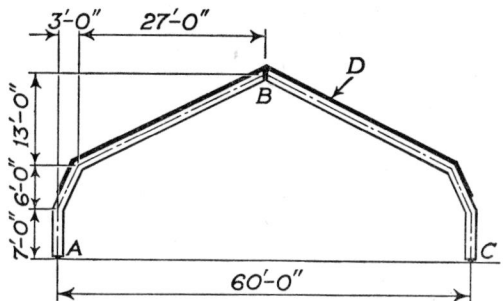

reinforcement for the positions of the maximum positive and negative bending moments.

Assume the following data:

Moment of Resistance of rectangular reinforced concrete beam
$$= 254 \times \text{breadth} \times \text{(effective depth)}^2$$
$$= \text{(area steel)} \times 16{,}780 \times \text{(effective depth)}.$$
Density of reinforced concrete = 150 lb/cu. ft.
Cover to reinforcement not less than one inch or the diameter of the bar.
The frames are supported laterally against buckling by the roof sheeting and brickwork walls.
Axial forces are to be ignored in the design of the sections.

(Univ. of Sheffield, Second Year Design, May 1961,
time allowed = 1 hour)

13. Design a simply-supported singly-reinforced rectangular reinforced concrete beam, 11 in. wide, to carry a load of 5,000 lb per ft run (inclusive of its own weight) over a span of 12 ft. If shear reinforcement is necessary give details of a system of stirrups to resist the maximum shearing force only. Curtail as many longitudinal reinforcement bars as possible before the supports and sketch, not necessarily to scale, a suitable system for these bars giving relevant dimensions to the curtailed bars. State the nominal mix of concrete used. Use mild steel reinforcement bars, the maximum size of which must not exceed one inch diameter for the longitudinal bars and ⅜ in. diameter for the stirrups. The overall depth of the beam must not exceed 2 ft 2 in. Formulae need not be proved and use should be made of B.S. C.P. 114 (1957) and the following formulae:

$$M_r = 0 \cdot 5\, p_{cb} n_1 a_1 b\, d_1{}^2$$

$$a_1 = 1 - \frac{n_1}{3}$$

$$n_1 = \frac{1}{1 + \dfrac{p_{st}}{15\, p_{cb}}}$$

the symbols being as defined in B.S. C.P. 114 (1957).

(Univ. of Sheffield, Second Year Design, Sept. 1961, time allowed = 1 hour)

14. The depth of the slab portion of a reinforced concrete T-beam is 5 in., and the tensile reinforcement is at an effective depth of 22·5 in. The beam is simply supported over a span of 20 ft and carries a uniformly distributed load. The maximum bending moment is 1,500,000 lb in., the maximum compressive concrete stress is 1,000 lb/sq. in. and the maximum tensile stress in the reinforcement is 20,000 lb/sq. in.

If the modular ratio is assumed to be 15, and Young's modulus for steel 30,000,000 lb/sq. in., calculate the maximum deflection of the beam, using the formula

$$\delta = \frac{5}{384} \frac{WL^3}{EI}$$

Ignoring the portion of the stem above the neutral axis, determine the breadth of the slab. Evaluate the corresponding area of the tensile reinforcement.

(Univ. of Sheffield, Second Year, June 1962, time allowed = 36 minutes)

(ANS. 0·311 in., 19·97 in., 3·71 sq. in.)

15. (a) A one inch diameter corner bar connecting a vertical column with a horizontal beam is required to transmit its full tensile force around the bend. Determine from first principles, using the following data, the necessary radius of curvature of the bend in the bar.

Permissible tensile stress in reinforcement, 20,000 lb/sq. in.
Permissible concrete bearing stress (for bend), 2,280 lb/sq. in.

(b) Determine from first principles the straight length of a $\frac{7}{8}$-in. diameter bar required for anchorage, such that a tensile stress of 30,000 lb/sq. in. can be developed without exceeding the permissible average bond stress of 120 lb per sq. in.

(Univ. of Sheffield, Second Year, June 1962,
time allowed = 36 minutes)

(ANS. (a) 6·89 in., (b) 54·7 in.)

16. The beams shown support channel reinforced wood wool slabs. The weight of these slabs, plus a screed and roofing felt on top and plaster beneath, is 15 lb/sq. ft. The rectangular precast reinforced concrete beams shown have an effective simply supported span of 30 ft. Design these beams to carry the roofing materials and a superimposed

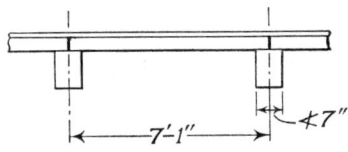

load of 15 lb/sq. ft, and forces due to handling. Illustrate with sketches, which do not need to be to scale, a suitable complete reinforcement system. Use B.S. C.P. 114 and assume any formula required, including:

$$M = 0 \cdot 5cn_1a_1bd^2 = A_sta_1\, d$$

where $\qquad a_1 = 1 - n_1/3 \qquad n_1 = \dfrac{m}{m + r} \qquad r = t/c$

and the remaining symbols have their usual meanings.

Assume a $1:1\frac{1}{2}:3$ mix of concrete and a permissible steel stress in tension of 20,000 lb/sq. in.

(Univ. of Sheffield, Second Year Design, June 1962,
time allowed = 1 hour)

17. A reinforced concrete beam carries a uniformly distributed load over a simply supported span of 40 ft. At mid-span the tensile reinforcement comprises four 1 in. dia bars. It is intended to run two of these bars through to the supports and to curtail the other two bars as near to the mid-span as possible. Determine:

(a) the distance from the support to the point where the second bar can be curtailed.

(b) the bond length to be given to this bar, excluding the additional nominal length provided for end anchorage. Prove any formula used and assume the following data:

Permissible tensile stress in steel, 20,000 lb/sq. in.
Permissible average bond stress in concrete, 120 lb/sq. in.

(Univ. of Sheffield, Second Year, Sept. 1961,
time allowed = 36 minutes)

(ANS. (a) 5·86 ft. (b) 27·8 in.)

18. The reinforced concrete T-beam shown carries a uniformly distributed load over a simply supported span of 30 ft. Determine its maximum deflection allowing for compressive stresses in the web and assuming the following data:

Permissible compressive stress in concrete in bending, 1,000 lb/sq. in.

Permissible tensile stress in steel, 30,000 lb/sq. in.

Young's Modulus for steel, 30,000,000 lb/sq. in.

Modular ratio, 15.

Deflection at mid-span $= \dfrac{5}{384} \dfrac{WL^3}{EI}$

where, $W =$ total load on span

$L =$ span

$E =$ Young's modulus

$I =$ Second Moment of Area of cross-section

(Univ. of Sheffield, Second Year, Sept. 1961,
time allowed = 36 minutes)

(ANS. 1·11 in.)

19. A reinforced concrete T-beam is singly reinforced, the effective depth of the reinforcement being 22·5 in., and the depth of the top flange is 5 in. The beam is simply supported over a span of 20 ft and carries a uniformly distributed load. The maximum bending moment is 1,500,000 lb/sq. in., the maximum compressive concrete stress is 1,000 lb/sq. in. and the maximum tensile stress in the reinforcement is 30,000 lb/sq. in.

Calculate the maximum deflection of the beam, using the formula

$$\delta = \frac{5}{384} \cdot \frac{WL^3}{EI}$$

where δ is deflection, W is total load, L is span, E is Young's Modulus, and I is Moment of Inertia.

Ignoring the portion of the stem (or web) above the neutral axis, determine from first principles the breadth of the flange and the area of the reinforcement.

Assume the following data:

modular ratio, 15

Young's Modulus for steel, 30,000,000 lb/sq. in.

(Univ. of Sheffield, Second Year, May 1961,
time allowed = 36 minutes)

(ANS. 0·4 in., 22·0 in., 2·45 sq. in.)

20. A rectangular reinforced concrete beam is singly reinforced with two 1⅛ in. diameter bars. The breadth of the beam is 10 in. and the effective depth of the steel reinforcement is 20 in. From first principles determine the maximum shear stress caused by a shear force of 10,000 lb. Assume the modular ratio is 15.

(Univ. of Sheffield, Second Year, May 1961, time allowed = 36 minutes)

(ANS. 58·0 lb/sq. in.)

21. The figure shows the cross-section of a reinforced concrete floor carrying a superimposed loading of 100 lb/sq. ft. The beams are continuous over spans of 30 ft such that the maximum support moment is 0·8 of the freely supported moment, and the maximum shear force is 0·6 of the total load on a span. Prove all formulae used and design a suitable section for the beam, so that no shear

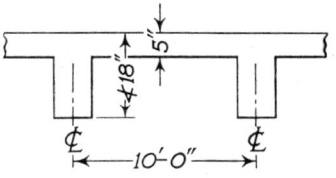

reinforcement is required. The following data may be used:

Permissible concrete stress in bending, 1,000 lb/sq. in.
Permissible concrete stress in shear, 100 lb/sq. in.
Permissible steel stress, 30,000 lb/sq. in.
Modular ratio, 15.
Density of reinforced concrete, 150 lb/cu. ft.

(Univ. of Sheffield, Second Year Design, May 1960, time allowed = 1 hour)

22. The reinforced concrete frame illustrated is pin-jointed at *A*, *B*, and *C*. It carries a uniformly distributed snow load of 15 lb/sq. ft. of plan area, and the roof sheeting, *D*, weighs 11·5 lb/sq. ft and spans between the frames which are at 10 feet centres. The frames are of in-situ construction and have a constant rectangular cross-section, the dimensions of breadth and depth to be in multiples of 4 inches to suit proprietory shutters. The frames are supported laterally against buckling by the roof sheeting and brickwork walls.

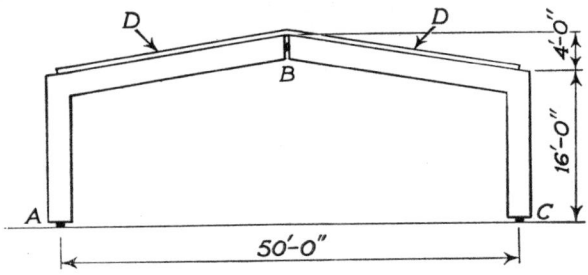

Design a suitable section and suggest suitable reinforcement for the positions of the maximum positive and negative bending moments. State whether or not shear reinforcement is required, but do not design such reinforcement. Prove all formulae and use the following data:

Permissible compressive stress in concrete in bending = 1,250 lb/sq. in.
Permissible shear stress in concrete = 90 lb/sq. in.
Permissible tensile stress in the reinforcement = 30,000 lb/sq. in.
Modular ratio = 15
Cover to reinforcement not less than 1 in. or the diameter of the bar.
(Univ. of Sheffield, Second Year Design, Sept. 1959,
time allowed = 1 hour)

23. A precast flooring or roofing system is illustrated. Each precast unit has a cross-section as shown. The minimum cover to the reinforcement is $\frac{1}{2}$ inch and the reinforcement bars must not exceed $\frac{1}{2}$ inch diameter. Assume high-tensile reinforcement is to be used, such that the permissible steel stress is 30,000 lb/sq. in.

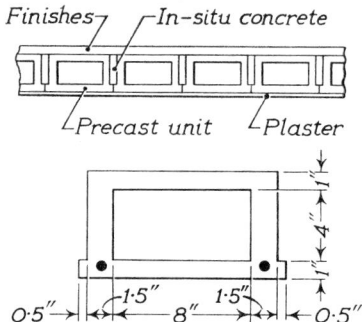

Various mixes of concrete can be used for the precast units but the permissible concrete stress must not exceed 1,875 lb/sq. in.

The precast units are not to be used for spans greater than 15 feet. The total load (comprising a super-imposed load of 15 lb/sq. ft and the dead weight of the completed floor) will not be less than 85 lb/sq. ft, and the deflection due to the super-imposed load must neither exceed $\frac{1}{360}$ of the span nor $\frac{3}{16}$ inch.

Determine the maximum span for which these units can be used. Under these conditions, recommend suitable tensile reinforcement and determine the minimum permissible compressive stress for the concrete. The full area of the concrete in compression must be taken into account in the calculations.

Assume that the precast units only must provide the full structural strength of the floor or roof. No calculations are required for the strength of the floor or roof transversely to the direction of the span.

Young's modulus for the reinforcement is 30,000,000 lb/sq. in. and the modular ratio is 15. The deflection of a simply supported beam carrying a uniformly distributed load is $\frac{5}{384} \cdot \frac{WL^3}{EI}$, with the usual notation.

(Univ. of Sheffield, Second Year Design, May 1959,
time allowed = 1 hour)

24. A singly reinforced concrete beam of rectangular cross-section, and breadth 10 inches, resists a shearing force of 8,000 lb. Determine from first principles the effective depth assuming the following data:

Maximum compressive stress in concrete in bending = 1,000 lb/sq. in.
Maximum shear stress in concrete = 100 lb/sq. in.
Tensile stress in the reinforcement = 30,000 lb/sq. in.
Modular ratio = 15.

(Univ. of Sheffield, Second Year, Sept. 1959,
time allowed = 36 minutes)

(ANS. 9·0 in.)

25. A reinforced concrete beam has five 1⅛-inch diameter bars as tensile reinforcement. It is simply supported and carries a total uniformly distributed load of 80,000 lb over an effective span of 20 ft. From first principles, determine the minimum number of the bars that it is necessary to continue through the supports. The maximum tensile stress in the reinforcement is 20,000 lb/sq. in., and the local bond stress must not exceed 200 lb/sq. in.

(Univ. of Sheffield, Second Year, Sept. 1959,
time allowed = 36 minutes)

(ANS. 3.)

26. The breadth of the top flange of a reinforced concrete T-beam is 20 inches, and the tensile reinforcement is at an effective depth of 22½ inches. The beam is simply supported over a span of 20 feet and carries a uniformly distributed load. The maximum bending moment is 1,500,000 lb/sq. in., the maximum compressive concrete stress is 1,000 lb/sq. in., and the maximum tensile stress in the reinforcement is 20,000 lb/sq. in.

If the modular ratio is assumed to be 15 and Young's Modulus for steel is 30×10^6 lb/sq. in., calculate the maximum deflection of the beam, using the formula

$$\delta = \frac{5}{384} \cdot \frac{WL^3}{EI}$$

Ignoring the portion of the stem above the neutral axis, determine an equation for the depth of the slab, and show that it is satisfied by a depth of 4·98 inches. Evaluate the corresponding area of the tensile reinforcement.

(Univ. of Sheffield, Second Year, May 1959,
time allowed = 36 minutes)

(ANS. 0·311 in., 3·695 sq. in.)

27. Discuss the basic assumptions of the elastic theory for the design of reinforced concrete sections to resist bending moments.

A reinforced concrete rectangular beam has a breadth of 6 inches and the tension reinforcement comprises two 1-in. diameter bars at an effective depth of 18 inches. It is designed such that the tensile steel stress is 20,000 lb/sq. in. If the modular ratio is 15 determine the corresponding maximum compressive concrete stress and the moment of resistance of the beam.

(Univ. of Sheffield, Second Year, May 1959, time allowed = 36 minutes)

(ANS. 1,219 lb/sq. in., 475,000 lb in.)

28. Discuss the relative merits of the 'working stress design' and the 'ultimate load design' for reinforced concrete sections.

Derive a general expression for the ultimate moment of resistance of an 'under-reinforced' rectangular section reinforced with mild steel in tension.

The rectangular cross-section of a singly reinforced concrete beam has a breadth of 9 in. and an effective depth of 20 in. Determine the maximum ultimate moment of resistance and the minimum area of tensile reinforcement required for 'balanced design' of the cross-section. Use Whitney's theory and assume that the ratio of the depth of the neutral axis to the effective depth is 0·537, the compressive strength of cylinders of the concrete is 2,000 lb per sq. in., and the yield stress of the steel is 40,000 lb per sq. in.

(Univ. of Sheffield, Third Year Honours, 1959, time allowed = 45 minutes)

(ANS. 2,400,000 lb in., 4·11 sq. in.)

29. The figure shows the cross-section of a barrel vault roof with a span of 78 ft between stiffening beams. The total loading on the shell portion of the roof may be taken as 50 lb/sq. ft of the curved surface. From first principles calculate the membrane reactions and *one* of the membrane displacements for the edge of the shell at mid-span. Describe briefly how these calculations could be continued to complete the design of this roof.

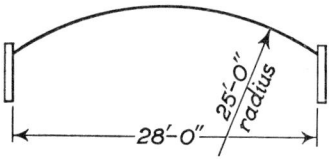

(Univ. of Sheffield, Third Year Honours, 1959, time allowed = 45 minutes)

30. The cross-section of a reinforced concrete column is as shown, a vertical load being applied at the point marked *A*. Determine from first principles the maximum permissible value of the vertical load, assuming the following data:

Permissible steel stress in compression, 18,000 lb/sq. in.
Permissible concrete stress in compression, 760 lb/sq. in.
Yield stress of steel in compression, 36,000 lb/sq. in.
Yield stress of steel in tension, 40,000 lb/sq. in.
Young's modulus for steel, 30,000,000 lb/sq. in.
Maximum concrete strain in compression, 0·0033

For *tension failure*:
  (a) Depth of rectangular stress block = 0·85 (depth of neutral axis).
  (b) Average stress of rectangular stress block at failure = 1,520 lb/sq. in.

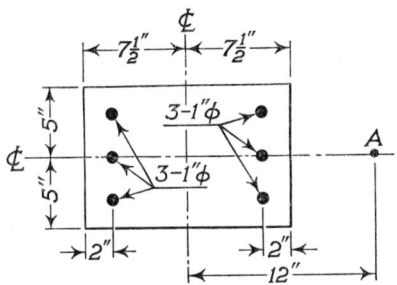

For section *entirely in compression*:

$$P = \frac{P_o}{1 + \left(\dfrac{P_o}{P_b} - 1\right)\dfrac{e}{e_b}}$$

where P is the permissible load on a short column subject to both direct load and bending, e is the eccentricity of a load on a column, P_b is the maximum value of P for a *tension failure*, e_b is the value of e corresponding to P_b, and P_o is the permissible load on a short axially loaded column.
  Load factor = 2.

(Univ. of Sheffield, Third Year Honours, 1960,
time allowed = 45 minutes)

(ANS. 57,800 lb)

31. Derive from first principles, Schorer's fundamental differential equation for the bending of shells.

(Univ. of Sheffield, Third Year Honours, 1960,
time allowed = 45 minutes)

32. Discuss the relative merits of 'working stress' and 'ultimate load' design for reinforced concrete sections.
  A rectangular reinforced concrete beam has a breadth of 8 inches and has two ½-in. diameter bars as compression reinforcement, the concrete cover to these bars being 1 in. Determine the minimum

effective depth of the tension reinforcement and the corresponding area of this reinforcement, if the beam is to be designed to resist a moment of 1,500,000 lb in. at working loads. Assume the following data:

Load factor, 2.

Young's Modulus for steel, 30,000,000 lb/sq. in.

Yield stress of steel in tension and compression, 40,000 lb/sq. in.

A rectangular stress block:

(a) For *balanced* design: Depth of neutral axis = 0·5 × (effective depth of tension reinforcement).

(b) Ultimate average compressive concrete stress, 2,000 lb/sq. in.

(c) Maximum concrete strain in compression, $\frac{1}{3}$%.

(d) Depth of neutral axis equals depth of stress block.

(Univ. of Sheffield, Third Year Honours, 1961, time allowed = 45 minutes)

(ANS. 21·21 in., 4·614 sq. in.)

33. Derive expressions for the longitudinal, tangential, and radial displacements due to membrane forces in a cylindrical barrel vault roof carrying a loading of g per unit area of surface. Use load harmonics and neglect all but the first term of Fourier's series.

(Univ. of Sheffield, Third Year Honours, 1961, time allowed = 45 minutes)

34. Shorer's equation of compatibility of the edge load problem for a cylindrical shell roof can be stated

$$\frac{\partial^8 M}{\partial \theta^8} + 4a^2b^2M = 0$$

where M is the bending moment transversely to the span, at a point at mid-span and at an angular distance θ from an edge of the shell, and a and b are quantities dependent upon the dimensions of the shell. Show that the solution of this equation for M conforms to the generalized solution

$$Q\{Ae^{-J_1\theta}(\alpha \sin K_1\theta + \beta \cos K_1\theta) +$$
$$+ Be^{-J_1\theta}(\alpha \cos K_1\theta - \beta \sin K_1\theta) +$$
$$+ Ce^{-K_1\theta}(\gamma \sin J_1\theta + \delta \cos J_1\theta) +$$
$$+ De^{-K_1\theta}(\gamma \cos J_1\theta - \delta \sin J_1\theta)\}$$

where A, B, C, and D denote arbitrary constants determined by boundary conditions. α, β, γ, and δ denote numerical coefficients, and Q, J_1, and K_1 denote quantities dependent upon the dimensions of the shell (Q is unity in this particular instance).

Hence, if two symmetrical tangential forces corresponding to $4/\pi$ at mid-span are applied at opposite edges of a shell segment, explain the derivation of the following matrix equation and describe how it enables the relevant edge displacements to be determined:

$$\begin{bmatrix} a_3 & b_3 & c_3 & d_3 \\ a_2 & b_2 & c_2 & d_2 \\ a_4 & b_4 & c_4 & d_4 \\ a_8 & b_8 & c_8 & d_8 \end{bmatrix} \begin{bmatrix} A \\ B \\ C \\ D \end{bmatrix} = \begin{bmatrix} 4/(\pi Q_{T2}) \\ 0 \\ 0 \\ 0 \end{bmatrix}$$

where values such as a_2, b_2, c_2, d_2, etc., and Q_{T2} denote quantities dependent upon the dimensions of the shell.

(Univ. of Sheffield, Third Year Honours, 1962, time allowed = 45 minutes)

35. The cross-section of a short reinforced concrete column is shown, a vertical load being applied at the point marked A. Determine from

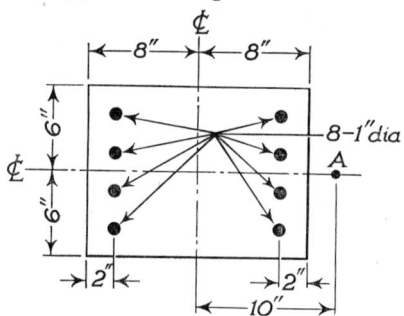

first principles the maximum permissible value of the vertical load, assuming the following data:

Permissible steel stress in compression, 18,000 lb/sq. in.
Permissible concrete stress in compression, 760 lb/sq. in.
Yield stress of steel in compression, 36,000 lb/sq. in.
Yield stress of steel in tension, 40,000 lb/sq. in.
Young's Modulus for steel, 30,000,000 lb/sq. in.
Maximum concrete strain in compression, 0·0033

For *tension failure*:
  (a) Depth of rectangular stress block equals 0·85 times depth of neutral axis.
  (b) Average stress of rectangular stress block at failure = 1,520 lb/sq. in.

For section *entirely in compression*:

$$P = \frac{P_0}{1 + \left(\dfrac{P_0}{P_b} - 1\right)\dfrac{e}{e_b}}$$

where P is the permissible load on a short column subject to both direct load and bending, e is the eccentricity of a load on a column,

P_b is the maximum value of P for a *tension failure*, e_b is the value of e corresponding to P_b, and P_0 is the permissible load on a short axially loaded column. Load factor, 2.

(Univ. of Sheffield, Third Year Honours, 1962,
time allowed = 45 minutes
(ANS. 88,800 lb)

36. Design a suitable cross-section for a rectangular reinforced concrete beam to resist a bending moment of 2,000,000 lb in. Prove all formulae used and assume the following data:—

Permissible stress of concrete in bending, 1,250 lb/sq. in.

Permissible stress of steel in tension, 20,000 lb/sq. in.

Modular ratio, 15.

(Univ. of Sheffield, Third Year Architects, May 1962,
time allowed = 36 minutes)

37. Design a reinforced concrete column of square cross-section to carry a vertical axial load of 60,000 lb. Prove all formulae used and assume the following data:—

Permissible stress of concrete in compression, 950 lb/sq. in.

Permissible stress of steel in compression, 18,000 lb/sq. in.

Modular ratio, 15.

Amount of reinforcement must be between 0·8 and 8 % of the gross cross-sectional area of the column.

(Univ. of Sheffield, Third Year Architects, May 1962,
time allowed = 36 minutes)

38. Discuss the relative advantages and disadvantages of reinforced concrete as opposed to structural steelwork construction.

(Univ. of Sheffield, Third Year Architects, May 1961,
time allowed = 36 minutes)

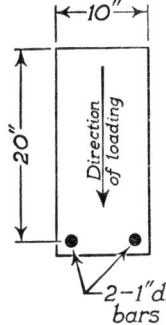

39. Determine from first principles the permissible moment of resistance of the reinforced concrete beam shown, given the following data:

Permissible concrete stress in bending	= 1,250 lb/sq. in.
Permissible steel stress	= 30,000 lb/sq. in.
Modular ratio	= 15.

(Univ. of Sheffield, Third Year Architects, May 1961,
time allowed = 36 minutes)
(ANS. 821,000 lb in.)

40. A reinforced concrete column has a cross-section 10 in. square and is reinforced with four 1 in. diameter steel rods. Determine the axial load it can carry if its effective length is 16 ft 8 in., the permissible stress in direct compression of the concrete is 950 lb/sq. in., the permissible stress of the steel in compression is 18,000 lb/sq. in., and the modular ratio is 15. Use the following extract from the British Standard Code of Practice C.P. 114 (1957), where R is the ratio of the effective length to the least lateral dimension of a column and C is the corresponding reduction coefficient for a load on a long column:—

R	15	18	21	24
C	1·0	0·9	0·8	0·7

(Univ. of Sheffield, Third Year Architects, June 1959,
time allowed = 36 minutes)
(ANS. 114,000 lb)

41. If the permissible concrete stress (in bending) = 1,250 lb/sq. in., the permissible steel stress = 30,000 lb/sq. in. and the Modular Ratio = 15, prove the following design formulae for a singly reinforced concrete beam of rectangular cross-section from first principles:—

(a) $M = 210bd^2$
(b) $M = 26,160A_s d$

where

M = moment of resistance of section.
d = effective depth of reinforcement.
b = breadth of section.
A_s = area of tensile reinforcement.

(Univ. of Sheffield, Third Year Architects,
Easter Terminal, 1960)

42. A reinforced concrete beam has a cross-section as shown. It is simply supported over a span of 20 ft, and carries a uniformly distributed load, including its own weight, of 1,200 lb per ft run. If the modular ratio is 15 and Young's Modulus for the steel is 30,000,000 lb/sq. in., determine the deflection of the beam at mid-span, using the formula:—

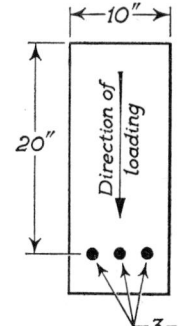

$$\delta = \frac{5}{384} = \frac{WL^3}{EI}$$

where,
δ = deflection,
W = total load on span,
L = span,
E = Young's Modulus,
I = Second Moment of Area
of cross-section.

N.B. Any other formulae used need to be proved.

(Univ. of Sheffield, Third Year Architects,
Easter Terminal, 1962)
(ANS. 0·02155 in.)

43. Discuss the properties of steel and concrete.

(Univ. of Sheffield, Third Year Architects,
Easter Terminal, 1962)

44. Describe laboratory methods of testing cement, concrete and steel.

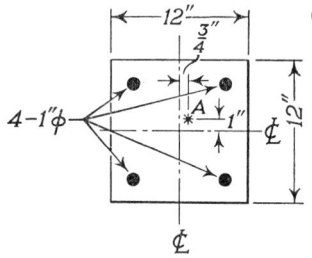

(Univ. of Sheffield, Third Year Architects,
Easter Terminal, 1961)

45. The cross-section of a short reinforced concrete column is shown. A vertical load of 70 tons acts through point A. Use an elastic analysis and the following data to determine the maximum and minimum compressive stresses in the concrete:

Modular ratio, 15.

Concrete cover to reinforcement, $1\frac{1}{2}$ in.

(Univ. of Sheffield, Third Year Architects, May 1960)
(ANS. 1,435 lb/sq. in., 208·0 lb/sq. in.)

46. A rectangular reinforced concrete beam has a breadth of 10 in. The effective depth of the tensile reinforcement is 22·5 in., and the effective depth of the compressive reinforcement is 1·5 in. Obtain from first principles, without making unnecessary assumptions, the amounts of compression and tension steel required to make the permissible moment of resistance of the section equal to 1,179,000 lb in., using the following data:

Permissible concrete stress (in bending), 1,000 lb/sq. in.

Permissible steel stress, 20,000 lb/sq. in.

Modular ratio, 15.

(Univ. of Sheffield, Second Year, May 1960,
time allowed = 36 minutes)
(ANS. 1·0 sq. in., 3·0 sq in.)

47. A rectangular reinforced concrete beam of breadth 6 in. has two 1 in. diameter bars as tension reinforcement at an effective depth of 15 in. and two $\frac{1}{2}$ in. diameter bars at a depth of $1\frac{1}{4}$ in. (to their centroid) from the top of the beam. At a section where the shear force is 6,000 lb, determine the local bond stress between the tensile reinforcement and the concrete. Prove all formulae used, and assume that the modular ratio is 15.

(Univ. of Sheffield, Second Year, Sept. 1962)
time allowed = 36 minutes,
(ANS. 74·4 lb/sq. in.)

48. A reinforced concrete T-beam of the section shown is simply supported and spans 20 ft. The beam is to carry the maximum permissible uniformly distributed load. Determine from first principles which bars should be continued over the supports, assuming that as many bars are curtailed as possible before the supports, and using the following data:

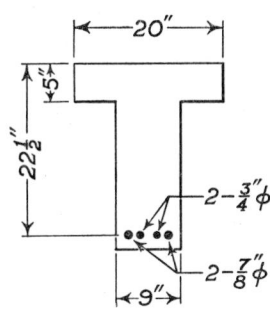

Permissible concrete stress (in bending), 1,000 lb/sq. in.
Permissible steel stress, 20,000 lb/sq. in.
Permissible local bond stress, 180 lb/sq. in.
Modular ratio, 15.

(Univ. of Sheffield, Second Year, May 1960, time allowed = 36 minutes)
(ANS. the two $\frac{7}{8}$ in. dia. bars)

49. A simply supported reinforced concrete T-beam is uniformly loaded over a span of length L. At mid-span the bending moment is 1,500,000 lb in., the maximum compressive stress in the concrete is 258 lb/sq. in., and the tensile stress in the reinforcement is 20,000 lb/sq. in. If the maximum deflection is $L/500$, determine L proving all formulae used. The following data may be assumed.

Effective depth of steel reinforcement = 22·5 in.
Young's Modulus for steel, 30,000,000 lb/sq in.
Modular Ratio, 15 and $\delta = \dfrac{5}{384} \dfrac{WL^3}{EI}$, with the usual notation.

(Univ. of Sheffield, Second Year, Sept. 1962, time allowed = 36 minutes)
(ANS. 45 ft 1 in.)

50. (a) A $\frac{7}{8}$-inch diameter corner bar connecting a vertical column with a horizontal beam is required to transmit its full tensile force around the bend. Determine from first principles, using the following data, the necessary radius of curvature of the bend in the bar.

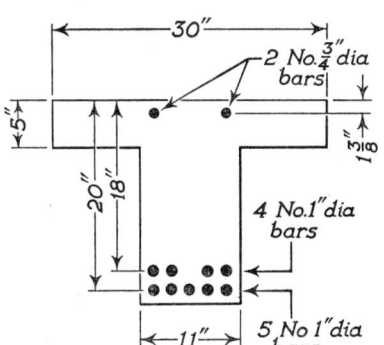

Permissible tensile stress in reinforcement, 20,000 lb/sq. in.
Permissible concrete bearing stress (for bend), 2,280 lb/sq. in.

(b) Determine from first principles the straight length of a $\frac{3}{4}$-inch diameter bar required for anchorage, such that a tensile stress of 30,000 lb/sq. in. can be developed without exceeding the permissible average bond stress of 120 lb/sq. in.

(Univ. of Sheffield, Second Year, Sept. 1960,
time allowed = 36 minutes)
(ANS. (a) 6·03 in. (b) 46·9 in.)

51. Design a rectangular beam to carry a uniformly distributed load of 265 lb per ft run, exclusive of its own weight, over a simply supported span of 30 ft. Only the sections subjected to the maximum bending moments and shear forces respectively need to be considered, but it must be ensured that the maximum deflection does not exceed 0·72 inch. Use the following data:—

Modular ratio, 15.
Permissible steel stress in tension, 30,000 lb/sq. in.
Permissible shear stress in concrete, 90 lb/sq. in.
Overall depth must be greater than 1 ft 6 in.
Beam is laterally stable.

$$M = 146bd^2 \qquad\qquad n = 0 \cdot 333d$$

$$q = \frac{F}{ab} \qquad\qquad \delta = \frac{5}{384}\frac{WL^3}{EI}$$

$$P = \frac{FS}{a} \qquad\qquad E = 2,000,000 \text{ lb/sq. in.}$$

where b = breadth of beam
d = effective depth of tensile steel
M = moment of resistance
q = shear stress
F = shear force
a = lever arm
P = total force in all arms of a stirrup
S = spacing of stirrups
δ = central deflection of simply supported beam
W = total load on span
I = second moment of area of equivalent concrete section.

(Univ. of Sheffield, Second Year Design, Sept. 1960,
time allowed = 1 hour)

52. A prestressed concrete beam, 4 in. wide and 6 in. total depth, is prestressed with one $\frac{1}{2}$ in. diameter high tensile steel rod at 1 in. from the bottom. The initial steel stress is 29,400 lb/sq. in. and the rod is bonded to the concrete after post-tensioning. If the shortening of the steel rod up to the time of loading due to shrinkage and creep is 66×10^{-6} per unit length, determine the maximum stress in the steel and concrete when the beam carries a load of 677 lb at each of the middle third points on a simply supported span of 5 ft 9 in. Assume the modular ratio to be 7·5.

(Univ. of Leeds, Third Year Theory and Design, 1952,
time allowed = 30 minutes)

53. Discuss the factors affecting the ultimate bending moment of prestressed concrete beams.

A symmetrical pre-tensioned beam of ⊥-section 8 in. by 4 in., with flanges 2½ in. deep contains 10 No. 8 gauge (0·160 in. diameter) wires at an average distance of 1½ in. from the bottom. If the cube crushing strength of the concrete is 5,000 lb/sq. in. and the tensile strength of the wire is 100 ton/sq. in., estimate the ultimate moment of the beam.

(Univ. of Leeds, B.Sc., 1945,
time allowed = 30 minutes)

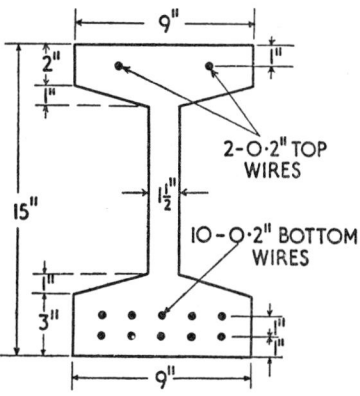

54. Calculate as accurately as possible the prestress at the top and bottom of the given section in the figure and sketch the stress distribution diagram. The stress in the tensioned wires is 115,000 lb/sq. in.

(Univ. of Leeds, B.Sc., 1952,
time allowed = 30 minutes)

55. A post-tensioned beam of span 50 ft and depth 3 ft has a uniform symmetrical cross-section of area 320 sq. in. and moment of inertia 54,000 in.[4] The prestress is provided by a cable tensioned to a force of 320,000 lb at transfer. If the beam is to carry a uniformly distributed live load of 1,400 lb per lin ft, and the minimum load is that due to the self weight of the beam, calculate the vertical limits within which the cable must lie, along the length of the beam. Any formulae used should be derived.

(Permissible stresses: compressive stress at transfer—2,000 lb/sq. in.; compressive stress at working load—2,400 lb/sq. in.; tensile stress at transfer—zero; tensile stress at working load—250 lb/sq. in.; loss ratio $(R_0) = 0·80$; weight of concrete = 150 lb/cu ft.)

(Univ. of Leeds, B.Sc., 1956,
time allowed = 30 minutes)

56. The figure shows the cross-section of a prestressed concrete beam in which the force exerted by the cable is initially 160,000 lb with a subsequent loss of 20%. If the compressive stress in the concrete must not exceed 2,500 lb/sq. in. or the tensile stress 400 lb/sq. in. at any

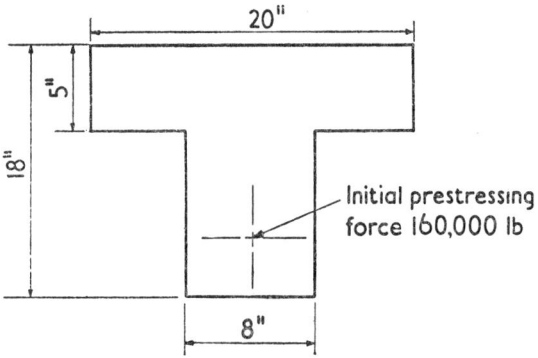

time, determine the highest and lowest possible positions of the cable at a point in the beam where the maximum bending moment is 1,180,000 lb in. and the minimum bending moment 186,000 lb in.

(Univ. of Leeds, B.Sc., 1959,
time allowed = 30 minutes)

57. A composite prestressed concrete floor, of cross-section illustrated in the figure, is to be designed to carry an imposed load of 150 lb/sq. ft over a span of 25 ft. The precast element is to be uniformly

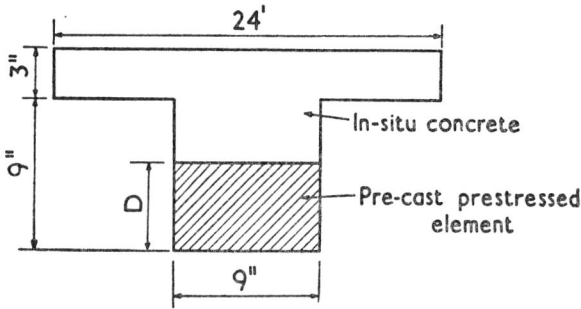

prestressed and supported on formwork while the *in situ* concrete is cast. If the tensile stress in the *in situ* concrete is not to exceed 500 lb/sq. in. and there is to be no tensile stress in the precast concrete, calculate the minimum depth (*D*) of the precast element, and its minimum prestress at transfer. Take the loss ratio (R_0) as 0·80.

(Univ. of Leeds, B.Sc., 1959,
time allowed = 30 minutes)

58. A pre-tensioned prestressed beam is of rectangular cross-section 8 in. deep by 4 in. wide and contains 8 wires at an average distance of $1\frac{1}{2}$ in. from the bottom and 2 wires 1 in. from the top of the beam. The wires are 0·160 in. in diameter with a tensile strength of 110 ton/sq. in.

and their effective stress, after deduction of all losses is 110,000 lb/sq. in.

If the beam is designed for a uniformly distributed load of 110 lb/ft, over and above its own weight, on a simply supported span of 18 ft, estimate the load factor against failure.

(Cube strength of concrete = 7,000 lb/sq. in.)

(Univ. of Leeds, B.Sc., 1959,
time allowed = 30 minutes)

59. A prestressed beam of uniform cross-section is continuous over two equal spans of 20 ft. The force in the prestressing cable is 48 tons and its profile is an inverted v 7 in. below the centroid of the concrete at each end, and 5 in. above the centroid at the centre support. Calculate the secondary prestressing moment at the centre support and the stable line of thrust. How could the same prestress be obtained with a reduction of cable friction at the centre support?

(Univ. of Leeds, B.Sc., 1959,
time allowed = 30 minutes)

60. The profile of a post-tensioned cable 50 ft long is parabolic with the mid-point 24 in. below the level of the ends. The cross-sectional area is 0·38 sq. in. and the modulus of elasticity 27×10^6 lb/sq. in. A force of 25 tons is applied to one end by means of a jack and an extension of 3·3 in. recorded, while a slip of 0·2 in. is measured at the end remote from the jack. If on anchoring the cable there is a further slip of 0·1 in. at the jacking end, calculate the coefficient of friction between the cable and the duct, and the final force in the cable (i) at the midspan point, (ii) at the end remote from the jack.

(Univ. of Leeds, B.Sc., 1959,
time allowed = 30 minutes)

61. A prestressed concrete beam of rectangular cross section 6 in. wide by 15 in. deep is required to support two symmetrical concentrated loads of 2,700 lb at the $\frac{1}{3}$ points of a simply supported span of 30 ft. The prestress is imposed by a single post-tensioned cable. There must be no tensile stress at the time of prestressing and the tensile stress under the maximum load must not exceed 200 lb/sq in. allowing for a maximum loss of prestress of 15%.

Assuming that the beam supports only its own weight at the time of prestressing, calculate the minimum possible force in the cable, its position at midspan and the maximum compressive stress in the concrete at midspan. Find also the upper and lower limits of the cable position at the support and sketch the profile of these limits along the length of the beam.

(Univ. of Leeds, B.Sc., 1961,
time allowed = 30 minutes)

62. A concrete beam 25 ft long and 10 in. deep by 5 in. wide is pre-stressed by six 0·276 in. parallel pre-tensioned wires which may be considered all to be located 3·25 in. from the soffit. The initial stress in the wires on the tensioning bed is 140,000 lb/sq. in. and the modulus of elasticity of the steel is 28,000,000 lb/sq. in.

If, when the prestress is transferred to the concrete, the centre of the beam is found to deflect 0·26 in. upwards, calculate the approximate modulus of elasticity of the concrete and the prestress in the wires.

(Univ. of Leeds, B.Sc., 1961,
time allowed = 30 minutes)

63. The cross-section of a precast pre-tensioned beam of span 30 ft is an inverted T 12 in. wide by 14 in. deep, with the web and flange both 3 in. thick. The effective prestress at the bottom of the beam, after all losses have occurred, is 1,800 lb/sq. in. (exclusive of stresses due to the dead weight). Concrete is to be added *in situ*, to form a composite rectangular beam 12 in. wide, the weight of this concrete being supported by the precast beam.

If the modulus of elasticity of the concrete is the same in both parts of the beam, and the density is 150 lb/cu ft, show that the maximum additional bending moment, without the occurrence of tensile stresses at the soffit, can be supported if the overall depth is about 17·6 in. Calculate this maximum moment, and find the maximum tensile stress at the bottom of the *in-situ* concrete.

(Univ. of Leeds, B.Sc., 1962,
time allowed = 30 minutes)

64. A road bridge of span 35 ft is to be constructed over a canal, using precast prestressed beams to avoid interruption of traffic. A pipe bay must be provided beneath the footpath to accommodate pipes of up to 6 in. external diameter. The loading on the road is the M.O.T. load, consisting of 220 lb/sq. ft, uniformly distributed, with a movable knife-edge load of 2,700 lb/ft. The load on the footpath is 150 lb/sq. ft, uniformly distributed.

(a) Design the bridge deck, using precast beams, **either** alone **or** in a composite construction with *in situ* concrete. Draw a cross-section to a suitable scale.

(b) Make detailed calculations and drawings of one of the precast prestressed beams.

(c) Write brief notes on the method of erection, including the method of lifting the precast beams.

(Univ. of Leeds, B.Sc. Design, 1952,
time allowed = 6 hours)

65. A prestressed concrete pile of cross-section 10 in. square contains 60 pre-tensioned wires of diameter 0·08 in. uniformly distributed over the section. The wires are initially tensioned on the pre-stressing bed with a total force of 30 tons. If the modulus of elasticity of the steel is 27×10^6 lb/sq. in., and that of the concrete is 4.5×10^6 lb/sq. in., calculate the respective stresses in the steel and concrete immediately after transfer of the prestress, assuming that up to this point the only loss of stress is that due to elastic shortening of the concrete.

If the concrete undergoes a further shortening, due to creep, of 0.2×10^{-6} per lb/sq. in. of stress, and a shrinkage of 200×10^{-6} per unit length, while there is a relaxation of 5 per cent of the steel stress due to creep of steel, find the greatest tensile stress which can occur in a pile 60 ft long when lifted at two points 14 ft from each end.

(Univ. of Leeds, Post-graduate Diploma, 1957,
time allowed = 45 minutes)

66. The figure is the cross-section at the support of a symmetrical concrete beam pre-stressed by two straight cables, each at a tension of 55,000 lb and distant 4 in. from the soffit. Calculate the principal tensile stress in the web at a distance of (a) 9 in. and (b) 13 in. from the soffit of the beam when the latter is simply supported and subjected to a shearing force of 30,000 lb at the support section. What vertical prestress would be necessary to eliminate the principal tensile stress at (a), and how could this be produced?

(Univ. of Leeds, Post-graduate Diploma, 1955,
time allowed = 45 minutes)

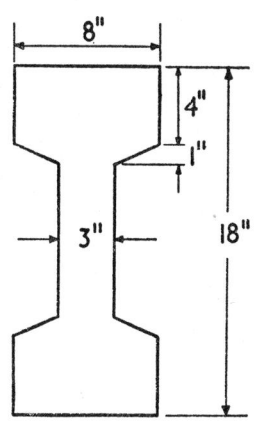

67. A rectangular pre-tensioned concrete beam has a breadth of 4 in. and depth of 9 in., and the prestress, after all losses have occurred, is 1,700 lb/sq. in. at the bottom, and zero at the top. The beam is incorporated in a composite T-beam, by casting a top flange of breadth 12 in. and depth 2 in. Calculate the maximum uniformly distributed load that can be carried on a simply supported span of 15 ft without any tensile stresses occurring.

(a) if the slab is externally supported while casting;

(b) if the pre-tensioned beam carries the weight of the slab and shuttering while casting, the shuttering being removed when the slab has hardened.

(Weight of concrete—150 lb/cu ft; Weight of horizontal shuttering 6 lb/sq. ft.)

(Univ. of Leeds, Post-graduate Diploma, 1956,
time allowed = 45 minutes)

68. A rectangular pre-tensioned concrete beam of 20 ft span is 12 in. deep and 4 in. wide. Since, in handling, the beam is liable to be turned upside down, it is decided to limit the tensile flexural stress in this position due to prestress and self-weight to 200 lb/sq. in. The compressive stress in the inverted position must not exceed 2,000 lb/sq. in. Disregarding all time effects, determine the resultant eccentricity and the required force in the wires after release. Adopting the same limiting stresses, calculate the allowable applied loading in the normal position. Show by clear diagrams the stress conditions at the centre of the span both in the inverted and normal positions.

Describe very briefly how this beam could be constructed.

Weight of concrete: 144 lb/cu ft.

(Univ. of Leeds, Post-Graduate Diploma, 1958,
time allowed = 45 minutes)

69. A floor 36 ft by 24 ft is supported by two main beams of 24 ft span at 12 ft centres, connected at the mid-points by a secondary beam of total length 36 ft, framing into the main beams. The main beams are each of rectangular cross-section 12 in. by 18 in. deep, prestressed by parabolic cables located 3 in. from the soffit at the midspan point and 9 in. from the soffit at each end, and tensioned to a total force of 200,000 at each end. The secondary beam is of rectangular cross-section 9 in. by 12 in. deep prestressed by a straight cable 4 in. from the soffit, tensioned to 100,000 lb.

Determine and sketch the line of thrust of the prestressing force through the main beams, and calculate the stresses in the concrete at the midspan point when the total loading (including weight of the beams) is 1,800 lb/ft on the secondary beam and 300 lb/ft on each of the main beams. Neglect the effect of torsion.

(Univ. of Leeds, Post-Graduate Diploma, 1958,
time allowed = 45 minutes)

70. The section of part of a composite prestressed concrete bridge deck is shown in the figure. The precast prestressed beams have the following properties.

Area of concrete, 54 sq. in.

Height of centroid, 3·09 in.

Moment of inertia, 324 in.⁴

Prestress at bottom, +1,475 lb/sq. in.

    ,, at top, −100 lb/sq. in.

Modulus of elasticity of concrete, 5,000,000 lb/sq. in.

The bridge has a span of 20 ft, and the precast beams are required to support the weight of the wet concrete infill without propping. When the infill has hardened, and may be assumed to have a modulus

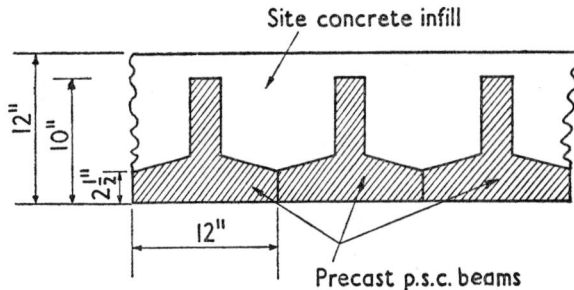

Site concrete infill

Precast p.s.c. beams

of elasticity of 4,000,000 lb/sq. in. a uniformly distributed load of 260 lb/sq. ft is applied. Calculate the stresses at the top and bottom of the precast beams and at the highest and lowest points in the concrete infill.

How would the stress distribution be modified by differential shrinkage of the infill concrete?

(Univ. of Leeds, Post-Graduate Diploma, 1960,
time allowed = 45 minutes)

71. Derive formulae giving the section moduli for the top and bottom of a prestressed beam in terms of the maximum and minimum bending moment, the permissible stresses in the concrete, and the ratio of the final prestress to the prestress at transfer. Discuss the practical significance of the minimum bending moment on a prestressed beam.

A prestressed beam of rectangular cross-section, with breadth equal to one-half of the depth, is simply supported over a span of 20 ft. If the maximum bending moment at midspan is that due to the beam's own weight, calculate the minimum depth for the following permissible stresses:

Compressive stress at transfer, 2,400 lb/sq. in.

     ,,   ,,   at working load, 2,600 lb/sq. in.

Tensile stress at transfer and working load, zero.

Loss ratio (R_0), 0·80.

(Univ. of Leeds, Post-Graduate Diploma, 1962)
time allowed = 45 minutes,

INDEX